# MIND, BRAIN AND ADAPTATION
# IN THE NINETEENTH CENTURY

# MIND, BRAIN
# AND ADAPTATION
## IN THE
## NINETEENTH CENTURY

---

*Cerebral localization
and its biological context
from Gall to Ferrier*

---

## ROBERT M. YOUNG
FELLOW OF KING'S COLLEGE, CAMBRIDGE

CLARENDON PRESS · OXFORD
1970

*Oxford University Press, Ely House, London W.*1

GLASGOW NEW YORK TORONTO MELBOURNE WELLINGTON
CAPE TOWN SALISBURY IBADAN NAIROBI DAR ES SALAAM LUSAKA ADDIS ABABA
BOMBAY CALCUTTA MADRAS KARACHI LAHORE DACCA
KUALA LUMPUR SINGAPORE HONG KONG TOKYO

*Made in Great Britain at the Pitman Press, Bath*

FOR MY PARENTS, MY WIFE,
AND MY TEACHERS:

RICHARD RORTY
IRWIN C. LIEB
WILBUR K. SMITH

But never can they behold the waking reality so long as they leave the hypotheses which they use unexamined, and are unable to give an account of them. For when a man knows not his own first principle, and when the conclusion and intermediate steps are also constructed out of he knows not what, how can he imagine that such a fabric of convention can ever become science?

Plato, Republic.

# PREFACE

But though the history of ideas is a history of trial-and-error, even the errors illuminate the peculiar nature, the cravings, the endowments, and the limitations of the creature that falls into them, as well as the logic of the problems in reflection upon which they have arisen; and they may further serve to remind us that the ruling modes of thought of our own age, which some among us are prone to regard as clear and coherent and firmly grounded and final, are unlikely to appear in the eyes of posterity to have any of those attributes. The adequate record of even the confusions of our forebears may help, not only to clarify those confusions, but to engender a salutary doubt whether we are wholly immune from different but equally great confusions. For though we have more empirical information at our disposal, we have not different or better minds; and it is, after all, the action of the mind upon facts that makes both philosophy and science—and, indeed, largely makes the 'facts'.

Arthur O. Lovejoy, 1936.

This question of origins is more than an abstract discussion of historical justice or truth. Modern psychology (physiological, experimental psychology) is faced by the same problems as all other scientific disciplines. In order not to go astray, in order to find new, safer and more direct paths, she must continuously re-examine her premises. In such re-examinations, it is not sufficient to analyse some recent work; one must go back to the real sources because they are the ones to reveal most clearly the virtues and the vices of a method.

Ackernecht and Vallois, 1956.

In calling this work a study in the history of biology, I am assuming the truth of what I have set out to show: that the history of research in psychology should be viewed as a development away from philosophy and toward general biology. The methods, concepts, and major assumptions which I have chosen to examine are those which I believe have played the most important role in psychology's movement in the nineteenth century from an epistemological enquiry to a study of the adaptations of organisms to their environments. The domain of psychology is bounded by the common-sense experience of the everyday lives of men and other organisms on the one hand and by physiology on the other. More than any other science, psychology is obliged to make sense to the layman, for its explanatory task is to make sense of the behaviour of the layman. Similarly, if it is to be a science it must demonstrate the relations between its phenomena and those of the traditional science to which they are most closely related, the physico-chemical science of physiology. Its task has been to develop categories of analysis which satisfy both the common man and the physiologist. It has very rarely succeeded in doing either of these. In fact, the most fundamental and perplexing problem in psychology has been, and remains, the lack of an agreed set of units for analysis comparable to the elementary particles in physics and the periodic table of elements in chemistry.

Since the nervous system, in conjunction with the musculo-skeletal and endocrine systems, mediates all aspects of experience and behaviour, it must, in principle, serve multiple functions. A number of these functions are discretely, and more or less uniquely, localized, in such centres as the somato-motor cortex and primary sensory projection areas. However, these same structures can be subjected to functional analyses beyond that of simple sensation and movement. For example, they are involved in the functions of contraction of the triceps, extension of the arm, striking an object, boxing, aggressiveness, self-preservation, and seeking acclaim—all at the same time. The problem for brain and behaviour research is whether or not there is anything to choose among these alternative analyses. If not, then there can be no straight-forward 'natural classification' of functions and thus no unique basis for a system of analytic units in psychology. Psychology will thereby have nothing analogous to the chemists' periodic table of elements. Rather, there will be a number of alternative tables, and the one that is used in a given situation will depend on the nature and the level of the functional analysis being conducted. In raising this issue here, I want to allude to a theme implicit in my argument: the problem of providing functional or purposive explanations within the context of Cartesian mind–body dualism set constraints on the study of cerebral localization which were not overcome within the period which is treated here; and, it seems to me, the problem is no less acute today.

Until the last decades of the eighteenth century, psychologists adopted their categories of analysis from philosophy. These were the attributes of mind in general: memory, reasoning, intelligence, imagination, and so on. The present study is designed to show that after psychologists began to attempt to *determine* a set of categories, they moved from the extreme of allowing the terms of everyday experience to dictate how the nervous system must be organized and must function, to that of allowing the categories of physiological analysis to dictate

the elements from which the phenomena of everyday life would have
to be synthesized.

The major ideas involved in this history were:

1. cerebral localization as an assumption about the functional
   organization of the brain,
2. sensation and motion as categories for the physiological analysis
   of the nervous system,
3. the principle of the association of ideas as the fundamental law
   of mental activity,
4. a changing context for psychology and physiology, from a
   primarily philosophical approach within the static framework
   of the 'great chain of being' to a biological approach based on
   the dynamic of evolutionary change.

This work is an attempt to show the relations between these ideas and
the various categories of function derived from philosophical speculation
and naturalistic observation in the nineteenth century, beginning with
the work of Franz Joseph Gall and culminating in that of Sir David
Ferrier. The result is a history of the ways in which psychologists
related various sets of explanatory elements to the phenomena which
they felt psychology should explain, and to the functions of the nervous
system. This story is closely linked with the development of methods
in psychology, from speculation to naturalistic observation and to
experiment, and I have attempted to show these. By the end of the
nineteenth century, psychologists had provided themselves with the
elements of an adequate methodology and an apparently adequate
set of explanatory terms in the physiological aspect of their subject
They had also grasped that their field of enquiry was not merely (or,
perhaps even primarily) the life of the mind but rather the life of organisms, including men, and their adaptations to their respective environments. What needed explanation was not the representation of reality
by the substance mind, but the adjustment to reality by organisms
which think, feel, and behave. My narrative ends just at the point at
which psychologists were beginning to realize that their methods,
their new approach to the subject, and their impressive findings
relating feeling and movement to the brain, still did not provide them
with an adequate set of elements for resynthesizing the phenomena
of everyday life. Consequently, in the last decade of the nineteenth
century a number of new approaches—some extending, some comple-
menting, and some rejecting the views of their teachers—branched off

from the parent tradition. At the present time vigorous attempts are being made to relate the results of this divergence: reflexology, behaviourism, psychoanalysis, brain and behaviour, factor analysis, and ethology. It is hoped that the present study can be of use in recalling the development of some of the issues which led these movements to take their separate ways; that it might also encourage the recall of the basic questions, thus prompting a re-assessment of whether or not we are—or should be—still addressing ourselves to them. I hope that I have made a case for the use of historical method in the analysis of *current* problems in science.

I became an historian of science as a result of my inability to derive a coherent picture of experience and behaviour from the findings of current psychology. I had studied philosophy and psychology as an undergraduate in preparation for a career in psychiatry. While at medical school I was overwhelmed by the confusion in current attempts to relate the concepts used in the explanation of normal and abnormal behaviour to the physiology of the organisms. I devoted some time during my medical course to an attempt to discover some of the basic issues which were causing confusion. A review of current literature led further and further into the history of neurology and psychology until I felt I had indentified two crucial concepts: brain localization, and the functions which various investigators had attempted to localize. Localization has been the reigning assumption in brain research, and the history of various concepts of function *is* the history of psychology. It can be argued that the mind–body problem finds its most precise scientific expression in the related problems of classifying and localizing the functions of the brain.

A regressive study of the literature led back to the inception of empirical localization research in the work of Franz Joseph Gall. I then left medical school in order to work as an historian and trace the development of concepts of localization and of function since 1798.

I have acknowledged all the sources which I have used, and cited the ideas and specific quotations I have drawn from them, but the conception, development, and results of the study are the products of my own independent research. My treatment of Gall, the development of sensory-motor physiology, Bain, Spencer, Jackson, Carpenter, and Ferrier are wholly original, except for the specific information which I cite in the text. It will be seen that my treatment of Magendie, Mueller, the early history of associationism, Broca, and Fritsch and Hitzig, consists of straightforward exegesis and draws heavily on secondary sources. The assessment of the place of their work in the history of cerebral localization and psychophysiology is my own. Finally, the importance of phrenology in many aspects of the histories of psychology and biology has come as a complete surprise to me. I originally studied Gall because his work was the starting point of empirical localization, and I planned to spend only a few weeks on phrenology. It will be seen that the result is quite far from what I anticipated. In a sense, then, I should acknowledge an important debt to Gall. The perspective on later work which his writings has provided has done more than any other single factor to shape my own view of the domain and aims of biological psychology.

My field of interest has received scant attention from professional historians of science and medicine. Therefore it has not been possible in most cases to extend or qualify the findings of other scholars. There are a few notable exceptions to this generally bleak situation: A. O. Lovejoy, Owsei Temkin, Erwin H. Ackerknecht, Elie Halévy, Richard Hofstadter, Ralph B. Perry, G. S. Brett, Jürgen Thorwald, Sir Henry Head, Sir Geoffrey Jefferson, Sir Michael Foster, A. Macalister, J. M. D. Olmsted, and L. S. Hearnshaw.

Professor O. L. Zangwill has shown a very gratifying interest in the progress of my work. His initial encouragement and continuing support made it possible for me to extend a one-year visit into a four-year course of research. Mr John Dunn is responsible for any sense of sharpened criticism and historical judgement that may be evident in this work. Mr Jeremy Mulford is responsible for the language of those parts of the chapter on Gall which are in English. Gerd Buchdahl, Mary Hesse, and Rita van der Straeten of the Whipple Science Museum, Cambridge, have helped and encouraged me in innumerable ways, as have Sydney Smith, Joseph Needham, and Ruth Schwartz-Cowan. The cooperation of the (now disbanded) British Phrenological Society, and especially the enlightened approach of its former President and Hon. Secretary, Miss Frances Hedderly, F.B.P.S., enabled me to have access to phrenological works not readily available in libraries. Though we cannot agree in our conclusions, I hope that their interests may have paralleled my own in indicating the debt which modern biology, psychology, and brain research owe to Gall. I should like to thank the staff of the following libraries for their cooperation in making manuscripts and books available to me, often for extended periods: the departments of Anatomy, Physiology, Pathology, and Psychology of the University of Cambridge, the British Museum, the Royal Society, the National Central Library, the University of Edinburgh, and the National Library of Scotland. Sheila Young has provided both the home that allowed me to pursue my research and many helpful comments. Lady Rosemary Fitzgerald has done an excellent job in checking the manuscript, Mrs Verna Cole has done the typing, and Mrs Marilyn Pole has been indispensable in proof reading and pre-pairing the index. At various stages my research has been supported by grants from the United States Public Health Service, the Wellcome Foundation (U.S.A.), and King's College, Cambridge.

*Cambridge 1969*                                                      R.M.Y.

# CONTENTS

# CONTENTS

# INTRODUCTION

When you are criticizing the philosophy of an epoch, do not chiefly direct your attention to those intellectual positions which its exponents feel it necessary explicitly to defend. There will be some fundamental assumptions which adherents of all the variant systems within the epoch unconsciously presuppose. Such assumptions appear so obvious that people do not know what they are assuming because no other way of putting things has ever occurred to them. With these assumptions a certain limited number of types of philosophic systems are possible, and this group of systems constitutes the philosophy of the epoch.

Alfred North Whitehead, 1925, p. 71.

During the seventeenth century there evolved the scheme of scientific ideas which has dominated thought ever since. It involves a fundamental duality, with *material* on the one hand, and on the other hand *mind*. In between there lie the concepts of life, organism, function, instantaneous reality, interaction, order of nature, which collectively form the Achilles heel of the whole system.

*Ibid.*, pp. 83–4.

. . . the point which I wish to make is that we forget how strained and paradoxical is the view of nature which modern science imposes on our thoughts.

*Ibid.*, p. 122

IN THE conclusion of *The Metaphysical Foundations of Modern Physical Science*, E. A. Burtt stresses the implications of the scientific revolution for the study of mind and the behaviour of men and animals.

. . . it does seem like strange perversity in these Newtonian scientists to further their own conquests of external nature by loading on mind everything refractory to exact mathematical handling and thus rendering the latter still more difficult to study scientifically than it had been before. Did it never cross their minds that sooner or later people would appear who craved verifiable knowledge about mind in the same way they craved it about physical events, and who might reasonably curse their elder scientific brethren for buying easier success in their own enterprise by throwing extra handicaps in the way of their successors in social science? Apparently not; mind was to them a convenient receptacle for the refuse, the chips and whittlings of science, rather than a possible object of scientific knowledge.[1]

Around the beginning of the nineteenth century people did appear 'who craved verifiable knowledge about mind in the same way they craved it about physical events'. What hope did they have of succeeding?

[1] Burtt, 1932, pp. 318–19.

With what did traditional science provide them as a foundation on which to build? It provided them with a psychology modelled on the new physics and a series of dualisms which, if transcended, raised questions which no nice man would ask and which, when asked by not-so-nice men, led to philosophical absurdities. They apparently had little hope of success.

This book is an attempt to explain the problems faced by the early scientific enquirers into psychological phenomena; to trace some of the attempts during the nineteenth century to make psychology an experimental, biological science; and to indicate briefly the problems bequeathed to the present century by the early empirical investigators of the relations among mind, body and the environment.

The price paid for the scientific revolution in the physical sciences was the isolation of mind from nature and of the study of purposive behaviour from the advance of the scientific method. The fragmentation of the world into primary and secondary qualities, outer and inner, body and mind, and the exclusion of final causes from science have plagued the study of mind and behaviour at least since Descartes. This heritage provides the philosophical context for the present work. Cartesian dualism supplied an ontological basis for the separation of mind and body, while the theory of representative perception separated the knowing mind from its external object for knowledge. Pre-nineteenth century psychologists were thus preoccupied with the ontological problem of how (or whether) the mind could interact with the body on the one hand and with the epistemological problem of how a mind can know an object on the other. These metaphysical issues effectively precluded empirical investigation of the relations of mind and brain, the laws governing psychological and behavioural phenomena, and the relation of mental functions to the environment. Speculation and uncontrolled introspection filled the void.

From the Greeks came the speculation that the mind is made up of a series of innate powers or faculties which were localized in the hollow ventricles of the brain: Sensation and Imagination in the anterior chamber, Reason in the middle, and Memory in the posterior. When attention shifted to the solid parts of the brain, the faculties were speculatively localized in different areas by different schools. When the innateness of the faculties was challenged by the belief that there is nothing in the intellect that was not first in the senses, it was not the classification of the faculties which was questioned, but their origin. The question of the mind's role in the economy of the organism in its

intercourse with the environment was not a central issue. Attention
was diverted from this by the separation of the mind from the brain
and from the external world, and the related separation of man from
other organisms.

Given this prologue, it follows naturally that I have chosen to study
the following themes in the history of nineteenth-century biology:
(1) attempts to relate the mind to the brain by means of the concept of
cerebral localization, and (2) attempts to specify the functions of the
brain in the relations between organisms and their environments.

Both the empirical study of cerebral localization and the attempt
to determine a set of functions which could explain the thought and
behaviour of men and animals in their natural environments began
with the work of Franz Joseph Gall (1758–1828). The first chapter of
this book is a critical exposition of the last edition of Gall's major work,
*Sur les fonctions de cerveau* . . . (6 vols., 1822–25), and an assessment of
his place in the history of biology. While remaining agnostic on the
philosophical mind-body problem, he thought he had discovered a
method for demonstrating the correlation of innate faculties and
identifiable brain areas. It is relatively incidental for present purposes
that his 'cranioscopic' method led to the pseudo-science of phrenology
and was abandoned in favour of experimental cerebral localization.
The influence of his concepts and his empirical approach remain
highly significant. Gall convinced the scientific community once and
for all that 'the brain is the organ of the mind' and argued strongly
that both its structure and functions could be concomitantly analysed
by observation rather than speculation. His second major contribution
lay in his rejection of the speculative faculties of Imagination, Reason,
Memory, etc., as inadequate for the explanation of the differences
among (1) species in nature, and (2) individual men and animals
within their respective societies. He rejected the sensationalism of his
contemporaries as irreconcilable with the facts of species and individual
differences, and considered their classification of the faculties as
irrelevant to the talents, propensities and needs of men and animals
in their everyday lives. Gall's attempted classification of the functions
of the brain remains significant, while the form in which he cast his
psychology was that of the fallacious 'faculties', which point to important functions while begging the question of their origins and elements.
Gall's third main contribution was to stress how much men and
animals have in common: in his view they share 19 of the 27 fundamental faculties. It should be emphasized that Gall's biology was

pre-evolutionary and that he accepted the prevailing concept of a static 'chain of beings'. However, in extending the comparative method to man he adhered to the continuous gradations in the chain more faithfully than those who had placed a wide gulf between men and animals. The influence of his approach and of some of his specific findings on later workers with a more adequate biological theory is considered in detail, while an attempt is made to clarify the limitations of his own static conception. As G. H. Lewes (an exponent of the implications of Gall's work) pointed out, by placing man firmly in nature Gall 'rescued the problem of mental functions from Metaphysics, and made it one of Biology'. 'In his vision of Psychology as a branch of Biology, subject therefore to all biological laws, and to be pursued by biological methods, he may be said to have given the science its basis.'[1]

Gall laid the foundations of empirical research into the relations of the functions of the brain to that organ and to the environment. However, once the empirical method replaces speculation, the relative merits of simple naturalist observation and of controlling nature by experiment become apparent. Those who came after Gall were quick to criticize his correlative and anecdotal method and to seek to learn more by direct intervention into the functioning brain by surgical excision—the method of ablation. Similarly, while Gall had a great deal to say on the psychological issue of '*What are* the functions of the brain?' he made no contribution to the physiological issue of *how* the brain functions. His theory called for a one-to-one correlation between his faculties and cerebral 'organs', and Gall failed to seek the elements of which both the faculties and their cerebral bases were composed. In a sense he allowed his valid biological questions to dictate to the anatomy and physiology of the brain.

The history of brain and behaviour research after Gall involves the progressive acceptance and success of the experimental method in favour of his relatively crude correlations. Units into which both the physiology of the brain and its functions could be analysed were provided from the older psychological tradition: sensation and motion. This paradigm was applied to progressively higher parts of the nervous system from 1822 onwards. On the psychological side, the sensory-motor view was applied to mental processes by the school known as the Association Psychology. Gall's classification of the functions of the brain was abandoned, and most investigators reverted to those which

[1] Lewes, 1871, pp. 425 and 423.

he opposed. These, in turn, were viewed as complexes of associated sensations and motions. The question of the validity of cerebral localization provided the background against which psychophysical thinking occurred. Thus, the remaining chapters of the book are concerned with the rise of experimental neurophysiology from Flourens to Ferrier in the context of the assocation psychology, sensory-motor physiology and the theory of evolution. Pierre Flourens, François Magendie, and Johannes Mueller were the main exponents of the experimental method in research on the nervous system in the second quarter of the nineteenth century, and the relevant work of each is considered in some detail. Flourens provided the techniques which made brain research an experimental science. His findings, however, excluded the cerebral cortex from any role in motor functions and opposed localization of functions. His results provided the main support for the reluctance with which experimentalists applied the categories of sensation and motion to the organ of mind. The cortex and its functions were set apart from the analysis of the rest of the nervous system, and Flourens was explicit in his loyalty to Descartes and was vehemently opposed to Gall. Magendie began with different philosophical assumptions but also failed to transcend the older speculative approach to the higher functions. He maintained that their study was a branch of physiology, but the supposed physiological discipline involved was 'Ideology', the philosophical analysis of ideas into their sensory elements. However, while his eonceptions looked backward where the functions of the brain were concerned, he laid the foundations for later work by providing an experimental basis for the functional division of the spinal nerve roots into sensory and motor. Mueller's experiments and his standard handbook set the seal of orthodoxy on Flourens' view of the cortex and Magendie's findings on the spinal cord. He also conducted one sort of analysis for sub-cortical functions and another for the cortex: the cortex subserved the Will, which (somehow) 'played on' the lower centres 'like the keys of a pianoforte'.

Concomitant developments were occurring in psychology which prepared it for integration with the new sensory-motor physiology. One aspect of the association psychology would fit it naturally for such an integration—its sensationalism. However, this same feature— reflecting the epistemological preoccupation of the tradition—looked back to the old philosophical context of associationism, with its roots in Locke and Gay and its development by David Hartley and the Mills. In the nineenth century, associationists developed an interest in motion (and therefore behaviour) and brought this more balanced view into contact with the study of the nervous system. These developments occurred in the work of Alexander Bain, who did more than any other single figure to free psychology from its philosophic context and make it a natural science in its own right. The emphasis on learning as a consequence of doing (*i.e.*, of motion) which he developed from the work of Müeller laid the foundations for the interest in behaviour which came to dominate psychology by the turn of the century. By means of an analysis of Bain's writings it is possible to trace the integration of the association psychology with sensory-motor physiology in principle, though Bain was still reluctant to apply the sensory-motor paradigm to the cerebral cortex.

Where Bain had enriched the association psychology with a new interest in motion and had provided it with an important alliance with experimental neurophysiology, Herbert Spencer gave it a new foundation in evolutionary biology. A detailed analysis of Spencer's intellectual development helps to show the emergence of the assumptions of modern psychology from elements of phrenology, associationism, sensory-motor physiology and the theory of evolution. Spencer's psychological work, like that of Bain, grew out of an early interest in phrenology. However, where Bain had turned away from the biological approach of the phrenologists, Spencer drew heavily on it to stress the relations of mental phenomena, and the needs of the organism, to the environment. Learning became the continuous adjustment or adaptation of internal relations to external relations. The shortcomings of Bain's work are presented by means of an analysis of his book on phrenology and the study of character, and Spencer's careful criticism of his work from the new viewpoint of evolutionary associationism.

Returning to the development of brain research, the conceptions of Bain and Spencer are brought together and applied to the cerebral cortex in the clinical neurological work of John Hughlings Jackson. New evidence for localization of functions is provided by the findings of Pierre Paul Broca (whose links with the methods and assumptions of phrenology are noted) and Fritsch and Hitzig. Broca's localization of the lesion in loss of speech (aphasia) provided the first convincing evidence of cerebral localization, while his correlative method and faculty psychology were criticized by the experimentalists. Fritsch and Hitzig proved the role of the cortex in muscular motions and demonstrated experimentally the electrical excitability of the cerebral hemispheres, both of which had been denied since before Flourens.

Sir David Ferrier united the conceptions of Bain, Spencer, and Jackson with the findings of Broca and Fritsch and Hitzig and inaugurated the classical period of experimental cerebral localization. Ferrier played the central role in the localization of the cortical areas representing the five senses and numerous discrete muscular motions. These developments are briefly reviewed. More careful attention is paid to his attempt to derive a comprehensive psychology from sensory-motor psychophysiology. It provides an excellent vehicle for the examination of the problem bequeathed to the present century: how to relate biologically significant functions with a cortex organized in sensory-motor terms and psychological units of associated sensations and motions (which were soon to be viewed objectively as stimuli and responses).

Ferrier's classical work was completed by 1886. In the sixty years between the publication of Gall's work on *The Functions of the Brain* and the appearance of Ferrier's volume of the same name (in a second, much enlarged edition) the study of the brain and its functions had become an experimental science based on the theory of evolution. Concomitantly, mind had ceased to be viewed as an isolated substance, the role of which was representation of reality and the investigation of which was a branch of metaphysics. The study of mind had become a biological science concerned with an important function of the organism, and its role in adaptation to the environment was just beginning to be investigated. It will be seen that this book is an historical study which attempts to show the implications of philosophical assumptions as they affected, and continue to affect, the *scientific writings* of students of mind and brain. An attempt has been made to give a sense of period by the use of extensive quotation, contemporary commentaries, and reviews of the works of lesser figures.

The implicit conclusion of my argument is that a coherent integration of evolution and the study of man will not be achieved until the implications of the evolutionary principle of continuity and the concepts of function, adaptation, and utility are more consistently opposed to the legacy of Cartesian dualism on the one hand and the assumptions of the association psychology on the other. The wider context in which I hope my narrative will be viewed is the attempt to apply the categories of science to the interpretation of man's place in nature. Viewed philosophically, it attempts to show that the intervention of evolutionary theory failed to transcend the metaphysical commitment to the separation of mind from body and the related separation of man from the rest of nature. This is an aspect of a more general issue: the problem of finding some means of adhering to the assumptions of modern science as applied to man at the same time that the end of the tale gives us back a recognizable personal and interpersonal world. I hope that the book does show some of the ways in which a simple application of the ideas of corpuscular matter and motion to the study of mind, brain, and adaptation impoverished psychology. Beyond that I now feel that the problem of finding a way to transcend Cartesian dualism requires one to broaden the context of the enquiry to embrace the eighteenth and nineteenth-century debates on the principle of continuity which included natural theology, geology, and evolutionary theory as applied to the behavioural and social sciences.

In spite of the evidence which is offered in this book which indicates an integration of psychophysiology with evolutionary theory in the work of Spencer, Lewes, Jackson, and Ferrier, further investigation has shown that these developments were relatively isolated from the general evolutionary debate. In this study I have attempted to broaden the perspective within which certain aspects of nineteenth-century psychology, physiology and neurology should be viewed. At a later date I hope to place these developments within the context of the debate on man's place in nature, a debate which drew heavily on paradigms drawn from psychology, but the participants were unwilling or unable to concede that mental functions could be integrated within the general movement of naturalism with which the evolutionary debate was primarily concerned. It is hoped that this study, complemented by an interpretation of the broader movement, might serve as a basis for a philosophical critique of the conceptual limbo within which the behavioural and social sciences still find themselves. Certain aspects of this critique have already begun to emerge, and references to the relevant articles appear at the end of the bibliography.

# GALL AND PHRENOLOGY:
## SPECULATION *versus* OBSERVATION *versus* EXPERIMENT

**phrenology:** *n.* a doctrine that the excellence of **mental faculties** or **traits** is determined by the size of the brain area upon which they depend and that this can be judged by the development of the skull overlying the area. Modern psychology rejects entirely the **faculty psychology;** and modern neurology has entirely disproved the kind of brain localization asserted in phrenology. The practice today is a form of quackery.

H. B. and A. C. English, 1958.

Phrenology has been psychology's great *faux pas*.
J. C. Flugel, 1951.

No one can refuse them the merit of patient enquiry, careful observation, and unprejudiced reflection. They have performed the useful service of rescuing us from the trammels of doctrines and authorities, and directing our attention to nature; her instructions cannot deceive us. Whether the views of Gall and Spurzheim may be verified or not, our labours in this direction must be productive, must bring with them collateral advantages. Hence they may be compared to the old man in the fable, who assured his sons, on his death-bed, that a treasure was hidden in his vineyard. They began immediately to dig over the whole ground in search of it; and found, indeed, no treasure; but the loosening of the soil, the destruction of the weeds, the admission of light and air, were so beneficial to the vines, that the quality and excellence of the ensuing crop were unprecedented.
William Lawrence, 1822.

SOME distortion is inevitably involved in beginning an historical study at a point in time. In this instance the problem is increased by the fact that the starting point could be seen not only as arbitrary but also as absurd. Franz Joseph Gall (1758–1828) was, after all, the founder of what was later known as phrenology: the belief that important traits of character can be determined from a study of the bumps on the skull. Phrenology, of course, is nonsense; it has received no serious attention from the scientific community in the present century. To read about it in a book that is readily available today one must look in Gardner's *Fads and Fallacies in the Name of Science*, where it shares a chapter with the pseudo-sciences of physiognomy, palmistry, and graphology.[1] Even in the 1840's phrenology was in such bad repute that Professor Adam Sedgwick felt that he could best indicate his low opinion of Robert Chambers' *Vestiges* by stressing its links with 'phrenology (that sink-hole of human folly and prating coxcombry).[2] It would seem, therefore, that some explanation is required for beginning a study in the history of science that is concerned with the functions of the brain, with the works of Gall.

Cerebral localization may be defined as the doctrine that various parts of the brain have relatively distinct mental, behavioural, and/or physiological functions. Speculative localization of functions, based on the belief that the brain is the organ of the mind, is as old as Hero-philus and Galen, that is, as old as anatomy and physiology themselves. In the fourth century A.D., Nemesius localized specific faculties in different parts of the brain, and this approach was the dominant characteristic of medieval analyses of the relations of brain to mind. However, these localizations had three features which fail to recommend them to us. They were ventricular; they were speculative; they were based on a faculty psychology. Medieval ventricular localization was allied with a pneumatic physiology which does not here concern us. Its faculties were derived from the Platonic division of the mind into sense and intellect or from the tripartite Platonic soul of passion, spirit, and reason. These divisions were increased until seven to nine faculties were usually mentioned: sensory perception, intellect, memory, and imagination were the faculties most often mentioned, while attention, language, judgement, will, and movement also appeared in various classifications. The usual localizations were sensation and imagination in the anterior ventricles, reason or thought in the middle, and memory in the posterior. Vesalius began the attack on these notions by protesting against those philosophers who 'fabricate, like a Prometheus, out of their own dreams . . . some image of the brain, while they refuse to see that structure which the Maker of Nature has wrought.'[3] Neverthe-less, after men had begun to look directly at brains, and after the emphasis had been shifted from the ventricles to the solid portions of the brain, these same faculties were still speculatively localized in various cerebral structures. The issue of faculty psychologies will concern us as we look at Gall's views.

[1] Gardner, 1957, pp. 292–8.
[2] Quoted in Gillispie, new ed., 1959, p. 165.
[3] Singer, 1952, p. 4. On the early history of localization, see Soury, 1899; Macalister, 1885; Pagel, 1958; Woollam, 1958; Magoun, 1958; Clarke, 1962.

The position just before Gall began his investigations can be gathered from the view held by Prochaska. He published a *Dissertation on the Functions of the Nervous System*, in 1784 at Vienna, twelve years before Gall took his medical degree there. He pointed out that the theory of cerebral localization, though probably valid, had as yet no scientific basis.

But since the brain, as well as the cerebellum, is composed of many parts, variously figured, it is probable, that nature, which never works in vain, has destined those parts to various uses, so that the various faculties of the mind seem to require different portions of the cerebrum and cerebellum for their production.[1]

The 'divisions of the intellect', each of which 'has its allotted organ in the brain' are given by him as 'understanding, . . . the will, and imagination, and memory.[2] However, Prochaska qualifies his analysis by saying.

Hitherto it has not been possible to determine what portion of the cerebrum or cerebellum are specially subservient to this or that faculty of the mind. The conjectures by which eminent men have attempted to determine these are extremely improbable, and that department of physiology is as obscure now as ever it was.[3]

In 1799, Xavier Bichat, the eminent anatomist whose tissue theory transformed histology, could still maintain confidently that the brain was the seat of the intellect but was not the seat of the passions.[4] This was the state of affairs around the time when Gall began his investigations.

Gall's work is the proper beginning point because his was the first empirical approach both to the nature of the faculties and to their localizations. Gall's work will be considered here in terms of four separate issues: What are the functions of the brain? How are they localized in the brain? How can one determine the functions and their localizations? Finally, Gall's method will be contrasted with that of experiment.

## What are the Functions of the Brain?

Gall's detailed analyses of the functions of the brain and their localizations have been totally abandoned by subsequent investigators

---

1 Prochaska, translated Laycock, 1851, p. 446.
2 Ibid, p. 447.
3 Ibid., p. 446.
4 Bichat, no date, pp. 62–3, 252.

except for some very lucky guesses. However, it is still the case that his great contribution to psychology and to the understanding of the nervous system was the thesis that behaviour and the functions of the brain, as well as its functional organization, are amenable to objective observation. Before Gall, psychology was a branch of the philosophic discipline of epistemology, and divisions of the brain into functional regions had never been empirically related to behaviour. Gall combined a principle of analysis into behavioural and anatomical units with a requirement that we actually look to external nature rather than rely on introspection alone for our classifications of mental and behavioural phenomena.

Gall reports that the object of all his researches is 'to found a doctrine on the functions of the brain. The result of this doctrine ought to be the development of a perfect knowledge of human nature.'[1] He bases his psychophysiological system on the following suppositions:

1. That moral and intellectual faculties are innate.
2. That their exercise or manifestation depends on organization.
3. That the brain is the organ of all the propensities, sentiments, and faculties.
4. That the brain is composed of as many particular organs as there are propensities, sentiments, and faculties, which differ essentially from each other.[2]

As a methodological corollary to these suppositions, Gall makes a fifth assumption:

And as the organs and their localities can be determined by observation only, it is also necessary that the form of the head or cranium should represent, in most cases, the form of the brain, and should suggest various means to ascertain the fundamental qualities and faculties, and the seat of their organs.[3]

As his cranioscopy or theory of bumps was accepted more and more uncritically by him and his followers, it guaranteed the brevity of attention which scientists paid to his detailed findings. It was the undoing of his psychological and physiological work.

The beginnings of Gall's psycho-physiology arose from childhood observations made on his playmates. He notes that each of them had 'some peculiarity, talent, propensity, or faculty, which distinguished

[1] Gall, translated Lewis 1835, I, 55.
[2] Ibid., I.
[3] Ibid., I.

im from the others'. In particular, he notes that those who learn by
heart with great facility have 'large prominent eyes'.[1] He discovered
his same correlation in schoolmates and later on fellow-students at
university. These chance observations might provide any thoughtful
observer with enough material for a conjecture, which he might
formulate as a hypothesis and set out to test. It will become apparent
that Gall's method encouraged him to formulate the hypothesis but
failed to provide the means for testing it. He could find supporting
observations, but he could not falsify it.

Gall makes the induction:

> I could not believe, that the union of the two circumstances which had
> struck me on these different occasions, was solely the result of accident.
> Having still more assured myself of this, I began to suspect that there must
> exist a connection between this conformation of the eyes, and the facility of
> learning by heart.[2]

Having made the induction, he generalizes it:

> Proceeding from reflection to reflection, and from observation to observation,
> it occurred to me that, if memory were made evident by external signs, it
> might be so likewise with other talents or intellectual faculties. From this
> time all the individuals who were distinguished by any quality or faculty,
> became the object of my special attention, and of systematic study as to the
> form of the head.[3]

It should be noted that Gall has so far been doing straightforward
physiognomy.

The step in his reasoning which changes our view of Gall from being
the founder of an empirical psychology based on physiognomy (which,
as I shall try to show, is very interesting in its own right) to being the
founder of a very advanced functional psychology and the modern
concept of cerebral localization, is the following:

> I had in the interval commenced the study of medicine. We had much said
> to us about the functions of the muscles, the viscera, etc., but nothing
> respecting the functions of the brain and its various parts. I recalled my
> early observations, and immediately suspected, what I was not long in
> reducing to certainty, that the difference in the form of heads is occasioned
> by the difference in the form of the brains.[4]

[1] Gall, 1835, I, 57–8.
[2] Ibid., I, 58–9.
[3] Ibid., I, 59.
[4] Ibid., I.

Given these two sorts of data—external signs and marked propensities or talents—Gall believed that he had a method for discovering the functions of the brain and their local organs in the nervous system. He also arrived at the novel, and historically very significant, conviction that the functions *had to be discovered* and that this was a task for the naturalist, not the philosopher. In order to maintain this conviction, though, he had to find an answer to the prevailing belief among the followers of Locke and Condillac that all faculties, propensities, and talents are derived from experience: the sensationalist hypothesis that men are born equal and become different through education and accidental circumstances.

We have now raised two issues: the belief in external signs of character, and the problem of the sources of the faculties, propensities, and talents. In order to appreciate Gall's position on these matters, it is necessary to examine his views in the light of two traditions: physiognomy and the sensationalist psychology deriving from Locke.

Duncan, King of Scotland, assures us that 'There's no art/To find the mind's construction in the face.[1] Gall would have agreed,[2] but since the time of Aristotle, attempts have been made to infer character (and to achieve insights about the macrocosm) by studying the external signs of bodies.[3] The specific claims of contemporary physiognomists were absurd, but there is something to be learned from the aims of their pseudo-science: the attempt to find stable and reliable phenomena in the objective world of matter and motion which indicate mental or emotional phenomena which cannot be observed directly. It is as an alternative to introspection that physiognomy recommends itself. Gall rejected as useless the holistic and vague assertions of Lavater that all parts of the body reflect all others to one who is observant enough to see, but he did grasp the significance of Lavater's belief that all truths are 'truths of the surface'. Lavater could only correlate external signs with characterological observations and believe that he had reliable guides. Gall felt that he could demonstrate the dependence of his external signs on the size of the underlying portions of the cerebral hemispheres. In the event, Gall too was wrong, but his hypothesis was extremely plausible at the beginning of the last century, and it played a very important part in the transition from speculations about

---

[1] Shakespeare, *Macbeth*, I. iv. 11–12.

[2] Gall, 1835, V, 261 ff.; Ibid., I, 17–18.

[3] See Thorndike, 1958; VIII, 448–75; Macalister, 1885, XIX, 3–5; Allport, 1937, pp. 65–78; Lavater, translated Holcroft, 1804.

unspecifiable physiological homogeneity to the experimental study of the brain.

The second tradition in the light of which Gall's work should be viewed is the sensationalist psychology derived from Locke. Locke had set out to explore the nature of the human understanding by considering 'the discerning faculties of a man, as they are employed about the objects which they have to do with'.[1] The tradition which derived from Locke's work gave rise to an intellectualist psychology about the limits of understanding, the sources of ideas and the relations between minds and objects in the processes of learning and knowing. The categories and operations which Locke defined and studied were therefore intellectual ones. His first task was to free philosophy from the tyranny of Platonic and Cartesian special sources of knowledge—the innate ideas. It was in reaction to this rationalist extreme and in the name of empiricism that Locke put forth a *tabula rasa* view of the origin of the contents of the understanding. Locke's views reached Gall in the more extreme form of Condillac's sensationalism. Condillac rejected the second of Locke's sources of ideas, reflection. He sought to derive all the faculties and even instincts from simple sensations, and the principle of seeking pleasure and avoiding pain. Condillac's method was typical of the sensationalists: he spoke in the name of empiricism while he conducted his arguments by means of elaborate speculations about the successive addition of the senses to a statue.[2] Condillac's method of analysis and sensationalist convictions were represented by the movement called 'Idéologie', whose influence prevailed in Paris when Gall reached there in 1807.[3]

It was therefore natural for Gall to express his own theories in relation to the conceptions of Locke, Condillac, and their contemporary disciplines, Cabanis and Destutt de Tracy. He rejected the tenets of sensationalism and sought to replace their epistemological psychology with a biological one. He replaced the *tabula rasa* view of the mind with a theory postulating a set of innate, inherited instincts transmitted in the form of cerebral organs, whose activity varied with the size of the respective organs. He argued that the senses were the instruments of these instincts instead of their source.

In rejecting the *tabula rasa* view, Gall was not rejecting empiricism. In fact, he argued that it was the sensationalists who had failed to be

---

[1] Locke, 5th ed., 1961, I, 5.
[2] Condillac, translated Carr, 1930.
[3] See Cabanis, 2nd ed., 1805; Rosen, 1946; Boas, new ed., 1964; Temkin, 1946 and 1947; Vartanian, 1960.

empirical enough. They had failed to observe nature and to note the extreme variations among men and among different species of animals, differences which could not be accounted for in terms of their immediate environments and experiences alone. There was something 'biologically given' in the abilities of men and animals, and it was this that Gall maintained in the face of the sensationalism of his time. He was not upholding the doctrine of innate ideas; he was upholding differences in natural endowment. This viewpoint led him to reject the optimism of the more sanguine environmentalists and to insist that the moral perfectibility of the human species is confined within the limits of its organization.[1] He held this same view with respect to different species and to different individuals within a given species. The ethical and forensic implications of this position gave Gall much trouble within his own thought, and their recognition by critics had led to the proscription of his lectures in Vienna and to constant charges of materialism and fatalism, which he answered feebly as seen from our vantage point.[2] However, these issues in his thought cannot be treated here. The important point is that Gall's concept of innateness served biology, not revelation or a Socratic doctrine of reminiscence.

Gall attempted to replace the speculatively derived, normative, intellectual categories of the sensationalists with observationally determined faculties which reflected the activities, talents and adaptations of individual organisms and were the determinate variables in individual behaviour. In setting out to search for such categories, Gall insisted on the unity of man with the rest of nature, and applied the methods of the naturalist to man more thoroughly than had been done before. His aim was that psychology should cease to be the domain of the speculative philosopher and should become the special study of the naturalist and physiologist.[3] That is, Gall saw the study of the functions of the brain—what is now called psychology—as a biological science. There is no simple dichotomy between a representational psychology and an adaptational one—between the epistemological and biological views of the goals of psychology. Locke and Gall both speak in terms of adaptation. But when Locke does so, he is concerned with the adaptation of the understanding to its proper objects for knowledge;

---

[1] This view extends to man's appreciation of the Deity: the pervasive religious ideas of man and revealed religion would have been absolutely impossible if the human species had not been endowed with the appropriate nervous apparatus for having these experiences. Gall, 1810–19, IV, 256.

[2] See Gall et al., translated Combe, 1838; Temkin, 1947; Lange, 3rd ed., 1925.

[3] Gall, 1835, I, 62.

the operations of the understanding are performed for the sake of reaching true inductions. He assures us that God has given men 'whatsoever is necessary for the conveniences of life and information of virtue; and has put within the reach of their discovery, the comfortable provision for this life and the way that leads to a better'.[1] Our senses, faculties and organs are fitted to the conveniences and exigencies of this life and our environments.[2] Locke's analysis is not concerned with what these environments require and how the faculties are specifically adapted to them; it is concerned with the instrument for knowing objects—the understanding. Gall's position on this issue is in some respects a striking anticipation of the adaptational or functional view of psychology which was developed half a century later in the wake of the theory of evolution. The functional viewpoint which Gall shares with later workers also inevitably concerns itself with the adaptation of the mind to its proper objects, but in a wider context; the role of mind in the interactions of a behaving (not primarily a knowing) organism with its environment. The basic issue is not the content of psychological experience but the activities of the man or animal which do or do not promote survival or mastery over the physical and social environments. However, Gall's psychology is pre-evolutionary. In stressing its functional, biological form and contrasting this with the older elementist, epistemological psychology of the Lockean tradition, it is necessary to keep this important historical limitation in mind.

While Gall differs profoundly from previous psychologists on the point of what adaptations are *for*, he is nearer Locke than the post-Darwinian psychologists on the question of how adaptations occur. He did not believe that they evolve through the dynamic interaction of organisms with their respective environments by means of natural selection. Rather they are set for all time by the place of an organism in the 'great chain of being'.[3] This static view of nature was the major generalization in biology until it was replaced by the theory of evolution. It dominates the details of Gall's psychology, making his faculties isolated and independent and leading to a relatively uninteresting character typology that almost completely fails to fulfil the promise of his most exciting conception of the domain of psychology.

The grounds for Gall's rejection of the old faculties were that they were neither determinate for individual and species differences, nor

---

[1] Locke, 1961, I, 7.
[2] Ibid., I, 250-3.
[3] The classical discussion of this concept is Lovejoy, new ed., 1960.

empirically derived. His rejection of faculties which are normative, or concerned with mind in general, in favour of those primitive characteristics of human nature which might explain individual differences, is the basis for his recognition as the first modern empirical psychologist of character and personality.[1]

Gall reviews the categories of psychological analysis that had been put forward by various philosophers and physiologists, with special emphasis on those of the sensationalists.[2] His conception of the domain of psychology makes their categories quite useless. Gall's faculties are designed to serve a purpose quite different from those of the philosophers. He sees the goal of psychology as a differential one with its domain as the behaviour, roles, talents and differences of men and animals. Since the normative psychology which he opposed was preoccupied with mind in general and the relations between the mind and potential objects for knowledge, Gall argues,

Whether we admit, one, two, three, four, five, six, or seven faculties of the soul, we shall see, in the sequel, that the error is always essentially the same, since all these faculties are mere abstractions. None of the faculties mentioned, describes either an instinct, a propensity, a talent, nor any other determinate faculty, moral or intellectual. How are we to explain, by sensation in general, by attention, by comparison, by reasoning, by desire, by preference, and by freedom, the origin and exercise of the principle of propagation; that of the love of offspring, of the instinct of attachment? How explain, by all these generalities, the talents for music, for mechanics, for a sense of the relations of space, for painting, poetry, etc?[3]

Gall does not deny the existence of the philosophers' categories. They have meaning but only as abstractions and generalities:

they are not applicable to the detailed study of a species, or an individual. Every man, except an idiot, enjoys all these faculties. Yet all men have not the same intellectual or moral character. *We need faculties, the different distribution of which shall determine the different species of animals, and their different proportions of which explain the difference in individuals.* All bodies have weight, all have extension, all are impenetrable in a philosophical sense; but all bodies are not gold or copper, such a plant, or such an animal. Of what use to a naturalist the abstract and general notions of weight, extent, impenetrability? By confining ourselves to these abstractions, we should always remain in ignorance of all branches of physics, and natural history. This is precisely what has happened to the philosophers with their generalities. From most ancient to the most modern, they have not made a step further, one than another, in the exact knowledge of the true nature of man, of his

---

[1] See Bain, 1861; Lewes, 2nd ed., 1857 and 3rd ed., 1871; Allport, 1937; Spoerl, 1935–6.
[2] Gall, 1835, I, 80–83.     [3] Ibid., I, 84.

inclinations and talents, of the source and motive of his determinations.[1] [*Emphasis added*].

With the judgement that 'The most sublime intelligence will never be able to find in a closet, what exists only in the vast field of nature,[2] Gall turns his attention away from speculations and toward common society, family life, schools, the jails and asylums, medical cases, the press, men of genius, and the biographies of great or notorious men. Gathering together the variations among the individuals he has observed, and adding to these the results of his comparative studies of animals, he concludes that they cannot be explained in terms of the faculties of the philosophers. In general, he maintains that 'every hypothesis, which renders no reason for the daily phenomena which the state of health and the state of disease offer us, is necessarily false'.[3] It is this requirement, to explain individual differences, that leads Gall to insist both on the innateness[4] and the plurality of the faculties and their organs.[5]

Having rejected the normative faculties of the philosphers, Gall was required to supply an alternative interpretation of the significant factors in mental life. It has already been mentioned that he viewed the brain and its functions in terms of an analogy with other bodily organs and their functions, and that his movement from mere correlation of external signs with striking behaviours to his emphasis on the brain was the most significant step in his reasoning.[6] Gall's second, third, and fourth basic suppositions were intimately concerned with the consideration of mind, behaviour, and character as *functions* of the brain. There are three stages in Gall's thought on the issue: his analogy of organ and function, the relations between this analogy and the traditional mind-body problem, and his reversion to a faculty psychology.

Gall juxtaposes his physiognomical discoveries with the prevailing ignorance of the functions of the brain and its various parts. He uses the analogy with other organs and their functions repeatedly in his arguments to establish that the brain is the organ of the mind. For example, in arguing against the view that every other function has a particular apparatus of its own—seeing, hearing, salivating, producing bile—he asks of Nature, 'But, if she has constructed a particular apparatus for each function, why should she have made an exception of the brain? Why should she not have destined this part, so curiously contrived, for particular functions?'[7]

---

[1] Gall, 1835, I, 88–9.   [2] Ibid., V, 317.   [3] Ibid., V, 251.
[4] Ibid., I, 137.   [5] Ibid., II, 268.   [6] See above, p. 13.
[7] Gall, 1835; II, 99–100.

3

His approach to the traditional mind-body problem is to argue that the soul or mind is not a principle, acting purely by itself, which produces the faculties and propensities. Rather, '*The faculties and propensities of man have their seat in the brain*'.[1] The whole of the second volume of *The Function of the Brain* is concerned with showing that the faculties and propensities depend on organization and that the organization involved is the brain. This was not a new view. It is said to have been held by the author of the first work which mentions the brain, the *Edwin Smith Papyrus*.[2] It was held by Hippocrates, who identified the brain as the cause of all of the operations of the understanding.[3] In defending himself against the charge of materialism that led to the proscription of his lectures in Vienna, Gall argues forcefully, and in detail, for the antiquity and repeated appearance of the belief that the brain is the organ of the mind.[4] Cabanis had even used the specific 'functional' argument:

In order to form for one's self a just notion of the operations which result in the production of thought, it is necessary to conceive of the brain as a peculiar organ, specially designed for the production thereof, just as the stomach is designed to effect digestion, the liver to filter the bile, the parotids and the maxillary and sublingual glands to prepare the salivary juices.[5]

However, no one before Gall argued for the dependence of the mind on the brain in such detail, specifically disproving the role of other organs, specifically including all the intellectual and moral propensities, and demonstrating countless instances of the parallelism between variations in the brain and variations in mental and behavioural phenomena. He showed all this by means of comparative studies on animals, the development of children, ageing, and diseases of the brain. Gall demonstrated again and again that the functions varied as the brain varied. It was Flourens, no friend of Gall's psychophysiology, who acknowledged that

the proposition that the brain is the exclusive seat of the soul is not a new proposition, and hence does not originate with Gall. It belonged to science before it appeared in his Doctrine. The merit of Gall, and it is by no means a slender merit, consists in having understood better than any of his predecessors the whole of its importance, and in having devoted himself to its

[1] Gall, 1835, I, 10.
[2] Castiglioni, 2nd ed., translated Krumbhaar, 1947, p. 57.
[3] Hippocrates, translated Adams, 1949, p. 138.
[4] Gall, 1838, pp. 315–21.    [5] Cabanis, 1805, I, 152–3.

demonstration. It existed in science before Gall appeared—it may be said to reign there ever since his appearance.[1]

Having established this conclusion, Gall sets out to systematically exploit it. The whole of the third volume of his *Functions of the Brain* is devoted to the proof of the plurality of the functions of the brain and the plurality of their 'organs'. Again, he argues by analogy with other organs. If each of the senses has its own specific material basis, then each of the functions of the brain has its own organ. The analogy of mental and behavioural phenomena as functions of a structure or organ could not be fully appreciated until it had been firmly established that the brain is the organ of the mind. When one does begin to exploit the analogy of the brain with other organs, one is led naturally to consider what role it plays in the economy of the organism and its interactions with the environment. Here are the beginnings of a functional psychology, and one can see that this approach naturally led Gall to a concern for the phenomena of everyday life, character, talents, and roles in society. The change of emphasis from a psychology of the soul as an insulated substance, which performs intellectual operations in relation to objects for knowledge, also becomes clear and natural. Locke's epistemological analysis and the faculty psychologies of Reid and Stewart are concerned with the operations, faculties, and powers of mind as an autonomous substance, while Gall concentrates on the mind as a function and considers its functional role.[2]

Gall's understanding of the explanatory goals of psychology was immensely enriched by his concept of mental activity and behaviour as functions of the brain. Yet, having proposed the concept of function as an alternative to the old faculty view, he retreats into the latter in his detailed psychology. To be sure, his faculties are of a new kind, given their functional framework, but they are faculties none the less, and his detailed psychology suffers from all the defects of the faculty view.

The circularity of faculty psychologies has been recognized since

---

[1] Flourens, translated Meigs, 1846, pp. 27–8.

[2] George H. Lewes was impressed by Gall's biological point of view and observational method. Lewes' chapter on Gall in his *History of Philosophy*, gives an excellent and balanced view of the value of Gall's approach and principles, while rejecting Gall's detailed attempts at psychological explanation. On the issue of functional thinking, Lewes says, 'He first brought into requisite prominence the principle of the necessary relation, in mental as in vital phenomena, between organ and function. Others had proclaimed the principle incidentally, he made it paramount by constant illustration, by showing it in detail, by teaching that every variation in the organ must necessarily bring about a corresponding variation in the function'. (Lewes, 3rd ed., 1871, II, 416).

Galen,[1] and the point was reiterated by Descartes, Locke, and Flourens before Herbart's criticism sounded its death knell. The form of explanation used by medieval psychologists, by Wolff, Reid, and Stewart, and by the phrenologists has been uniformly criticized by late nineteenth and twentieth century psychologists for confusing classification with explanation. Faculties are only class concepts invested with a fictional reality. Faculty psychologists change questions spuriously into answers by animating the operations of the mind or abilities, activities or other dispositions. Such descriptive terms become hypostatized, and take on the qualities of an occult agent, cause, or power. For example, Thomas Reid moves directly from the description of classes of mental operations to the postulation of a faculty or power as active agent: 'The words *power* and *faculty*, which are often used in speaking of the mind, need little explication. Every operation supposes a power in the being that operates; for to suppose anything to operate, which has no power to operate, is manifestly absurd.[2] Gall's faculty psychology confuses 'function' as a classificatory concept for a number of related behaviours, with the cause or causes of those behaviours.

When Gall explains that a woman loves her children very much because a large cerebral organ produces a strong faculty of 'love of offspring', or that a man can reproduce very easily verbal material that he has heard or read because he has a highly developed 'memory for facts', he is giving no more of an explanation than Molière's physician, who explained that opium produces sleep because it has a soporific tendency. However, in rejecting Gall's faculties as explanations one should not ignore the importance and novelty of the questions he begs and the classification of functions which he offers. It is possible to accept his approach to the functions of the brain and even some of the functions themselves as novel problems for psychological analysis, without lapsing into the circularity of faculty psychology.

Leaving aside the problems raised by the form of Gall's psychology, it could easily be shown that each of the functions which Gall proposed as basic has emerged again as a function investigated by modern brain and behaviour research, using the concept and techniques of cerebral localization. There is no point in producing a detailed list of these functions, since variations in the operational meaning of the terms would reduce it to an elaborate pun. However, the point should not be missed that the fundamental functions which Gall derived from his naturalist observations and which were ridiculed as fanciful by subsequent

[1] Riese, 1959, pp. 22, 24.    [2] Reid, 6th ed., 1863, I, 221.

investigators have re-appeared as problems in recent research. A few examples should suffice: sexual instinct, maternal behaviour, self-defence, carnivorous instinct, verbal memory, sense of locality, language, music, numerical ability, conscience—each of these has had its modern investigators and localizers.

## How are the Functions Localized?

Except for his purely neuroanatomical discoveries, the only indisputable contribution that Gall made to the history of science is the concept of cerebral localization. It is this concept that makes Gall's work classical, in that all subsequent research involved taking some stand on the issue of whether various functions are localized in specific parts of the brain. Some investigators conducted much of their work in explicit opposition to cerebral localization, some accepted a more or less modified form of the doctrine as their basic assumption about the functional organization of the brain, and others confined their use of the concept to a technique for either pathological and clinical studies, or physiological research. The role which this concept played in subsequent clinico-pathological and physiological research in the work of Broca, Fritsch and Hitzig, Hughlings Jackson, David Ferrier, and other investigators in the nineteenth century and its continued use up to the present, will be discussed in the following chapters. However, one judgement by a later investigator may briefly indicate the debt of later workers to Gall's initiative.

The minute anatomy of the convolutions was unknown in the time of Gall, and he based his phrenological theories rather on the external prominences of the skull—on cranioscopy—than upon a careful study of the convolutions to which these prominences corresponded, and although his conclusions must be considered in many instances arbitrary and hypothetical, still I would say, 'Let not the spark be lost in the frame it has served to kindle,' for in spite of all that has been said against Gall, and all that has been written in depreciation of his labours, beyond all doubt his researches gave an impulse to the cerebral localization of our faculties, the effect of which is especially visible in our own days; and I look upon his work as a vast storehouse of knowledge, and as an imperishable monument to the genius and industry of one of the greatest philosophers of the present age. The localization of cerebral function may be said to have received the first real impetus from Gall, for before his time no such attention was given to the subject as deserved the name of systematic study.[1]

---

[1] Bateman, 2nd ed., 1890, p. 319. Cf. the judgement of Wm. Lawrence quoted above on the first page of this chapter.

For the present, I should like to confine my attention to the role which the concept of cerebral localization played in Gall's psychological and anatomical investigations. The main point that will emerge from this analysis is that while the *concept* of cerebral localization was central to his theory, direct investigation of the brain and specification of clearly defined areas on the cortex played almost no part in his work. Gall had elaborated his four basic principles and many of the details of his theory before the first publication of his views in 1798.[1] J. C. Spurzheim, his pupil and colleague from 1800 to 1813, says that Gall had 'not yet begun to examine the structure of the brain' by 1800.[2] He had been elaborating his views about the functions of the brain as early as 1792, and gave a public course on the subject at least as early as 1796. His views at that time included the argument that the brain is necessary to the manifestations of mind, 'of the plurality of the mind's organs, and of the possibility of discovering the development of the brain by the configuration of the head'.[3] 'Between 1800 and 1804 he modified his physiological ideas, and brought them to the state in which he professed them at the commencement of our travels' (1805).[4] Gall had met an intelligent woman with extreme hydrocephalus whose intellectual capacities were apparently unimpaired and had reached the conclusion that 'the structure of the brain must be different from what it is commonly supposed to be. He now felt the necessity of examining the mind's organ anatomically'.[5] The neuro-anatomical investigations which he then began to make with the help of Spurzheim, and which were the basis of his well-deserved reputation for dissection and discovery, were completely unrelated to his doctrines of function and his organology. They were concerned with dissection method, subcortical and medullary structures, the nuclei of cranial nerves, the decussation of the pyramids, the continuity of grey matter with the white fibrous matter,[6] and a very odd doctrine about the unfolding of the hemispheres in hydrocephalus. His neuroanatomical work was not inconsistent with his organology, but was irrelevant to it. The anatomical exposition in his 1808 memoir, the first volume of his *Anatomie*, and the anatomical debates in the final volume of *The Functions of the Brain* are not integrated conceptually with the detailed exposition of his psychology and craniology-organology in the rest of his works.[7]

[1] Gall, 1835, I, 6–19.    [2] Spurzheim, 1826, pp. ix–x.    [3] Ibid., p. ix.
[4] Ibid., p. x.    [5] Ibid.    [6] See Temkin, 1953.
[7] Flourens stresses this point in his critical work on phrenology. In his discussion of the memoir which Gall and Spurzheim submitted to the National Institute in 1808, he says that

The key to this very baffling discontinuity in Gall's exposition is that here, as with his naturalist principles, his functional viewpoint, and his critique of philosophical psychology, he enunciates important principles which he was unable to carry out in practice. Thus, Gall insists on connecting anatomy and physiology (which, for him, means psychology) in principle, since the brain is the organ of the mind, but he cannot demonstrate the details of the relations between brain and mind. When the Committee of the National Institute reviewed the memoir submitted by Gall and Spurzheim, they discussed the anatomical findings and conclusions, but insisted that it was not within their province to connect these with Gall and Spurzheim's physiological doctrine of the special functions of the different parts of the brain.[1] Gall was very indignant about this decision, since he (I think rightly) took them to be separating anatomical studies from physiological studies *in principle*. The Committee had said that Gall's anatomical discoveries came within their province, but that the physiological doctrine 'in no way comes under the cognizance of the class, since it ultimately depends upon observations relative to the moral and intellectual disposition of individuals, which certainly are not within the sphere of any academy of sciences'.[2] To Gall this separation of the sciences of anatomy and physiology was founded on the assumption that the functions of the brain 'have no immediate and necessary connection with its structure'.[3] His reply is based on the organ-function paradigm that had become central to his thinking: 'Can any one advance that motion and secretion have no relation to the organization of the muscles and viscera; and that digestion and the circulation of the blood have not an inseparable affinity with the stomach and the heart? etc.'[4] The principle at stake was whether the brain was the organ of the mind. To rule out investigations of the mind connected with the study of the brain was to deny this fundamental truth.

Gall considered this matter of principle to be quite a different question from that of the proper *method of discovery* of the functions of

---

it does not contain 'one word of *special anatomy, of secret anatomy*, of what might be called *antomy of the Doctrine*; or, in other terms, and as it would be expressed at the present day, of *phrenological anatomy*. . . . The anatomy of Gall's memoir is nothing but very ordinary anatomy . . . it is sufficiently clear that, whatever side we take upon these questions [i.e., anatomical debates on conventional issues about the organization of the brain in which Gall played a leading part], his doctrine assuredly would neither gain nor lose any thing'. (Flourens, 1846, pp. 70–71. Cf. pp. 72–4.)

[1] Tenon et al., 1809, pp. 36–7.    [2] Ibid., pp. 36–7.    [3] Gall, 1835, VI, 29.
[4] Ibid., VI, 30.

the brain. In practice, 'the discovery of the functions of the brain is made independent of the knowledge of its structure . . .'[1] There is no doubt in Gall's mind about the priority of behavioural studies in his own work.

The knowledge of the functions has always preceded that of the parts. It is, also, as I have said elsewhere, without the aid of the anatomy of the brain, that I have made all my physiological discoveries; and these discoveries might have existed for ages, without their agreement with the organization having been detected.[2]

A detailed analysis of the history of discovery of each of his fundamental functions supports this description of his method. In no case does anatomical information play anything more than a confirmatory role in his elucidation of the functions. He presents detailed arguments containing both in principle and historical objections to show that the study of structure has never led, and never could lead, to a knowledge of the functions of the brain. He holds this position against the findings of simple dissection, neuropathological studies, mutilations (ablations) and comparative anatomy.[3]

Gall's argument against morphological and experimental researches on the brain is based on the view that they cannot themselves give a knowledge of the functions of the brain, and that without such knowledge they are meaningless. The reason that the attempts at cerebral localization before his work had failed was because no attempt had been made to find first the 'radical, fundamental, primitive faculties'.[4] There could be no cerebral organs for the abstract, metaphysical, speculative faculties of the philosophers. No amount of philosophical speculation or of morphological investigation could be of the slightest use until the fundamental faculties were discovered from observation of the habits of animals and of the moral and intellectual characters of individuals in nature and in society. Instead of conducting minute researches on brains, physiologists must first gain a knowledge of the 'diversity of mechanical aptitudes, instincts, propensities, and faculties, which constantly attend this variety of organization'.[5] In the light of the extreme physiological reductionism that occurred in the last three decades of the nineteenth century, one must acknowledge that Gall's

[1] Gall, 1835, VI, 29.     [2] Ibid., II, 25–26.     [3] Ibid., III, 88–104.
[4] Ibid., III, 82.     [5] Ibid., VI, 192.

view of the priority of behavioural and psychological investigations was ignored.[1]

Thus there was no doubt in Gall's mind that we must first know the functions before we can learn anything important from the direct study of the brain. He is not entirely consistent, though, on the role of brain studies after the functions have been elucidated by behavioural studies. In his own special doctrine he uses anatomical, pathological, clinical, and comparative findings when they confirm his psychological findings. As the founder of craniology, he does not doubt that the correlation between a striking behaviour and a cranial prominence is telling him something about the brain. The point that he insists on is that one must first know the functions. If anatomical and experimental findings confirm his behavioural discoveries, all is well: they ought to do that.[2] If physiological findings are in opposition to anatomical findings, the issue is slightly obscure. Ordinarily, Gall is quite clear on this point. Consistent with his view that the brain is the organ of the mind, he takes the position early in his work that 'A doctrine of the functions of the brain, if it is in contradiction with its structure, must be necessarily false'.[3] However, in the conclusions to his last volume, written after vehement controversies with the experimental findings of Flourens, Rolando and others, and the publication of the anatomical findings of a number of comparative anatomists, Gall retreats from this firm stand and appears to betray his own fundamental thesis. A charitable view of the following quotation might be, though, that he is protecting his reputation against the day that he might be found a bad anatomist but a good psychologist. His conclusion is

That the fate of the physiology of the brain is independent of the truth or falsity of my assertions relative to the laws of the organization of the nervous system, in general, and of the brain in particular, just as the knowledge of the functions of a sense is independent of the knowledge of the structure of its apparatus.[4]

If it is understood clearly that Gall places anatomical investigations

---

[1] It is interesting to note that in later work Hebb came forth with a position very similar to Gall's: 'a physiologically oriented theory of behavior must remain a *psychological* theory. It will have to employ constructs derived from behavior which could not have originated with neurological data, even if subsequently one finds a way of relating them to such data'. (Hebb, 1959, p. 635.) Gall would have agreed emphatically with Hebb that the direct study of brain function can never be a substitute for psychology, although he might have been less enthusiastic than Hebb in believing that it contributes essentially to psychology, except—Gall would have said—in principle and as confirmatory of psychological findings. (Hebb, 1959a, p. 269.)

[2] Gall, 1835, VI, 80.     [3] Ibid., VI, 30.     [4] Ibid., VI, 237–8.

as a secondary matter in his search for the functions, one can still ask to what extent he attempts to specify the localization of functions in the brain substance. In the first place, his localizations are confined to the cortex: to areas that could exert an effect on the conformation of the skull. In the second place, they are in all cases offered as a confirmation of a localization he had made in the belief that the cranium serves as a faithful cast of the underlying brain. It is always the brain that he is writing about, but given the faith he had in the craniological hypothesis, he was not systematic in actually looking at brains. His faith in cranioscopy became so complete that at one point he says that 'There is no other possible means of discovering the functions of the cerebral parts'.[1] Nor do his writings indicate when he was looking at brains and when he was inferring the existence of the cerebral organ from prominences on the overlying cranium. He occasionally specifies an observation made directly on a brain. He assure us that each time he checked the brain against the cranium, his findings on the cranium were confirmed.[2] But when he specifies the convolutions which make up an organ for a given function, one often has no way of knowing whether the evidence for this included direct observations on brains. He merely specifies the convolutions by a number of one of the brains in his atlas. He does not pretend to be able to 'circumscribe exactly the extent of each organ'.[3] His organs do not divide according to the convolutional patterns of the brain.[4] Gall was content to specify the areas and to admit freely that he neither knew the functions of all the cerebral parts nor the precise limits of those parts whose function he had specified.[5] He left the precise delimitation of the cerebral organs to future investigators and contented himself with saying that in discovering the functions of the brain he had made their task meaningful for the first time, and immensely easier.

The conclusion one reaches about Gall's work on localization is that he was more interested in the nature of the functions than in their localization, and that he had more to say about localization in principle than in practice. Finally, given the inability of later workers to confirm his craniological methods, the approach he took to direct observation of the brain leaves much to be desired. The principal merit of his work, then, is a conceptual one, not an empirical finding or set of findings. He drives home the point by constant reiteration and exemplification

---

[1] Gall, 1835, II, 34.
[2] Ibid., VI, 86. Cf. III, 25, where he answers his critics on this point.
[3] Ibid., VI, 85–6, Cf. II, 249–50     [4] Ibid., VI, 20.     [5] Ibid., VI, 86.

that 'the study of the organization of the brain should march side by side with that of its functions'.[1] By juxtaposing on nearly every page statements about behaviour to statements about the brain, and sub-suming both into a naturalistic, biological framework, he created a way of thinking that future investigators with more precise techniques and an experimental methodology could follow and exploit impressively.

What has been said so far about Gall's views on neuropsychology has been concerned with the investigation of the functions of the brain. For Gall the functions of the brain was the behaviour of the organism, and he called their study 'physiology'. The science of functions addressed itself to the question of what the functions are. This conception of physiology seems foreign to the activities of most modern workers who call themselves physiologists, while Gall's activities and observations would be quite natural to a modern psychologist or ethologist. This is a matter of the state of physiology in Gall's day. Sir Michael Foster points out that as the hypothesis that animal and vital spirits are the cause of physiological phenomena was progressively replaced by the materialist concept of organs as machines and their actions as functions, there was a period when people were little concerned with *how* an organ produced a function and were content with 'the mere enunciation of the function as the chief end of physiological inquiry'.[2] If one asks what Gall had to say about *how the brain functions* as opposed to *what are the functions* of the brain, he has little to offer. Those who did oppose his attempt to discover the organs and their functions sometimes objected that until he could specify how the brain produced its functions in the same way that one could specify how the stomach produces digestion, he had no doctrine of the physiology of the brain. The implication was a dualist one: that since the phenomena of the brain were of such an entirely different order from the phenomena of experience and behaviour, the task was an impossible one.[3] Gall's answer was that with many organs one can only specify the dependence of the function on the integrity of the structure. One can specify the structure, its function and their covariances concerning the stomach, the blood, the semen, and the external organs of sense. 'Thus we know the facts, and some conditions which are requisite in order that these facts should occur; but the why and the wherefore are almost always unknown to us. Well, this is precisely as much as we know in regard to the intellectual faculties and moral qualities.'[4] His science was in no worse a situation than other

---

[1] Gall, 1835, II, 46.
[3] Gall, 1835, III, 70–1. Cf. below, pp. 80–2.
[2] Foster, 1885, p. 10.
[4] Ibid., III, 74–5.

branches of physiology. Given the state of physiology at the beginning of the nineteenth century, Gall's reply was quite fair and proper. He not only had almost nothing to say about physiology as we now understand it—the study of material and efficient causes—but he felt no need to be embarrassed about the fact.

Neuroanatomical and nuerohistological studies had not advanced far enough to place any effective 'givens' in the path of how Gall chose to view the functional organization of the brain. There were no awkward facts that any theory had to explain. The divergence since Gall's time of what is known about the fine structure of the brain and the language used to describe it, from knowledge and descriptions of behaviour and experience, makes his position enviable. The problem of relating the language of psychology to the language of physiology and of finding some means of translating between these two universes of discourse did not exist for Gall. Subsequent advances in the study of the brain have made the task not easier but immeasurably harder. Gall's problem, as he saw it in 1798, and throughout his work was almost absurdly simple. 'As I suppose a particular organ for each one of our independent qualities, we have only to establish what are the independent qualities, in order to know what are the organs which we may hope to discover'.[1] He says very little more about the nature of the cerebral organs than that they constitute 'the material condition which renders possible the exercise or the manifestation of a faculty'.[2] He does specify that the organs are made up of 'a greyish, pulpy, or gelatinous substance'. This substance constitutes the hemispheres of the brain and is the ramification of the various fibrous bundles (our fibre tracts of white matter). The variations in the size of these ramifications depend on the size of the nervous bundle. These determine the activity of a given cerebral organ and thus the importance of the corresponding faculty in the behaviour of the organism. Gall does not develop this view further and does not attempt to connect it with his detailed neuroanatomical investigations.

Since there were no 'givens' from detailed neuroanatomical studies of the cortex, Gall could allow his method and sources of data to dictate the categories which he derived for relating brain function to behaviour. The kinds of behaviour which were the sources of his fundamental categories came from the extremes of society: marked propensities, talents, monomanias, and animal activites. From these he derived a faculty psychology. Then, from the context of his craniological method

[1] Gall, 1835, I, 14.    [2] Ibid., I, 234.

nd belief in it as an accurate reflection of the structure of the underly-
ng brain, he could argue that since we analyse behaviour in this way,
he brain must be organized to produce it in this way. Thus, to the
modern physiological question of how the brain is functionally organized
o produce behaviour, he would have answered 'By having an organ
hat produces (or is the material instrument of) each kind of behaviour
which we observe to be fundamental. Each category of behaviour
nas its own organ'. This is a simple one-to-one correlation. Since his
data were correlation of striking behaviours with cranial prominences,
the direct application of his psychological categories to the brain seemed
perfectly legitimate.

   The history of brain and behaviour research in the present century
can be seen as a progressive abandonment of faith in a one-to-one
correlation between the categories of analysis and the functional organization of the brain on the one hand, and the analogous variables in
behaviour on the other. The simple faculty-organ view has given way
to a progressive divergence of the understanding of behaviour from that
of the structural organization and physiological functioning of the brain.

   In the last three decades of the nineteenth century the one-to-one
view was revived but the relative emphases on psychological and brain
categories were almost completely reversed. Instead of allowing
psychological categories to dictate to the brain, the categories of
physiological analysis dictated that all thought and behaviour were the
result of the association and combination of sensory and motor substrata. Gall's organology, which was eminently suited to a faculty
psychology, was replaced by a different view of cerebral localization
which referred to cerebral areas for each of the classical sensory
modalities and for movements. Within this scheme certain 'centres'
for specified movements, and punctate localizations for specific sensory
modalities were determined. The complex functions which Gall had
made the basis of his faculty psychology were abandoned, and attempts
at explaining complex psychological phenomena were confined to the
thesis that the normative intellectual functions of thought, volition,
speech, etc., were the complex products of sensory and motor elements.
This work emerged from a combination of association psychology with
clinical and physiological interests, and the view of mental processes
was explicitly based on the prevailing conception of the constitution
of the cerebral hemispheres as consisting of centres related to sensory
and motor tracts.[1]

[1] Ferrier, 2nd ed., 1886, Chapter 12.

Gall's localizing assumption became a methodological tool for the discovery of critical cerebral determinants for given behaviours under controlled conditions. If a behaviour ceases to occur on ablation of a given structure, the inference should be restricted to the conclusion that that portion of the brain is a necessary condition for the performance of the behaviour under the conditions of the experiment. From this initial datum, it is necessary to go on to discover the remaining portions of the nervous system which, in combination, are *sufficient* to produce the behaviour. This requires both the working out of a complicated set of functioning neural circuits, each part of which is necessary for the behaviour to occur, and the combined use of stimulation, ablation, degeneration, and recording techniques. This is the neurophysiological aspect of the current version of the problem that seemed relatively simple to Gall.

The behavioural aspect is at least as complicated, since it requires the specification and control of environmental conditions which provide a valid test of the function in question. The series of experiments which meets this requirement must combine in such a way that all of the operational meanings of the function are tested and related to the neural circuits necessary and sufficient for its production.

The difficulties involved in the two aspects of the problem and in integrating the data from the two universes of discourse can be gathered from a reviewer's comments on a recent symposium on *Brain Mechanisms and Learning*.

It is clear that technical skill and methodical sophistication in analysing brain-behaviour relationships are steadily rising. A comparison of this work with research of say, 25 years ago, seems staggering. And yet the neurological basis of learning remains mercurial. [This is partly due to the complexity of the learning process.] More fundamental, perhaps, is the marked difference in units of analysis appropriate to the two domains—the neurological units being bursts of impulses occurring in a brief period of time, the behavioural units being turns in a maze or a memory of an event that occurred years previously. The operations relating the two are, for the most part, missing, so that research must content itself with either simple correlations—the hippocampus gives 5 to 6 c.p.s. wave-trains as an animal approaches food— or a listing of necessary neurological conditions (rarely has it been possible to state precisely the sufficient conditions) for certain forms of behaviour to occur—the monkey must have two intact frontal lobes to perform delayed response efficiently.[1]

Gall's method of inferring functions directly from behaviour and its

[1] Weiskrantz, 1962, pp. 125–6.

ne-to-one correlation with a portion of the brain seems a long way
from the logical and empirical complexities of current methods and
concepts.

*How can the Functions and their Localizations be Determined?*

Many of the elements of Gall's method for discovering the fundamental faculties and the seats of their organs have already been mentioned. However, as a preliminary to contrasting his method with that
of Flourens and the experimental physiologists, it may be useful to
examine the sources of data he employed purely as methodology and
independent of the nature of his psychology and psychophysiology. It
has been pointed out that he had nothing but ridicule for the introspections and speculations of the philosophers, for the physiognomy of
Lavater,[1] and for the investigation of the brain independent of the
study of behaviour. Gall was quite self-conscious about the methodology
he followed and spells it out in detail. It is clear from his description
of the history of discovery of each of his faculties (which he provided for
all but three of the twenty-seven fundamental faculties), that he
actually used the methods that he said he did. Whatever reservations
one may have about the craniology involved in almost all these methods,
it is important to remember that all of them were empirical methods
and that this was a new feature in psychological investigation. Gall
lists nine methods:[2]

1. *Correlation of propensities, sentiments, and talents drawn from common
language, with cranial prominences.* When he met or heard of a man or
animal endowed with a striking talent or propensity, he sat out to
determine if this remarkable behaviour was the work of nature:
a truly fundamental faculty. (The criteria for deciding which remarkable
behaviours referred to fundamental faculties will be considered separately.) The main criterion was that it be manifested *independent* of the
other characteristics of the individual or species. When he found
men or animals with an eminent talent or propensity he examined the
form of the head for a cranial prominence. He collected and compared
as many such correlations as he could find.

2. *Counter-proof.* Individuals who had a moderate degree of a given
quality or none at all were examined for lack of the corresponding
cranial prominence.

---

[1] See Gall, 1835, V, 261–6; I, 17–18. Gall proposed a study, *Pathognomy*, which was to
replace physiognomy. It was perhaps his least fortunate idea and its 'findings' go far beyond
the most flagrant excesses of cranioscopy. (See Ibid., V, 266–94.)

[2] Ibid., III, 108–130.

3. *Correlation of marked cranial prominences with the faculties and qualities of individuals.* When Gall saw a striking head prominence he would engage the individual in conversation to determine his propensities and talents. He travelled to schools, foundling homes, hospitals, prisons, and lunatic asylums, and obtained information on remarkable heads and remarkable talents wherever he could.

4. *Collection of head casts.* Gall collected and measured the casts of hundreds of individuals remarkable for either their talents and propensities or their cranial conformation. More or less systematic comparisons were made of like faculties and like skulls.

5. *Collection of crania.* When Gall found a common character in ten or twenty casts or skulls, he combined these data with those obtained from other methods.[1]

The above are the principal methods Gall used. Of the rest, he says, 'The following methods have assisted me less in discovering the fundamental qualities and faculties, than, in proving their discovery.'[2]

6. *Correspondence between skull and underlying organ.* After Gall had marked out a number of protuberances on the skull, he then began to see how far these prominences corresponded with the underlying brain. He assures us that no exceptions were found to such correspondence in sound or middle-aged brains.

7. *Comparative anatomy and physiology; natural mutilations of the brains of animals.* Gall argued that nineteen of the twenty-seven fundamental faculties were shared between men and animals. After the fundamental faculties had been discovered in man, he turned to species differences in the behaviour and crania of animals. By natural mutilations, Gall meant that the step-wise addition of organs and faculties in the 'chain of being' provided a more trustworthy method of discovery than the artificial mutilations of such experimental physiologists as Flourens.

---

[1] Gall's zeal for collecting skulls and busts was notorious and the subject of many contemporary jokes. He made collections both in Vienna and Paris, and parts of both still exist. By 1802 he had collected more than 300 skulls and 120 casts. Most of this collection remained in Austria. The collection which he made in Paris contained over 600 pieces which were bought from his widow (in exchange for a pension) on the advice of Cuvier and Saint-Hilaire, and placed in the Musée de l'Homme in Paris. The collection is still there, although its catalogue was removed by the Germans in 1941. A recent attempt at reconstructing the catalogue shows that it contained over 70 criminal busts, and those of various talented people. A complete catalogue of the collection appears in the *Phrenological Journal and Miscellany* **6**, 1829–30, 480–99; 583–602; and **7**, 1831–2, 27–36; 181–5; 250–3. Its existence was unknown to Ackerknecht and Vallois at the time they made their reconstruction from a manuscript found at the Musée de l'Homme. (Ackerknecht and Vallois, translated St. Léon, 1956, pp. 37–86; Ackerknecht, 1956, pp. 294–308, provide an index to their reconstruction.) Further information on phrenological collections in France and Britain is given in Laycock, 8th ed., 1859, p. 563.

[2] Gall, 1835, III, 120.

The large number of observations on the behaviour of animals included in Gall's work give him a legitimate claim to be the writer of the first systematic animal psychology, seventy years before the work of Romanes which is usually given this distinction. Gall was as convinced of the continuity of animal and human functions as any post-evolutionary animal psychologist, and a number of his fundamental faculties drew heavily on observations of animals for their evidential support.

8. *Accidental mutilations.* Gall rejected experimental ablations, but he was prepared to accept evidence from the accidental injury to a part of the brain as confirmatory evidence for a localization that was already established on other grounds. However, he would accept neither experimental ablations nor clinico-pathological correlations as evidence for a localization that had not already been established. He offered reasons both practical and in principle why nothing could be learned from such experiments used alone.

9. *The succession and arrangement of organs.* After the faculties and their organs had been discovered by strictly empirical methods, Gall believed that their harmonious arrangement in the brain constituted another proof of the validity of his discoveries. He found the faculties common to man and animals in one part, those unique to man in another, those of indispensable function in the most protected places, and those of like function adjacent to one another.

Other sources of data which Gall fails to mention in his methodological exposition include quotations from famous authors, paintings and busts of doubtful authenticity, and anecdotes from any source. In practice, Gall's interest in a given faculty or propensity was almost always derived from a striking individual or a cranial prominence. It is this correlation which forms the basis of most of his faculties, and none was discovered without the aid of cranial prominences.

The most serious problem raised by Gall's method was the determination of which classes of behaviour represented fundamental faculties, and which were merely the result of combined activity of other, fundamental faculties. In raising this issue, Gall was addressing himself to the most perplexing problem in psychology: its lack of an agreed set of units of analysis. Gall believed that he had solved this problem, and his solution was very sophisticated by modern standards: isolate the variable by observing its pathological manifestations, and its changes independent of other functions.[1] There was hardly a single

---

[1] For the twentieth-century version of this approach, see Spearman, 1927; for the relations between this work and Gall's, see Spoerl, 1935–6.

4

faculty of Gall's which did not raise the problem of whether or not it was a fundamental, primitive, radical function. He had rejected the philosophers' faculties precisely because they were not determinate for individual behaviour, and he had to show that his own functions were. Gall sought to find an extreme manifestation of each of the faculties he thought to be fundamental, and to find it varying independent of others by its development at a different period from others (e.g., instinct for propagation), its striking appearance in a character that is otherwise unremarkable (e.g., a poet or musician who is not remarkable in any other sphere of life), its activity while others are paralysed (e.g., an idiot who is talented at mimicry), its difference between the sexes (e.g., caring for offspring), and its difference between species (e.g., the constructive talents of beavers and spiders compared to horses and cows).[1] Gall's most trustworthy criterion is the exaggeration of a given quality in geniuses and maniacs. Thus, he argued that there is a monomania for each of his faculties, and searches the writings of Pinel for cases that could be construed as insanity involving one of his fundamental faculties. It is in their extreme activity that the faculties most readily reveal their natural language, and Gall thus draws heavily from the extremes of society: criminals, prodigies, geniuses, lunatics. 'In conformity to principles, I have more than once announced, we may infer, that when, in disease, some particular quality is manifested in a much higher degree of activity than the others, it is fundamental'.[2]

Given such sources of fundamental faculties, Gall sometimes has difficulty in specifying the role the faculty plays within the normal range of behaviour. He preferred to leave some doubt about the normal function of a given exaggerated manifestation than to draw premature conclusions.[3]

The structure of Gall's theory can be seen as a series of one-to-one correspondences:

| 1<br>STRIKING<br>BEHAVIOUR | implies<br>causes | 2<br>FACULTY | implies<br>causes | 3<br>CORTICAL<br>ORGAN | implies<br>causes | 4<br>CRANIAL<br>PROMINENCE |
|---|---|---|---|---|---|---|
| (talent,<br>propensity,<br>mania) | | (innate<br>instinct) | | (activity<br>varies<br>with size) | | (size varies<br>with under-<br>lying organ) |

Gall observed data of classes 1 and 4 and went on to argue to 2 and 3. The faculties were the only unobservables in the theory, but Gall was often unable to obtain direct evidence about the cortical organs, since most of his observations were made on living organisms. His usual

---

[1] Gall, 1835, III, 133–5.      [2] Ibid. IV, 162.      [3] Ibid. V, 248.

rocedure was to infer the existence of both 2 and 3 from an observed
orrelation of 1 and 4. It appears from his writings that Gall was
xtremely predisposed to see a cranial prominence or large cerebral
rgan when he already had evidence of a striking behaviour. In practice,
ie falsifiable part of the theory was the correlation of striking behaviours
ith cranial prominences. Gall's failure to falsify this covariance can
e explained partly by the difficulty of palpating the living skull, but
ie main problem lies in his anecdotal method. He sought cases con-
rming his theory, and each new case strengthened his belief that he
ad found a valid correlation. This selection of cases is the most serious
anger of the naturalistic and anecdotal methods which he employed.
'he problem of selecting cases for the method of clinico-pathological
orrelations remained until sophisticated statistical methods of case
election and suitable control procedures were developed in the present
entury. In Gall's day, the only substitute available for the anecdotal
iethod was that of experiment, and this was the method which Gall
ejected, while Flourens and later workers used it to provide informa-
ion about cerebral localization of functions which Gall failed to
iscover.

Before turning to the contrast between Gall's method and that of the
xperimentalists, it is worth noting how impressive Gall's achievement
vould have been had his simple one-to-one correlations proved valid.
'irst, psychology would have 'become possessed of an apparently
omplete list of human powers, faculties and tendencies, in terms of
vhich the whole human mind could be fully and accurately described'.[1]
econdly, the problem of the functional organization of the brain would
ave been solved as the result of a single discovery. Finally, it would be
ossible to diagnose individual character and ability at a glance,
liminating the need for further personality psychology, psychology
f individual differences, and vocational guidance and selection.[2]

## Gall's Critique of the Experimental Method

Gall's simple one-to-one correlations between cranial prominences
nd striking behaviours did not prove to be the key to the functions of
he brain or to its functional organization. The simple and obvious
nswer to why this was the case is that the craniological hypothesis was
vrong, and investigations based on this hypothesis could therefore
ead only to error. Gall has been praised for his insistence that the
letermination of the functions of the brain and the seat of their organs

---

[1] Flugel, 2nd ed., 1951, pp. 37–8.    [2] Ibid., p. 38.

was a problem which could be satisfactorily answered only by observa tion, and that it was the job of the naturalist or physiologist to make suc observations. On this issue, as with so many others, one finds Ga advocating something in principle which he was unable to carry ou satisfactorily in practice. Gall's naturalism must be viewed in two way In the light of the speculations to which he was reacting, it was a immense step forward. The application of a consistent naturalism t man was a new approach in the first quarter of the nineteenth centur One is thus impressed with Gall when he insists that 'The naturalis above all, is the slave of nature; he ought to know what is; afterward he can give himself up to his vain desire of knowing why, *what is, i as it is*'.[1] Or that he has 'conducted my reader by a path to which natur herself had directed me'.[2] 'I devoted myself entirely to observatio waiting patiently and resignedly for the results it would bring me.' Looking back from Gall to earlier workers, these statements are im pressive. However, the second view one must take is forward from Gall, and it is here that his version of naturalism led him deeply int error, and was superseded by the experimental and control procedure that he rejected. Once the necessity for observation is established, th relative merits of the anecdotal and experimental approaches begi to emerge.

The striking thing about the craniological technique is not that it i based on an absurd assumption. The belief that the importance of function was reflected in the size of its cerebral organ—which, in turr determined the conformation of the overlying cranium—was a per fectly plausible hypothesis given the state of anatomical and physic logical knowledge in the first decades of the nineteenth century. Th striking thing is that this hypothesis was not found to be untrue by th phrenologists, that many thousands of observations were gathered i support of it, and that phrenologists are still gathering such evidenc and being convinced by it. The explanation of the establishment an perpetuation of the evidential basis for craniology lies in the lack c rigour with which Gall's methods were applied. Gall was deceiving himself in claiming to be the slave of nature, waiting patiently for th results brought by nature or found along the road on which sh conducted him.[4] In doing so he was attempting to ally himself with naïve inductivist view of scientific method, the so-called true Baconia

---

[1] Gall, 1835, III, 28.    [2] Ibid. IV, 141.
[3] Gall, 1822–25, III, 169. (Quoted in Ackerknecht and Vallois, 1956.)
[4] E.g., Gall, 1835, III, 264.

method of gathering facts from which inductions emerge. This view of scientific method neither represented Bacon accurately, nor did it truly describe the activities of any scientist. Gall's own description of his methods shows how he sought certain kinds of facts in the light of a preconceived hypothesis (which he had initially derived from a naïve induction in his childhood). But even if Gall had applied his own method rigorously, the inaccuracy of the craniological technique would have soon become apparent. His detailed presentation of the discovery of the faculties and their organs shows that he used all the methods mentioned, but that he did not apply each method to each faculty. He drew data from each method in so far as it was found to *support* his initial hypothesis. In short, he sought only confirmations. It is not his naturalism that is at fault; it is his anecdotal method and his standards of evidence.

It may help us to see both the plausibility and the error of his anecdotal method if a sample argument is given. Gall's presentation of the 'carnivorous instinct' or 'disposition to murder' is one of the fullest of the twenty-seven faculties.[1] The discovery of this fundamental faculty was based on two findings. In comparing the skulls of animals he noticed a consistent difference between carnivorous and frugivorous species, i.e., that 'in the carnivora, there are cerebral parts above and behind the ear, not possessed by the frugivora. . . .'[2] Second, the skulls of a parricide and of a murderer were sent to him. There were many differences, but 'there was, in each, a prominence strongly swelling out immediately over the external opening of the ear'.[3] He concluded that the brains of carnivores and murderers are developed in the same region and asked himself if this conformation was connected with the disposition to kill. His discussion of the natural history of the instinct in animals consists mostly of anecdotes about a particularly carnivorous lap-dog Gall owned.[4] In his presentation of the external appearance and seat of the organ in animals, he discusses the variation of the relevant prominence with the extent of carnivorous habits, and includes a discussion of a collection he had made of heads of dogs and cats. Over fifty species and their habits are mentioned. The evidence for the existence of a carnivorous instinct in man is as follows: The attitude of individuals toward suffering varies independent of education and class. He gives a series of anecdotes about individuals who delighted in witnessing the death of other men in executions and battles. These are

[1] Gall, 1835, IV, 50–119.    [2] Ibid., IV, 50.    [3] Ibid., IV, 51.
[4] Ibid., IV, 51–54.

mingled with cases where individuals delighted in torturing animals and in seeing both animals and humans suffer and die. He then gives several cases of murderers who were notorious for their delight in senseless killing. Next, he appeals to history for the cruelties to Jews, the history of Rome, the Spaniards in the Americas, and the French Revolution. Finally, he turns to sadistic, cruel, and murderous tyrants, detailing the activities of Caligula, Nero, and Louis XI and listing others from Sylla [sic] to Henry VIII and Catherine de Medici. After this barrage of cruelties, he concludes: 'Who, now, will dare to maintain, that there is not in man an innate propensity, which leads him to the destruction of his own species? Where is the creature, that evinces more ferocity towards all other animals, not excepting his fellows, than man?'[1] Turning to evidence for the independent activity of the propensity, Gall cites four cases of idiots who murdered, four cases quoted from Pinel of supposed murderous monomania, four cases Gall observed, and thirteen more culled from various written and verbal sources of insanity involving murder and sometimes mixed with suicide. In discussing the seat and external appearance of the organ in man he cites over twenty-five skulls in detail including those of many famous criminals which he examined and on which he found the requisite prominence. Finally, he cites the busts and paintings of famous murderers, all of which 'bear the outward mark of a cruel and bloody character'.[2]

This presentation of the data supporting one of Gall's faculties and its organ has been given in some detail so that there will be no basis for doubting Gall's accuracy, sincerity, or honesty when, in other places, he assures the reader that 'Since the discovery of this organ, hardly a day has passed, that I have not discovered confirmations either positive or negative of this truth'.[3] Or 'I have made thousands of observations on this subject, and have never found an exception'.[4] The point is that Gall's whole method was geared toward *seeking confirmations*. Where confirmations were concerned, he had almost no standards of evidence. His writings are filled with anecdotes about patients, famous people, animals, criminals, observations made by him, quotations from the scientific writings of others, reports in the press, quotations from literature. All are given equal credence so long as they support his views. It would not make sense to ask that Gall use control procedures and statistical methods, or conduct his work in the light of

---

[1] Gall, 1835, IV, 68.    [2] Ibid., IV, 118.    [3] Ibid., V, 183.
[4] Ibid., V, 197.

falsificationist view of scientific method, all of which are products of the last quarter of the nineteenth century and have only come into their own in the last few decades. The anecdotal method which he used was the standard approach in human and animal studies until Galton (1884) and Thorndike (1898). Nor was measurement yet involved in such studies when Gall worked. What one can ask, though, is that Gall seek and treat counter-examples with the same seriousness that he did confirmatory findings, and that he apply the same standards to apparent exceptions to his views that he applied to supportive evidence.

An example which illustrates both the lack of standards and the different treatment afforded to supportive and counter evidence is his approach to busts and other indirect evidence.

have elsewhere said, that painters, draftsmen, engravers, and sculptors, sacrifice truth to erroneous notions of beauty, and endeavor to render less striking those uncommon forms, which they sometimes meet with in their models.[1]

Or

These two lengthened protuberances give to the superior part of the head, a great breadth and so singular a form, that painters, engravers, and sculptors rarely venture to present them in all their prominence.[2]

Thus, Gall is not worried if a representation of an individual with a striking propensity does not display the requisite prominence. On the other hand,

Still, there occur, from time to time, forms so striking, that the likeness absolutely depends on it, and then the artist is obliged, in spite of himself, to remain true to nature. In this way we obtain some faithful portraits of remarkable persons. The busts and portraits of Caligula, Nero, . . . all bear the outward mark of a cruel and bloody character.[3]

Finally, he argues from busts of Homer, Socrates, and Christ and (while granting that they were not taken from the originals while they lived) insists that since the sculptors must have used the greatest analogous men of their own times, craniology is still confirmed. When his expectations were not fulfilled, he had various means available for explaining away the facts. If the prominence were small, the propensity could exist because of the circumstances, e.g., a father murdering the

---

[1] Gall, 1835, IV, 117–18.　　[2] Ibid., V, 153.　　[3] Ibid., IV, 118.

man who deflowered his daughter;[1] or it could be due to brain disease
A large organ can produce uncharacteristic behaviour because of it
combination with the activity of other organs or with education, habit
example, etc.[2]

All we can confidently maintain is, that, *caeteris paribus*, a person who has
this organ large, will be more easily induced to commit homicide, than one
not naturally disposed to it by his organization.[3]

Gall's faith in his method led him to some quite ludicrous conclusions
In his discussion of the 'faculty of distinguishing the relations of colours
(which includes the talent for painting), he relates that

We were especially struck by a bookseller at Ansburg, blind from birth, who
maintained, that it is not the eye but the intellect, which recognizes, judges
and creates the proportion of colours.[4]

Gall relates that this man was able to arrange coloured beads in a
harmonious manner, that he felt a pain in the appropriate area of the
the head when doing so and that he displayed the appropriate crania
prominence.[5] The relationship which Gall develops between pride
(*hauteur*) in man and birds which fly high in the air, depends on similar
cranial prominences, and the extravagance of the analogy shows just
how far he was prepared to go on the basis of bumps alone.[6] Because
some of his organs were situated in areas lying on the underside of the
brain in areas which touch the orbital plate, it was necessary for him
to infer the size of four separate faculties from the conformation of the
eyes and eyelids.[7] Finally, Gall was forced to deny the existence of the
frontal air sinuses in most people in order to retain the cranioscopic
evidence for his 'sense of locality'.[8] In his general remarks about the
limitations of the cranioscopic method, Gall is often very modest and
claims only that he can make valid inferences when the cranium does
provide a faithful cast of the underlying brain. However, in his actual
use of the method, he is very often uncritical in the extreme. Cranioscopy
was Gall's most trusted method. It is ironic, therefore, that this is the
only one of all his postulates and methods which has no analogue or
direct descendent in modern work, except, of course, among practising
phrenologists.[9]

[1] Gall, 1835, IV, 108–10.     [2] Gall, 1835, I, 244–6.     [3] Gall, 1835, IV, 110.
[4] Gall, 1835, V, 53.     [5] Ibid.     [6] Gall, 1835, IV, 170–81.
[7] Gall, 1835, V, 4, 8, 19, 91.     [8] Gall, 1835, IV, 263–4.
[9] However, the narrower forms of physical anthropology *can* trace their ancestry to Gall's
cranioscopy, both directly and via Hunt and Broca. See Ackerknecht and Vallois, 1956,
pp. 27–8; Hunt, 1868–9.

Beginning with Gall, phrenologists have had two characteristic reactions toward evidence. If it can be construed to support phrenology, it is proclaimed as confirmatory. If not, it is explained away. Gall dealt with a case of large, projecting eyes coupled with an unremarkable memory by suggesting that the large eyes might have been due to rickets or hydrocephalus.[1] Or, the talent might have been lost due to excesses or diseases.[2] In later years counter-examples were put forward more forcefully, and they were explained away. In Paris, a young boy was found with remarkable calculating ability and a depression where the prominence for number should have been. Broussais and Domoutier defended phrenology by explaining that his calculating ability was really a manifestation of other faculties acting in combination.[3] A cast of half of Napoleon's skull which was unfavourable to phrenology was first criticised as a poor rendering and then answered by reference to parts of his skull which were not in the cast and therefore unavailable for examination.[4] Finally, it is reported that when Descartes' skull was found to be remarkably small in the anterior and superior regions of the forehead, where the rational faculties were localized, Spurzheim replied that Descartes was not so great a thinker as he was held to be.[5]

In 1857, G. H. Lewes called for phrenologists to 'cease for the present their accumulation of *corroborative* instances, and direct all their efforts to the accumulation of *contradictory* instances'.[6] This advice was friendly and was aimed at helping phrenologists to approach nearer to truths he felt they half grasped. It was not taken, and by 1871 he concluded that others had done the job for them with the result that precise scientific observations had shown that cranioscopy and its localizations did not correspond with the facts, and thus failed to gain general acceptance.[7] Nevertheless, phrenologists were undaunted in their search for confirmations, and attempted to appropriate any finding that in any way supported their theories. In 1894, W. Mattieu Williams attempted to vindicate phrenology by citing Ferrier's motor localizations as confirmations of Gall.[8] 'If Ferrier had said that the leg is advanced "as in *strutting*", instead of "as in walking", his fidelity to Gall would have been quite perfect, and the significance of his description more intelligible.' The stimulation had been made at the point of Gall's organ

---

[1] According to Castiglioni, exophthalmic goitre was known clinically in the first quarter of the nineteenth century, but Gall makes no reference to this alternative explanation. (Castiglioni, 1947, p. 781.)

[2] Gall, 1835, V, 13.    [3] Lewes, 1857a, p. 668.

[4] Ibid., pp. 669–71.    [5] Ibid., pp. 671–2.

[6] Ibid., p. 674. Cf. a similar sympathetic treatment by Carpenter (1846, pp. 520 ff.).

[7] Lewes, 1871, II, 446–7. Cf. Haight, 1968, pp. 166, 188.    [8] Williams, 1894, Chapter 9.

of vanity.[1] Dr Bernard Hollander's works are filled with case material which 'confirms phrenology'.[2] If one meets phrenologists and has an opportunity to observe their absolute sincerity, some understanding and sympathy emerges for their insistence that (as one wrote to me) 'the only reason that I may appear enthusiastic is because day by day I find constant confirmation of it'.

Lest this appear a totally aberrant view held by credulous men who are unacquainted with standards of evidence in biology, it might be added that it was shared by Alfred Russell Wallace, co-discoverer of the theory of evolution by natural selection. Wallace read Combe's *Constitution of Man* as a young man (1844), and was convinced of the truth of phrenology and even of 'phreno-mesmerism', the belief that hypnotized subjects expressed the emotion appropriate to a given phrenological organ when the operator touched the requisite area on the cranium. Wallace conducted his own experiments and was satisfied with the evidence he obtained.[3] He had his head delineated by two phrenologists in 1847 'with such accuracy as to render it certain that the positions of all the mental organs had been very precisely determined'.[4] He remained convinced of the truth of phrenology, and explained Ferrier's findings as follows: 'The supposed "localization of motor areas" by Professor Ferrier and others, which are usually stated to be a disproof of the science, are really one of its supports, the movements produced being merely those which express the emotions due to the excitation of the phrenological organ excited'.[5]

The fact that Wallace could hold these views highlights the dangers of the naturalistic method. His own theory was based on the fact that many, many observations were explained by the hypothesis of evolution by natural selection. The more observations collected on the subject, the more the hypothesis was accepted. Both Darwin and Wallace used great numbers of naturalistic observations and pieces of anecdotal evidence to support the theory. The analogy between the theory of evolution and that of craniology is instructive. Granted, the standard of evidence was usually higher in the evolutionary work. But, logically it was in the same position as phrenology for most of the nineteenth century. It rested on naturalistic observations and a mass of anecdotes collected more or less systematically. Doubt remained whether the causal relations proposed by the theory were real, or only mistaken inferences from correlations reflecting the union of chance circumstances,

---

[1] Williams, 1894, pp. 180–1.     [2] Hollander, 1901, n.d., 1931.
[3] Wallace, 1905, I, 234–6.     [4] Ibid., 257–62.     [5] Ibid., 262.

ntil the theory was demonstrated by the experimental production of
arieties by selection. Huxley had stressed this point and wrote (about
887) 'In my earliest criticisms of the "Origin" I ventured to point
ut that its logical foundation was insecure so long as experiments in
:lective breeding had not produced varieties which were more or less
ifertile; and that insecurity remains up to the present time.'[1] The
ifference is, of course, that experimental confirmation was forth-
oming. Formally, the issue between Gall and Flourens is exactly the
ime as that involving evolution.

The whole issue of Gall's method, and of the subsequent history of
hrenology, turns on the view which Gall took of his first finding, the
orrelation of 'saucer-eyes' and facility in learning by heart: 'I could
ot believe, that the union of the two circumstances which had struck
ie on these different occasions, was solely the result of accident.'[2]
;all and later phrenologists firmly believed that the correlations which
hey found between cranial prominences and notable behaviours,
upported by data from each of the other methods they used, reflected
ausal relations. It has been clear since Hume that any inference from
bserved conjunctions to causality is an act of faith. The Humean
oncept of causality views the most *constant* conjunctions in this
ceptical way. Ample evidence of the inconstancy of some of the
onjunctions observed by the phrenologists has been given above.
Iad they applied their own methods rigorously, this would have
merged. Since they did not, and since statistical methods were not
.vailable to them, the only alternative was that of experiment. Both
aturalistic observation and anecdotes are recognized as valid sources
f evidence, but can best be tested by controlling one variable and
bserving changes in another. The naïve inductive view of naturalists
uch as Gall was based on a misconception of 'true Baconian principles',
or Bacon had stressed the importance of experiment as more revealing
han mere naturalism. 'Human knowledge and human power meet in
ne; for where the cause is not known the effect cannot be produced.
Nature to be commanded must be obeyed; and that which in con-
emplation is as the cause is in operation as the rule.'[3] Where effects

---

[1] Huxley, 1900, I, 170.     [2] Gall, 1835, I, 58–9.
[3] Bacon, 1960, p. 39. Concerning the study of natural history, Bacon says, 'Next, with
egard to the mass and composition of it: I mean it to be a history not only of nature free
nd at large (when she is left to her own course and does her work her own way)—such as
hat of the heavenly bodies, meteors, earth and sea, minerals, plants, animals—but much
nore of nature under constraint and vexed; that is to say, when by art and the hand of man
he is forced out of her natural state, and squeezed and moulded. . . . Nay (to say the plain
ruth), I do in fact (low and vulgar as men may think it) count more upon this part both for

can be produced by direct manipulation of a given variable, th inference from constant conjunction to causality requires much le of an act of faith. The methods used by the phrenologists allowe them to demonstrate the covariance between specifiable events, a can astrologers, some of whose predictions are also borne out by sub sequent events. However, neither the phrenologists nor the astrologe can demonstrate that the relationships are causal by producing th effects by means of manipulation of the supposed causes.[1]

Why did Gall not avail himself of experimental method? He was no ignorant of this, nor, as his anatomical discoveries show, did he lac the technical skills required for carrying out experiments. In fact, Gal and Spurzheim, assisted by others, did conduct numerous experiment in response to Flourens' experimental determination of the functio of the cerebellum in regulating locomotion, and of the equipotentialit of the cerebral hemispheres for the senses and intellectual functions The results contradicted Flourens directly in some cases and wer strikingly variable and unrepeatable in others.[2] Gall's reaction to thes findings was to mount a full-scale attack on the use of the experimenta method in nervous physiology. Before reviewing his argument on should note that this attitude of Gall's was in no way unusual. From th vantage point of the mid-twentieth century, Flourens' work marks th beginning of the experimental physiology of the nervous system whicl led to Fritsch and Hitzig, Ferrier, Munk, and Goltz, and to Sherrington Franz, Lashley, and current workers. In 1822, the year Flouren published his first memoir, Magendie also published his experimenta determination of the functions of the spinal roots. A measure of the unstable reputation of the experimental method, even at the time when it was beginning to give these impressive results, is the fact that the co-discoverer of the Bell-Magendie Law was himself opposed to anima experimentation on scientific and moral grounds and based his findings

helps and safeguards than upon the other, seeing that the nature of things betrays itself more readily under the vexations of art than in its natural freedom.' (Ibid., p. 25.)

[1] Bain stressed the logical position in which phrenology was placed by its method, by reference to the chapter in Mill's *Logic* (Book iii, Chapter 22) on 'Co-existences Independent of Causation': 'He points out that such propositions demand uniformity without a break, in order to establish them in their generality. There must not be one single real exception, otherwise the rule is as completely void as if there were not one instance in its favour. Consequently, every instance that seems to contradict the general affirmation must be met and shown to be only an apparent exception'. Mill's example is the correlation of crows and the colour black and the possibility of a white one appearing. This criterion lends urgency to Lewes' objections cited above. (Bain, 1861, pp. 59–60.)

[2] Gall, 1835, III, 247–52. Cf. Gall, 1835, VI, 177–9.

primarily on anatomy.[1] Bell wrote in 1823, 'Experiments have never been the means of discovery; and a survey of what has been attempted of late years in physiology, will prove that the opening of living animals had done more to perpetuate error, than to confirm the just views taken from the study of anatomy and natural motions. . . .'[2] It has been pointed out that this view was shared by many eminent physiologists on the basis that the experimental physiology of the nervous system had shown very little up to that time.[3]

Gall had both technical and theoretical objections to the experimental approach used by Flourens. These appear in two parts of *The Functions of the Brain*: in the third volume he attacks Cuvier's laudatory review of Flourens' memoir of 1822, where the discovery of the regulatory function of the cerebellum is reported; volume six is devoted to answers to various criticisms of Gall's work which were brought by comparative anatomists and physiologists, and includes an answer to Flourens which, in this case, was based on a reading of Flourens' memoir itself.[4] The issue between Gall and Flourens on method is particularly striking in that it involves the functions of the cerebellum, where their respective findings were unequivocal and sharply opposed. Gall's methods had revealed that this structure was the organ of the sexual instinct ('Instinct of Generation, of Reproduction; Instinct of Propagation'),[5] while Flourens, on the basis of surgical ablation experiments, concluded that it was responsible for the coordination of voluntary movements.[6] For Gall's critics, Flourens' discovery was an important basis for rejecting phrenology. Cuvier had high praise for Flourens. He describes the experiments in detail and concludes, 'This discovery, if repeated experiments, with all proper precautions, establish its truth, will do the greatest honour to the young observer whose work we have just analysed.'[7] He closes with the remark that Flourens presented new details and new facts 'which are as new as precious for science'.[8] After considering the controversy between Gall and Flourens on this issue, a contemporary English commentator concludes that Flourens' discovery and Gall's inadequate reply weigh heavily against the claims of phrenology. 'In the present state of matters, it appears to us no small proof of the validity of Flourens' doctrines, that so acute and so captious a controversialist, on a point

---

[1] See Liddell, 1960, pp. 50–1.  [2] Quoted in Olmsted, 1944, p. 117.
[3] Ackerknecht and Vallois, 1956, pp. 22–3.  [4] Cf. Gall, 1835, III, 97–100, 255–63.
[5] Gall, 1835, III, 141–239. Gall *et al.*, 1838, pp. 1–94.
[6] Flourens, 2nd ed., 1842, pp. 37–43 and 133–41; 163n–4n.
[7] Quoted in Gall, 1835, III, 255.  [8] Ibid.

so injurious to his system, has made so weak an assault, and has been reduced to such sorry subterfuges.'[1]

Since subsequent research has given such an unequivocal judgement in this controversy,[2] a review of the basis of Gall's opposition should be instructive. For Gall the issue was not only that of the function of the cerebellum but the legitimacy of direct experimental intervention into the processes of nature, particularly by ablation or 'mutilation'.

Gall's technical objections were: (1) The state of anatomical knowledge is too primitive for such operations: 'And how can we remove from the brain a single organ? Does any one know the commencement, the termination, or the limits of an organ?'[3] (2) Surgical techniques are not precise enough: 'Finally, how can we remove a part without affecting those that are contiguous to it? How can we remove the cerebellum, especially in the mammalia, without injuring the *medulla oblongata* and all the parts with which it communicates.'[4] (3) Surgical controls are too primitive to test the alternative hypotheses. The animal will not survive long enough to test Gall's view: 'Let us suppose that M. Flourens wishes to determine, by the ablation of the cerebellum, whether this part is or is not the organ of the instinct of generation, how will he be enabled to make the animal live sufficiently long, to decide whether the animal retains or has lost this instinct?'[5] This problem leads him to suggest that Flourens' findings may be artefacts: 'Is it astonishing, that the animal successively loses the faculty of flying, standing upright, of performing regular motions, of raising himself up when he is gradually ceasing to live?'[6] (4) Using the results of various experimenters, as well as his own, he argues, 'That it is impossible to perform exactly the same operation, or experiment, a second time, and that not only each different experimenter, but the same man, in

---

[1] Anon., 1824, p. 154.

[2] A 1955 issue of the *Phrenological Newsletter* still pictured the cerebellum as the seat of the sexual functions, while the standard compendium on that organ by Dow and Moruzzi and the exhaustive review of brain research and reproductive behaviour are most emphatic in saying that 'completely negative results were obtained' on all stimulation and ablation experiments on the alleged sexual functions of the cerebellum (Dow and Moruzzi, 1958, p. 308; cf. Ibid., p. 6), and that 'This concept has never been supported by evidence from animal experiments'. (Sawyer, 1960, p. 1225.) Finally, none of the areas in the brain which have been shown to be involved in sexual functions is near to, or has particularly close functional relations with, the cerebellum. For the history of cerebellar physiology, see Dow and Moruzzi, 1958, pp. 3–6.

[3] Gall, 1835, III, 244.     [4] Ibid.

[5] Ibid. Cf. Gall, 1835, VI, 137.

[6] Ibid., 257. Cf. Ibid., 98–99 and the less extreme position—allowing for *both* his conception and Flourens' (Gall, 1835, VI, 137)—in a passage written after he had read Flourens' memoir. However, this is only a passing concession, since he caustically rejects Flourens' findings in his conclusion (Ibid., 148).

ach new experiment, must necessarily obtain different results. . . .[1] n fact, Flourens could and did overcome these objections in his xperiments on the cerebellum. One can argue, though, that his xperiments on the cerebrum suffered from his inability to isolate and blate anatomically discrete structures.

Gall's theoretical objections were in part derived from the technical nes. (1) The problem of isolating structures surgically was connected vith the fact that all parts of the nervous system are connected with all thers. The structure of the brain thus requires that 'a part being vounded or irritated, wounds or irritates all the rest',[2] His conclusion s 'That it is in fact impossible to prevent the reciprocal influence of he different parts of the nervous system, or to isolate irritations, lesions, nd mutilations, and obtain specific, isolated results. . . .'[3] (2) Even if 'lourens' findings were accurate, they would not exhaust the functions f the organ:

Neither should we ever forget, that one and the same part may have its eneral vital function, and its particular animal function beside. If it were rue, that the lesion of the tubercles in birds, always causes convulsions, it s not the less true, that the tubercles are destined for vision. So, also, the erebellum may participate in the vital function of the *medulla spinalis* and *medulla oblongata*, and, at the same time, have a particular animal function.[4]

3) Comparative observations which are not made in conjunction vith studies on man cannot be conclusive. Gall puts this so strongly in ne place that it casts doubt on his own use of comparative observations: It is absurd to think of applying the vague, arbitrary, varying and perhaps, poorly observed results of experiments on hens, pigeons, and abbits, to the moral and intellectual faculties of man.[5] In the case of 'lourens' work, this is a fair criticism of his inferences about the erebrum. From his analysis of Flourens' work Gall concluded,

With the exception of the influence, that the lesions of the cerebellum xercise on the medulla oblongata and medulla spinalis, there exists, neither in the state of health, nor in that of disease, any relation or proportion, petween the cerebellum and the regularity of the motions of the faculty of ocomotion.[6]

---

[1] Gall, 1835, VI, 239. Cf. Ibid., 153, and Gall, 1835, III, 197.
[2] Gall, 1835, VI, 239.     [3] Ibid., Cf. 155–6.
[4] Gall, 1835, III, 244–5. It has been pointed out that this argument was used by later phrenologists to accommodate the findings of the sensory-motor localizations of Ferrier. In spite of this specious use of the point by Gall and later phrenologists, one feels that in some sense it must be valid. See above, p. viii.
[5] Gall, 1835, VI, 239; cf. Gall, 1835, III, 98.     [6] Gall, 1835, III, 262.

His conclusion about the ablation method was equally extreme:

Thus, all these experiments, by mutilation or ablation, confirm what I hav
before said, that, at most, we can obtain but few results, almost always ver
doubtful, in relation to the phenomena of irritability and sensibility, th
functions of certain viscera, and those of voluntary motion. But never sha
we obtain the least knowledge of the special functions of the cerebellum c
the integral parts of the brain.[1]

Finally, on the basis of the inability of the experimentalists to isolat
either anatomical structures or the behavioural results of their ablations
both in principle and in practice, he concludes against the whol
approach of experimental localizations. 'We see, then, throughout th
brain, the parts very materially complicated, which renders any locali
zation absolutely impossible.'[2] 'This beautiful idea of localization i
then only a fine and presumptous chimera.'[3]

The simplest judgement one could make about these conclusion
would be to take a vantage point in the 1870's, and pronounce then
categorically wrong. A more sympathetic view acknowledges tha
judgement as historically accurate but maintains that Gall had excellen
reasons for his conclusions, given the state of anatomical and physio
logical technology in the 1820's. His conclusions about the possibility
of experimental localizations appear in a context of how little wa
known of the connections in the nervous system. Gall's error was no
in his conclusions. Rather, it lay in his failure to distinguish objection
based on lack of knowledge and technology from logical, theoretica
objections. He tended to slip rather easily from the limitations of the
contemporary state of knowledge to declarations about what was ever
to be possible. The reason for this is not simply that Gall had a taste
for prophecy but was bad at it, but had more to do with his conception
of the explanatory goals of physiology. He was committed to the
explanation of the individual differences which account for the talents,
propensities, and instincts of men and animals. He was, albeit erroneously, convinced that he had a method for determining these. Whatever
the merits of his own method, one can follow him in his declaration of
the irrelevance of the experiments which were then being done to the
concepts of function which he sought. Gall's remarks about experimental
localization should not therefore be read as bad guesses as seen from
1870 or 1873. In fact, his judgement about the ablation method granted
that it could lead to discoveries about 'the phenomena of irritability

[1] Gall, 1835, III, 245; cf. Ibid., 263 and Gall, 1835, VI, 117.     [2] Gall, 1835, VI, 158.
[3] Ibid., 156; cf. Ibid., 238–9.

and sensibility, the functions of certain viscera, and those of voluntary motion'. Far from failing to anticipate the possibility of such discoveries, he predicted them. The point was, as he saw it, that these had no bearing on the 'special functions' of the brain and cerebellum. It was by a radical reduction of the explanatory goals of localization research to include only the phenomena of sensation and motion, and a concomitant reduction of the basic elements of their psychological correlates, that the late nineteenth-century localizers could claim to account for life and mind. Since subsequent research in the nineteenth century did take this course, it seems only fair to end this review of Gall's position with a full quotation of his conception of the goals of localization research. While rejecting his methodological tirade against experiments one is very struck by the challenge he makes to subsequent research.

It must, however, be remarked, that my objections or observations against the lesions and mutilations, are particularly directed against those who, by this means, wish to learn the animal functions of the cerebellum and brain. I understand by animal functions, the mechanical aptitudes, instincts, propensities, and intellectual faculties; but, as far as these are concerned, all the experimenters are yet at an enormous distance. Almost always, they confine themselves, as Haller, Zinn, Lorry, Lancerotte, Rolando, Flourens, etc., did, to an exploration of the nature and the relations of the phenomena of irritability, excitability, motion, whether spontaneous or voluntary, and sensibility. To this end, we ought to accord to them, especially M. Flourens, the merit of having devised very ingenious and sometimes conclusive experiments. But he confines himself, so far as sensibility is concerned, like the philosophers, to generalities which are really very nearly the same in reptiles, fishes, birds, the mammalia, and man. All are excitable, all have sensibility, all have also volition; and if to eat, drink, walk, fly, leap, crawl, swim, can be included under the empire of the intellectual faculties, they all possess intelligence. Thus, it is in these points of view solely, that true and constant results, obtained from experiments performed with address and discernment, on young and inferior animals, merit our attention.

But so soon as we desire information on the mechanical aptitudes, the different propensities, instincts, and intellectual faculties, experimenters leave us in an absolute desert. It is as if these faculties and qualities did not exist, or that there does not exist any relation between them and the nervous system. They never make mention of an instinct, propensity, or determinate talent. It is known that animals have the propensity for propagation, that they love and take care of their young, that they travel, build, sing, lay up provisions, recollect places, things, and persons; that they unite together for life, etc., but all this is nothing according to the experimenters, but sensibility, or at most, modified intelligence. That such an animal is of a mild disposition, and another, savage; that such a one delights to live on the peaks of mountains,

5

whilst another never leaves the valleys; that some construct and others do not; that some unite in marriage and others do not; that some live in society and others remain isolated; all this is not worth the trouble of searching out the cause in the animal organization, it is all explained by the unity of the brain, and, if we hesitate ever so little, even without a brain. Very well! gentlemen physiological experimenters, clear up to us a single one of these points. Before my discoveries, you did not think of this; now the materials are in your hands. Cut, pinch, prick, remove, cause your martyrized animals to live as long as you will, and show us which of those faculties continues or ceases to manifest itself! You cannot deny the existence of these qualities and faculties, since all the actions of man and animals attest them, or prove to us that it belongs only to their volition, to the direction of what you call intelligence, that the tiger has the propensities of the tiger, the sheep those of the sheep; that the male nightingale sings, and that the female and so many other species of birds do not sing; that such a man, in spite of all obstacles, excels in poetry, in a spirit for observation, in a talent for music, and that another, with all the faculties, all external encouragements, never rises above mediocrity, etc.; that such a species of animals is continually on the round of gradual perfection; that such an instinct appears and disappears at such an age, such a season; where will you show us the material conditions of these phenomena at the point of your scalpel! None of you thus far have had either the philosophy or the courage to meet these questions; otherwise you would have soon been convinced of the insufficiency and nullity of your cruel experiments.[1]

Here, then, terminates this work, which, for fifteen years, the learned have been impatiently expecting. I should have wished to defer it still longer, to bring the fruits of my researches to greater maturity; but the final hour draws near, and I must be content with leaving this first effort in the physiology of the brain, far less perfect than it will be fifty years hence.[2]

Fifty years later David Ferrier wrote a work with the same title as Gall's: *The Functions of the Brain* (1876). In what follows an attempt will be made to trace some aspects of the psychological assumptions and physiological research leading from Gall to Ferrier. It may be useful here to provide a preview of the end point of these developments in order to show the sharp differences from Gall without the benefit of the intervening changes. Ferrier not only ignores Gall's strictures, but he introduces his work with the claim that

Experiments on animals, under conditions selected and varied at the will of the experimenter, are alone capable of furnishing precise data for sound

---

[1] Gall, 1835, VI, 160–62. It should be noted that in addition to his technical, theoretical, and psychological objections to experiments, Gall had a horror of such practices, which he considered to be cruel. (See Ebstein, 1924, p. 271.)

[2] Gall, 1835, VI, 293.

nductions as to the functions of the brain and its various parts; the experiments performed for us by nature, in the form of diseased conditions, being
rarely limited, or free from such complications as render analysis and the
discovery of cause and effect extremely difficult, and in many cases practically
impossible.[1]

The functions which interested Gall had no place in Ferrier's analysis,
nor were the questions which Gall raised even addressed. Ferrier and
the sensory-motor psychophysiologists of the late nineteenth century
reverted to the normative psychology of the philosophers. The relations
of brain structure and function to personality and to the study of
individual differences were not investigated by them and were not
studied seriously until the second quarter of the present century. The
categories of function used by these workers, by the post-Darwinian
animal psychologists, and by the early brain and behaviour researchers
of the 1930's, were those of the normative medieval and Lockean
psychologies: memory, intelligence, reason, etc. Ferrier reduced the
phenomena of experience and behaviour to the functions which Gall
had recognized as amenable to experimental analysis: irritability,
sensibility, and muscular motion. This reduction was justified in the
name of a sensationalist philosophy and an associationist psychology
which considered Gall's functions as syntheses of primitive sensory and
motor elements. The faculties, functions, and instincts could not themselves serve as explanatory concepts but had to be explained in terms
of associated sensations and movements. In arriving at this view of the
functions of the brain, Ferrier reduced psychology to an appendage of
sensory-motor physiology. The development and rationale of this
reduction provide the subject of the following chapters. At the same
time constant reference will be made to the influence of phrenology
on later developments.

[1] Ferrier, 1876, p. xiv.

## 2

# EXPERIMENTAL SENSORY-MOTOR
# PHYSIOLOGY AND
# THE ASSOCIATION PSYCHOLOGY

Pure empiricism does not lead us anywhere—not even to experience; muc
less, of course, to experiment. An experiment, indeed, is a question we pı
to nature. It presupposes, therefore, a language in which we formulate ou
questions; in other words, experiment is not the basis of theory, but only
way of testing it. Science does not result from an accumulation of facts
there are no facts that do not imply concepts.

Alexandre Koyré, 1954

## *The Rise of Experimental Sensory-Motor Physiology*

The developments from the end of Gall's work to the findings o
Fritsch and Hitzig, and Ferrier, that inaugurated the classical period o
cerebral localization involve five related themes: (1) the progressive
acceptance and success of the experimental method and the concomi
tant abandonment of Gall's correlative method and cranioscopy
(2) The development of the view that the nervous system is organized
in sensory-motor terms and the extension of this approach to progres
sively higher parts of the system. (3) The progressive application of the
sensory-motor view to mental processes within the Lockean tradition
of associationist psychology, involving both the abandonment of Gall's
organology and his concepts of function in favour of the functions he
opposed. These, in turn, were viewed as complexes of sensations
motions, and associations. Thus, both psychology and physiology
adopted a uniform set of explanatory elements which left little place for
cerebral organs or faculties. (4) The parallel continuation of the
assumption of cerebral localization within phrenology and its combina
tion with the above developments in physiology and psychology and
with clinical findings, leading to the localization of muscular movements
by Fritsch and Hitzig, and of muscular movements and the primary
sensory modalities by Ferrier. (5) The development of a new biological
context for psychological and physiological research—the theory of
evolution. The early evolutionists applied the principle of continuity to
mind and brain, but they failed to transcend the categories of function
which they inherited from philosophical psychology.

*Relations with the Orthodoxy: The Careers of Gall and Flourens*

Gall and Flourens agreed that the brain is the organ of the mind, and Flourens gave Gall credit for establishing this point unequivocally.[1] Except for this fundamental thesis, it is difficult to think of an issue on which they did not disagree. It is true that Flourens thought Gall a good anatomist, but he pointed out that Gall's anatomical discoveries were irrelevant to his doctrine of the functions of the brain.[2] Gall, on the other hand, finally granted the efficacy of Flourens' experimental methods for investigating irritability, sensibility, and motion but pointed out that such investigations held no promise of discovering the fundamental faculties or their organs. Thus, Flourens' methods and findings were irrelevant to the true aim of cerebral physiology as conceived by Gall. In view of their vehement opposition, it is ironic that it was Flourens, not Gall, who provided the first experimental demonstration of localization of function in the brain. He also provided the findings which dominated cerebral research for almost half a century, and methods which are still basic to neurophysiology. His findings eclipsed Gall's methods and assumptions and lent credence to his own. However, a more sophisticated use of Flourens' careful techniques, complemented by others, led eventually to the establishment of the very cortical localization of functions which Flourens opposed. Finally, the so-called 'new phrenology', which grew out of modified versions of Flourens' methods and Gall's assumption of cerebral localization, was based on a very different conception of the functions of the brain from that of either Gall or Flourens. They would have both opposed the conceptions of the sensory-motor localizers but for different reasons: Gall because their functions were not biologically significant and Flourens because they undermined his conception of the unity and independence of the mind. Neither would be sympathetic to the attempt to synthesize the whole of mental life and behaviour from associated sensations and motions, localized in the cerebral cortices. Of course, their protests were never heard. The conflict between Gall and Flourens antedates these developments by fifty years, and in contrasting them it will be convenient to consider their careers, methods, main findings, and assumptions in their contemporary context.

Jean-Pierre-Marie Flourens was born (1794) more than a generation after Gall (1758), and he lived until 1867, long enough to oppose Darwinism in his later writings. Gall's last work began appearing in the year that Flourens delivered his first experimental memoir (1822), and

<hr>

[1] See above, pp. 20–21.     [2] See above, pp. 24n–25n.

Gall was able to include a detailed and vehement criticism of the new experimental methods in the later volumes. Flourens, on the other hand, presided over the demise of phrenology and contributed substantially to the criticism which discredited Gall and his followers by writing *Examen de la phrénologie* (1842) and *De la phrénologie* (1863). Whereas Gall was a controversial rebel whose work was never accepted as part of orthodox science, Flourens was a member of the Establishment, and his career was advanced at every stage by important patronage. Gall's public lectures in Vienna were proscribed by Emperor Francis I in 1802, on the grounds that they led to materialism and were opposed to the principles of morality and religion.[1] Gall wrote a petition to the Emperor asking for a iair hearing, but it was denied,[2] and he left Vienna in 1805. He and Spurzheim demonstrated their doctrine in over thirty cities in the next two years, and arrived in Paris in 1807 with an international reputation.[3] Although Gall caused an immediate sensation, and his popular lectures were well attended, it was into society and not into scientific circles, that Gall and Spurzheim were welcomed.[4] When they submitted a memoir on their work to the Institute in 1808, the commission which reviewed it produced an equivocal report on their anatomical findings and refused to consider their physiological doctrines at all.[5] It is said that Napoleon took a personal interest in seeing that Gall was received coolly by the orthodoxy and even that Cuvier's initially sympathetic response to Gall's work was transformed under political pressure.[6] Gall continued to have a large popular following and a successful medical practice (including many prominent patients). He became a naturalized French citizen in 1819 and lived in Paris until his death in 1828. In spite of his acknowledged contributions to neuroanatomy, his efforts in 1821 to obtain admission to the French Academy of Sciences (though supported by Geoffroy Saint-Hilaire) were unsuccessful. His following among prominent scientists came only after his death and was always tainted with unorthodoxy and even liberalism (which had no place in Gall's own political opinions). Finally, his books were placed on the *Index*, and he was refused a religious burial, though his orthodox religious beliefs were firm. It has been suggested that some of Gall's disfavour among orthodox scientists

[1] Gall *et al.*, 1838, p. 309. Cf. Gall, 1835, I, 19.
[2] Gall *et al.*, 1838, pp. 309–35, 336–9.
[3] Gall, 1835, I, 65–66; Gall, 1835, VI, 119; Chevenix, 1828, p. 12; Temkin, 1947, p. 279.
[4] Ebstein, 1924; Chevenix, 1828, p. 16. Ackerknecht and Vallois, 1956, p. 10.
[5] Tenon *et al.*, 1809.
[6] Chevenix, 1828, pp. 15–16; Gall, 1835, I, 25; Gall, 1835, VI, 239–45; Ackerknecht and Vallois, 1956, pp. 10, 38, Temkin, 1947, pp. 300–13.

can be explained by his habit of speaking sensationally to popular audiences for a fee rather than confining his efforts to gaining the respect of the scientific community. Gall justified his practice as a means of gaining funds to finance his research and the publication of his large work,[1] but one suspects that his vanity was also involved.

The contrast between Gall's fortunes and those of Flourens is almost total. When Flourens arrived in Paris he bore a letter of introduction to the doyen of French science, Georges Cuvier, and was immediately received into the company of the most eminent scientists.[2] He began submitting memoirs to the Academy of Sciences when he was twenty-seven, and their reception by the Commission was as flattering and enthusiastic as that of Gall and Spurzheim had been flat and guarded.[3] In fact, Cuvier, Portal, and Pinel sat on both commissions. This support set the stamp of approval on his work and was largely responsible for its favourable reception in the scientific world.[4] Cuvier's patronage was quickly and amply justified by Flourens' work in the period 1822–24, and the young experimentalist received the newly established Montyon Prize in Experimental Physiology in both 1824 and 1825.[5] Before he was thirty-five he was elected to a seat in the Academy of Sciences, again with Cuvier's support.[6] Cuvier entrusted his protégé with his course of lectures on natural history at the Collège de France as well as his course in anatomy at the Museum in the Jardin des Plantes.[7] When Cuvier died in 1832, Flourens was offered his professorship, but instead took up a chair in Comparative Physiology specially created for him.[8] Finally, from his deathbed, Cuvier bequeathed to Flourens his post as one of the permanent secretaries of the Academy of Sciences, and this was confirmed by a vote a year later.[9] His eloquent eulogy to Cuvier was the first of a distinguished number which were collected and published in three volumes in 1857. In 1838 Flourens was chosen as a deputy from his home *arrondissement*.[10] Two years later he was received into the French Academy, and he took his seat as the successful rival of Victor Hugo, whose popularity in Paris was then at its height.[11] In 1846 he was elevated to a peerage. He was first given the ribbon of the Legion of Honour in 1832 and rose to the grade of Grand Officer by 1859.[12]

Flourens' honours were well-deserved. In a series of memoirs and books between 1819 and 1865 he made important contributions to all

[1] Ebstein, 1924.    [2] Olmsted, 1953, p. 292.    [3] Anon. 1824.
[4] Olmsted, 1953, p. 294.    [5] Ibid., p. 296.    [6] Ibid., p. 298.
[7] Ibid.    [8] Ibid.    [9] Ibid.
[10] Ibid., p. 299.    [11] Ibid., p. 290.    [12] Ibid., p. 301.

the following topics: the functions of the cerebrum, cerebellum medulla oblongata, and semicircular canals; the formation of bone and teeth; diseases in birds; respiration in fishes; trephining; and the use of chloroform as an anaesthetic. He edited the works of both Cuvier and Buffon, wrote numerous monographs, and took an active part in scientific debate and politics. From this active and prolific career, the aspect of his work which has brought him the most lasting recognition is his work on the nervous system. By the time he was forty, M. Mignet Director of the French Academy, claimed that Flourens' work ranked with the contributions of Albrecht von Haller, the founder of modern physiology, and Bell and Magendie. What Haller did for the peripheral nerves and Bell and Magendie did for the spinal nerves, Flourens had done for the major divisions of the central nervous system: he had determined their functions by experiment.[1] The distinctions conferred on Flourens were due primarily to the memoirs which were collected and published in 1824 as *Recherches Expérimentales sur les Propriétés et les Fonctions du Système Nerveux dans les Animaux Vertébrés* and expanded by two-thirds in the second edition of 1842.

In retrospect, Flourens' methods were more important to scientific progress than were his findings. Although many of his experimental results remain valid, others—and especially the assumptions which they supported—retarded cerebral research for almost half a century. It is for this reason that his methods, findings, and assumptions will be considered separately.

## Flourens' Method: Experimental Ablation

Where Gall had confined himself to naturalistic observations and correlation, Flourens was firmly committed to the experimental method. Gall claimed that he waited patiently for what nature brought; Flourens' approach was more active: 'I picture to myself physiology, a probe in her hand, eagerly turning over unknown soil in order to discover there the sources of life, and to make them redound to the profit of humanity.'[2] He grants the importance of observation as a necessary prerequisite to experiment, but alone it is insufficient: 'It is too complicated to be comprehensive and too limited to be truthful.'[3] Experiment reproduces all that observation shows, but it goes further, joins isolated facts, completes them, and explains them.

[1] Olmsted, 1953, p. 290.   [2] Quoted in Ibid., p. 302.   [3] Flourens, 1842, p. 248.

In a word, what observation has begun experiment finishes.[1] In the study of natural phenomena, there is thus a time for observation and a time for experiment. At first when one only tries to ascertain the obvious circumstances of these phenomena, observation suffices: then one wants to penetrate further into both the intimate constitution and the hidden resources; this is the task of experiment.[2]

Flourens was very attentive to Gall's technical objections to the experimental method, and he set out to overcome them in his conception of the task of cerebral physiology.

Everything, in experimental researches, depends on the method; because it is the method which gives the results. A new method leads to new results; a rigorous method to precise results; a vague method can only lead to confused results.[3]

Thus, the method which I have employed: 1st *isolate the parts;* 2nd *remove,* when necessary, *the entire parts;* and 3rd always *prevent the complication of the effects on the lesions due to the effects of effusions.*[4]

He criticizes his predecessors (Haller, Zinn, Lorry, Saucerotte, Rolando) repeatedly for failing to isolate the parts which they were removing. This imprecision led to the inconsistent results which had brought the experimental method into disrepute.[5] Similarly, he was careful to avoid causing injury which would obscure the direct effects of his operations. He chose only young animals with tender bones, a strong constitution, and less developed meninges.[6] In order to minimize blood loss further he exposed only the part on which he was operating and extended the lesion no farther than was necessary.[7] Finally, he waited until the effects of the operation itself had worn off, and kept his animals alive as long as possible so that his observations would not be complicated by the effects of operative shock, swelling, and pressure.[8]

His predecessors had relied largely on pricking, pinching, and compression.[9] Flourens' method was more precise and led to unambiguous results. Cuvier had high praise for this advance in methodology.

When, for instance, the brain was compressed, it was not well known, on what point of the interior the compression had most strongly acted; when an instrument was passed into the brain, the depth to which it extended was not sufficiently examined, nor into what organ it had been introduced. M. Flourens objects, with some reason, to the experiments of Haller, Zinn, and Lorry: and he has endeavoured to avoid this difficulty by operating principally by means of ablation, that is to say, by removing, whenever it

---

[1] Flourens, 1842, p. 248.    [2] Ibid.    [3] Ibid., p. 502. See below p. 231.
[4] Ibid., p. 510.    [5] Ibid., pp. vi, 252–4, 505–7.    [6] Ibid., pp. vii–viii.
[7] Ibid., pp. viii, 252–4.    [8] Ibid., Chapter IX.    [9] Ibid., pp. ix–x.

was possible, that particular part, the special function of which he wished to know.[1]

Flourens did not originate the method of ablation. Luigi Rolando had reported results based on this method as early as 1809.[2] However, it can be said that Flourens was the first to use it successfully, in his experiments on the cerebellum. Similarly, Flourens claimed that he was the first to remove all the cerebral lobes.[3]

It was the dramatic success of Flourens' precise use of ablation which established this method as a standard part of cerebral research. It has since been refined and complemented by very sophisticated methods of electrical and chemical stimulation, and by recording the electrical activity of areas varying in size from a whole lobe to a single neurone. However, the authors of the standard compendium on the cerebellum could still say in 1958,

There is a natural tendency, which is perhaps stronger in our time, to stress the importance of new approaches and to forget experiments made with older techniques. We believe that it would be particularly dangerous to indulge in this trend in a monograph on the cerebellum. The historical perspective of the reader would first of all be seriously distorted. Moreover, all the refinements in stimulating and recording techniques will never supplant ablation experiments. In fact, it is only through extirpation experiments that we may hope to know the main features of cerebellar function and to evaluate, more or less quantitatively, the relative importance of the different types of functional activity of this organ. . . . Stimulation experiments and electrophysiological studies can direct and suggest points for attack by ablation experiments, but can never take their place.[4]

It should be emphasized that this testimony to the utility of the ablation method does not provide unqualified support for Flourens' use of it. His findings on the cerebellum have remained valid. For practical purposes the function which he was investigating is unitary, and successive slices from an anatomically discrete structure provided him with trustworthy results. However, subsequent findings have not justified Flourens' method of ablating the cerebral hemispheres by successive slices. Gall rightly points out that this approach is contrary to the structure of the cerebrum. If some form of cerebral localization *were* valid, Flourens' slicing indiscriminately through the hemispheres would still result in increasing loss of all its functions as the slicing proceeded. 'The sole method of proceeding would be in conformity

---

[1] Flourens, 1842, pp. 71–72.    [2] Gall, 1835, VI, 125–6.    [3] Flourens, 1842, p. 508.
[4] Dow and Moruzzi, 1958, p. 7.

vith the true organization of the brain. . . . He mutilates all the organs
t once, weakens them all, extirpates them all at the same time.'
Consequently, Gall concludes, a million experiments of this kind would
ave no demonstrative value for cerebral localization.[1] Methods do
ndeed give the results.

Flourens maintains that 'the end and goal of all physiology and
pathology' is 'to deduce the alteration of the parts from the alteration
of the properties, and, reciprocally, the lesion of the properties from
he lesion of the parts'.[2] Where Gall's method had involved four
variables (striking behaviour, faculty, cortical organ, and cranial
prominence), Flourens considered the faculties to be already established
and the cranial prominence irrelevant. Consequently, his method
reduced to making inferences about the seats of faculties from changes
n behaviour consequent upon cerebral lesions. He said, in effect:
I removed this part, and the animal ceased to do that, so this must be
he seat of the faculty of that.' His conclusions were often based on
months of careful, daily observation of the post-operative behaviour
of his animals which he carefully recorded in his journal.[3]

From a modern point of view, however, his method was only half-
experimental. That is, he controlled the physiological aspect of his
experiments, but in the behavioural realm he was still a naturalist.
He carefully excised a part of the brain and then waited to see what
happened. There was no attempt to establish standard criteria for
loss of function. It is true that Flourens conducted tests, but these were
crude and unstandardized. For example, after removing both cerebral
lobes in a hen, he reports the following observations on the senses,
made five months after the operation:

I let this hen starve several times for as long as three days. Then I brought
nourishment under her nose, I put her beak into grain, I put grain into her
beak, I plunged her beak into water, I placed her on a shock of corn. She
did not smell, she did not eat anything, she did not drink anything, she
remained immobile on the shock of corn, and she would certainly have died
of hunger if I had not returned to the old process of making her eat myself.

Twenty times, in lieu of grain, I put sand into her beak; and she ate this
as she would have eaten grain.

Finally, when this hen encounters an obstacle in her path, she throws
herself against it, and this collision stops her and disturbs her, but to collide
with an object is not the same as to touch it. . . . She is collided with and she
collides, but she does not touch.[4]

[1] Gall, 1835, VI, 165–6. See below, pp. 231–2.   [2] Flourens, 1842, p. 57.
[3] E.g., Flourens, 1842, pp. 87–92.   [8] Ibid., pp. 90–1.

The process by which he draws conclusions from these observations as follows:

One judges that an animal does not have a certain sense when it does no use that sense any more.

An animal does not see any more when it knocks against everything tha is in its way; it does not hear any more when no sound changes its expression it does not smell any more when no odour attracts or repels it; it does no taste when no flavour attracts or angers it; it does not feel, it does not handl it does not touch, when it does not distinguish any object, bumps obstinatel against anything, and walks or advances against everything indifferently.

His experiments on the senses lack rigour, but one has only forma reservations about the legitimacy of these relatively simple inference from anecdotal evidence. However, he is quick to draw further con clusions which give rise to more serious reservations.

An animal which really touches a body, judges it; an animal which doe not judge anymore therefore does not touch anymore.

Animals deprived of their cerebral lobes have, therefore, neither per ception, nor judgment, nor memory, nor will: because there is no volitio when there is no judgment; no judgment when there is no memory; n memory when there is no perception. The cerebral lobes are therefore th exclusive seat of all the perceptions and of all of the intellectual faculties.[2]

His evidence provides no basis for these sweeping conclusions or for th categories of function which he uses without question.

This mixed method of controlled physiological manipulation an naturalistic observation of the resulting behavioural changes remaine characteristic of cerebral research throughout the nineteenth century It was not until 1898 that Thorndike introduced standard, quantitativ tests into the study of animal behaviour, and it was another decad before Franz and then Lashley integrated these methods with brai research and made controlled experimentation a standard feature o physiological psychology. These methods are still being slowly extende to studies on humans. Finally, it can be said that the design of standard quantitative, behavioural tests which isolate identifiable pieces o behaviour, that in combination are sufficient to characterize a give function, remains a task for the future.

A final reservation should be made about the inferences which Flourens drew from his ablations. He was working solely with animals and primarily with birds. In spite of the familiarity with comparative

[1] Flourens, 1842, pp. 96–7.  [2] Ibid., p. 97.

anatomy which he must have derived from his teaching, from editing the works of Buffon and Cuvier, and from his own experiments, he had no reservations about drawing sweeping inferences about the functions of the human brain from experiments on lower organisms. This had disastrous effects where motion was concerned, since, in fact, birds may have no motor cortex, and if they do it is small enough to be easily missed.[1] After the role of the cortex in motion had been established, Ferrier granted the validity of Flourens' findings on birds but rejected their extension to higher organisms.[2] More important, perhaps, the behaviour of Flourens' experimental animals did not require him to consider seriously the concepts of function which Gall had derived from his comparative studies on men and animals. As Gall rightly pointed out, 'these cruel experiments, when they are made on animals of an order comparatively low, are hardly ever conclusive for man. In chickens, pigeons, rabbits, guinea pigs, and even in newly born animals of a superior order, the whole animal life is not by any means under the dominion of the brain.'[3] He even doubts that lower functions could be better understood by this approach, though he grants that some doubtful results might be obtained on irritability, sensibility, functions of the viscera, voluntary motion, respiration, etc.[4]

*Problems and Main Results*

The foregoing analysis of Flourens' method and its limitations provides a basis for the study of his own conception of his work and for an exposition of his main findings. In his first memoir to the Academy of Sciences he describes his approach with elegant simplicity. The nervous system is the origin of sensations and movements and the site of the principle which wills, perceives, remembers, and judges. Do these constitute a simple property or many? Do they reside in the same or different parts of the system? If different, which parts serve each? No one before, he claims, has addressed these issues by direct experiments.[5]

The point of the question and the difficulty is only therefore to ascertain experimentally (for it is only thus that one can ascertain) which parts of the nervous system are used exclusively for sensation, which for contraction, which for perception, etc.

Obviously, only experiment on each part would show which parts are used exclusively for which property. I have therefore subjected to experiment,

[1] von Bonin, 1960, p. ix.    [2] Ferrier, 1890, pp. 5–8.
[3] Gall, 1835, III, 97–8. Cf. Hollander, 1909, pp. 10–11.
[4] Gall, 1835, III, 98.    [5] Flourens, 1842, pp. 1–2.

one by one and separately, the nerves, the spinal cord, the medulla oblongata, the quadrigeminal tubercles, the cerebral lobes and the cerebellum.[1]

The problems which Flourens addressed, like the method which he employed, derive from a tradition very different from Gall's naturalism. They were both concerned with the functions of the nervous system, but Gall set out to find new categories of analysis, while Flourens drew on the established problems of experimental physiology. The starting point for Flourens' investigations was the work of Albrecht von Haller, who has been called 'the founder of modern physiology'.[2] Haller was the author of the first modern handbook or systematic treatise in the field.[3] 'The year 1757 may be regarded in a certain sense as a red letter year in the history of physiology, as marking an epoch, as indicating the dividing line between modern physiology and all that went before. It was the year in which the first volume of the *Elementa Physiologiae* of Haller was published, the eighth and last volume leaving the press in 1765.'[4] This judgement is based on the modern treatment given in the work in his approach to anatomy and minute anatomy, and physical properties and chemical composition (so far as this was known). It particularly refers to Haller's own careful observations and sound judgement.

Flourens' experiments on animal functions stemmed directly from the concepts of Haller's treatise on the sensible and irritable parts of animals (1753). Nordenskiöld describes Haller's treatise as follows:

In this investigation he first establishes the fact that the organs of the body are partly irritable, partly non-irritable; why this is so, science cannot discover; it can only show that it is so. As irritable (*irritabilis*) he mentions such a part of the body as contracts upon being touched; as sensible (*sensibilis*), again, he defines a part of the body, contact with which induces an impression in the mind. Which organs belong to the one or the other category is a question which can be answered only by experiment. The performing of such experiments on live animals Haller finds highly revolting, but in the interests of truth it cannot in this case be avoided.[5]

Thus, Haller was a pioneer in physiological experiments on live animals in order to discover the functions of organs.

[1] Flourens, 1842, p. 3.
[2] Roget, 1838, II, 382; Nordenskiöld, translated Eyre, 1928, p. 238; Wolf, revised McKie, 1952, p. 469.
[3] Boring, 2nd ed., 1950, p. 16.
[4] Foster, 1901, pp. 204-5.
[5] Nordenskiöld, 1928, p. 236. Cf. Young, 1968, p. 256 and fn. 33.

n his footsteps there followed an increasing number of scientists who sought
y means of experiment on live animals—that is, vivisections—to ascertain
ne course of events in animal life, both in the isolated organs and in groups
nereof, to an every-increasing extent.[1]

Iis doctrine of irritability was a modification of a broader concept of
'rancis Glisson.[2] Haller argued that muscles were irritable, while
erves were the source of all sensibility. Later developments of the
oncept of irritability broadened it into a general attribute of living
natter, while the specific reaction of muscle gave rise to the narrower
oncept of contractility.[3] The concept of sensibility became the modern
oncept of nervous excitability, according to which the function of the
ervous system is the transmission of impulses which result in sensations,
nuscular contractions, and secretions.

Haller also conducted experiments on the brain and concluded that
he cortex must feel, though no movements resulted when it was
rritated.[4] On the question of cerebral localization, he admits that some
xperiments and phenomena of disease do support it, as does anatomical
vidence (e.g., the parts of the brain near the optic nerve are probably
oncerned with vision). However, he concludes that

Jur present knowledge does not permit us to speak with any show of truth
about the more complicated functions of the mind or to assign in the brain
o imagination its seat, to common sensation its seat, to memory its seat.
Iypotheses of this kind have in great numbers reigned in the writings of
ohysiologists from all time. But all of them alike have been feeble, fleeting,
and of a short life.[5]

In his first experiments Flourens set out to reform the nomenclature
of neurophysiology. A contemporary English expositor provides a
convenient summary of his argument. He wanted to eliminate an
ambiguity, whereby the nerves had been said to be 'irritable and sensible,
though they are merely organs for conveying the impressions which are
to call forth these properties elsewhere'.[6] He begins with the phenomenon that when one pricks a nerve it leads to contraction of a muscle
and to a sensation. These events are not the properties of the nerve
itself.

---

[1] Nordenskiöld, 1928, p. 374.
[2] See Foster, 2nd ed., 1924, pp. 284–8; Anon., 1824, p. 144; Brazier, 1959a, p. 13.
[3] See Verworn, 1913, Chapter 1.    [4] Foster, 1924, p. 292.
[5] Quoted in Ibid., p. 296.    [6] Anon., 1824, p. 144.

The nerve has therefore the property of receiving a peculiar impression which is conducted in both directions along its course, producing contraction at its extremities, and sensation somewhere at its origin in the great nervous centre, the brain and spine.[1]

Flourens proposed that the property, inherent in muscular fibres, of undergoing contractions under stimuli be called 'contractility'; that the property of experiencing sensations be called 'sensibility'; and that 'irritability' should refer to the property, possessed by nerves, of receiving impressions which give rise to sensation and motion without experiencing them.[2] Flourens' first experiments derive directly from this reasoning. He ligated a peripheral nerve in two places and stimulated above, below, and between the ligatures. The nerve was neither contractile nor sensible but conveyed irritations concerned with these properties. The same results occurred when he divided the spinal cord in two places, but the cord showed the additional property of combining muscular contractions to produce coordinated movements of joints or limbs. He then goes on to seek to discover by experiment what parts of the nervous system have the property of irritability.[3] In his laudatory review of Flourens' memoir, Cuvier summarizes the questions as follows:

1st from what points in the nervous system must artificial irritation set out in order to arrive at muscle;

2nd To what points in the system ought impressions be propagated in order to produce sensation;

3rd From what points voluntary irritation descends, and what parts of the system ought to remain intact in order to produce it regularly.[4]

In addition to sensation and movement, the nervous system is the seat of perception and will. But do perception and will reside in the same portion as sensation, and sensation in the same portion as movement? Flourens points out that the question of whether or not these are separate faculties has been debated over the centuries and still awaits solution.[5]

As a result of a very large number of experiments on different species (e.g., frogs, cocks, hens, pigeons, ducks, mice, moles, cats, dogs), some of which were conducted in response to Cuvier's criticisms of his first memoir,[6] Flourens arrived at the following conclusions:[7] Connection

---

[1] Anon., 1824, p. 144.    [2] Ibid.    [3] Ibid., pp. 145–6.
[4] Flourens, 1842, p. 68.    [5] Ibid., pp. x–xii.    [6] Ibid., pp. 60–86, 147–9.
[7] Flourens' arguments are rambling and repetitious, and his conclusions are scattered throughout the thirty-two chapters of his book. The following summary is based on a close reading of the book, but it would be pointless to cite the numerous repetitions of his findings and conclusions.

of nerve with muscle is required for muscular contraction, and connection with the brain is necessary for perception. If the peripheral end of a severed nerve is stimulated it produces muscular contractions, whereas stimulation of the central end produces pain. Thus, the two orders of phenomena—sensation and muscular irritation—are distinguished.[1] Following Bell, he finds the same separation of functions between the anterior and posterior spinal nerve roots, and the central and peripheral parts of the transected spinal cord.[2] He exposed the spinal cord from the sacrum to the cranium and up to the cerebral mass, and irritated successively higher parts. He found a point where muscular contraction ceased to be produced by laceration, pricking, and burning, and concluded that excitability (i.e., production of muscular contractions) is not a property of the whole system.[3] Stimulation of the cerebral hemispheres, corpus striatum, corpus callosum, optic layers, and cerebellum produced no movement, whereas stimulation of the bigeminal and quadrigeminal tubercles, the medulla and all lower structures produced movements ranging from violent convulsions to simple muscular contractions.[4] He concluded that the cerebral hemispheres do not immediately excite muscular contractions[5] and that neither the cerebral lobes nor the cerebellum is effectively the direct origin of any nerve.[6] Conversely, if he removed the cerebral lobes, the animal suffered a profound weakness, became lethargic and no longer moved spontaneously. When prodded it would move but in a purposeless way and soon settled back into its lethargic state.[7]

This evidence (along with that on the cerebellum, cited in the preceding chapter)[8] is the basis for Flourens' distinction between volition, muscular contraction, and coordination. The elements of muscular contractions are directly excited by the nerves; these are combined into movements by the nervous trunks, spinal cord, and medulla. Coordination of voluntary movements is the property of the cerebellum. Voluntary control—the will—is exclusively the property of the cerebral lobes.[9] He concludes that the intellectual faculty of will is independent of the locomotor faculties,[10] which, in turn, are independent of the principle of coordination. The will provokes movements but is not the direct cause of any.[11]

[1] Flourens, 1842, pp. 3–4.  [2] Ibid., p. 9.    [3] Ibid., pp. 16–17.
[4] Ibid., pp. 17–23.    [5] Ibid., pp. xiv and 19.  [6] Ibid., p. 22.
[7] Ibid., p. 239.    [8] See above pp. 47–50.  [9] Flourens, 1842, pp. xiii, 27–31.
[10] Ibid., pp. xiii, 50.
[11] Ibid., pp. 237–9. I am not here considering Flourens' work on the mechanism of respiration, the 'vital point' and the 'movements of conservation', all functions of the medulla. See Flourens, 1842, Chapter X.

In view of later developments in cerebral physiology, it is important to consider more closely Flourens' view that the hemispheres play no direct role in exciting muscular movements. A simple explanation of his path to this wholly erroneous conclusion has already been given: he worked primarily with birds, and uncritically extended his results to higher organisms. However, he also conducted experiments on mammals, and he explicitly considered paralyses due to cerebral lesions.[1] These lesions produced profound weakness and paralysis, though these often passed away as the animal recovered from the operation. He discusses crossed and direct effects in paralyses and convulsions, and recognizes the long-established fact that the motor impairment from cerebral lesions is a crossed effect. However, in this case, he makes no inference from the effects of lesions to the function involved and refrains from implicating the cerebral lobes in motor functions. This can only be attributed to the combined effect of his negative results on cerebral stimulation and the preconceptions which will be considered presently. There can be no doubt that he held this view without reservation. It is one of his most oft-repeated conclusions. When Rolando reported muscular contractions resulting from stimulation of the hemispheres of a pig and concluded that the hemispheres contain a group of fibres producing voluntary movement, Flourens confidently replied that Rolando only appeared to have induced such responses. They were actually due, Flourens argued, to the conduction of the current to the structures which immediately excite muscular contractions. 'My experiments establish that the hemispheres of the brain do not produce any movement.'[2]

From his experiments on sensory functions Flourens concluded that the nerves, spinal cord, medulla, bigeminal and quadrigeminal tubercles, and cerebral peduncles have the properties of conveying sensations, but that perception resides in none of these structures. He argues that each sense originates in the eminence which gives rise to its nerves (e.g., vision in the quadrigeminal tubercles and hearing in the nervous extension of the cochlea).[3] The distinction which he made between sensation and perception was based primarily on the fact that animals whose cerebral lobes had been ablated still responded to sensory stimulation, but they gave no evidence of appreciating the quality or meaning of the sensation. They failed to recognize or avoid objects, or to care for themselves in any way unless prodded.[4] It is extremely

---

[1] Flourens, 1842, Chapter XVI.   [2] Quoted in Walker, 1957, p. 103.
[3] Flourens, 1842, pp. 450-1. Cf. Gall, 1835, VI, 167-8.   [4] Flourens, 1842, pp. 123-5.

difficult to follow Flourens' arguments on this issue, and subsequent research has not supported his exclusion of sensation from the hemispheres. Also, the two editions of his book differ on this matter, and it appears that he was inconsistent in the first edition, while he consistently excluded sensation from the hemispheres in the 1842 edition.[1] However, the main lines of his position are unambiguous: sensation is distinguished from perception and intelligence. Perception and intelligence reside exclusively in the cerebral lobes. Ablation of a single lobe causes loss of sight in the opposite eye but the remaining lobe is sufficient for the preservation of intelligence.[2] Ablation of both cerebral lobes leads to loss of all perceptions at once. The animal becomes lethargic and fails to exhibit the instincts peculiar to that species.[3] It does not wish, remember, or judge.[4] He even ventures the conclusion that such animals are deprived of their dreams.[5]

Although Flourens' arguments about motion and will have been discussed here separately from those regarding sensation, perception, and intelligence, it should be emphasized that the sensory-motor distinction played no part in his view of the cerebral hemispheres. Although he localized different functions in different parts of the nervous system, he considered the hemispheres a unitary organ. Thus, he was an advocate of localization in the brain but not within the hemispheres themselves.[6] He stresses the conclusion that if one cortical faculty is lost all are lost: the cortex is a unitary organ whose functions constitute a unitary faculty.[7] Perception, intelligence, will, and all the subdivisions of these (memory, reasoning, judgement, desire, etc.) reside together in the hemispheres. Successive slicing of the cerebral lobes led to concomitant loss of all these faculties. If sufficient tissue remained, function would be restored, but if the ablation was carried too far the faculties remained permanently lost. Thus, while the nervous system had diverse parts with diverse functions, it acted in a unitary fashion, and within this grand unity the unitary cortex presided over lower functions.[8] These views provided the basis for opposition to

---

[1] The two editions should be compared systematically with a view to distinguishing the meanings of the term *sensation* in particular contexts. It appears from a partial comparison that Flourens substituted the term *perception* for *sensation* in the second edition wherever he was concerned with the functions of the cerebral lobes. See below, p. 213, and Boring, 1950, pp. 77–8.

[2] Flourens, 1842, pp. xv, 16, 24, 34.    [3] Ibid., pp. 131–2.

[4] Ibid., pp. xvi, 48–9.    [5] Ibid., p. 33.

[6] Flourens, 1846, pp. 32–3. Cf. Riese, 1949, p. 122.

[7] Flourens, 1842, pp. xvi, 244.    [8] Ibid., pp. 208, 235, 243.

cerebral localization, and the historical precedent for modern doctrines of mass action and cortical equipotentiality.[1]

## Flourens' Assumptions

Although Flourens worked primarily as an experimentalist until the publication of the second edition of his *Recherches* in 1842, in subsequent years he became increasingly concerned with the philosophical issues surrounding his work. In his eulogy of Flourens, Claude Bernard noted that after Flourens was elected to the French Academy in 1841, his work became 'a combination of philosophy, science and literature'.[2] It is indicative of his convictions (and extremely convenient for present purposes) that the first book which he wrote in this new vein was a polemic against phrenology: *Examen de la phrénologie* (1842). This work makes explicit the assumptions which had led Flourens to make a radical distinction between the sensory and motor parts of the nervous system on the one hand and the seat of perception, intellect, and will on the other. It also explains the basis of his vehement opposition to Gall's physiological and psychological doctrines.

Flourens' experimental methods were certainly an advance on Gall's naturalism, and if this were the only issue between them, it would be pointless to consider Flourens' objections in detail. Similarly, Gall has no defence against Flourens' accusation that his anatomical discoveries are irrelevant to Gall's own doctrine of the functions of the brain.[3] However, very basic issues are at stake in the conflict between their respective psychological views. It has been pointed out that Flourens granted that observation was a necessary prerequisite for experiment. Nevertheless, in his own work, Flourens made no attempt to *determine* by observation a set of psychological categories which were relevant to the adaptations of species and individuals to their respective environments. Such observations should have constituted an obvious prerequisite to his experiments, and Gall was quick to point this out. Before experimental ablations could bear fruit,

It would have been requisite to know what could be found, and what ought to be sought for, in the brain. It would also have been necessary, that the mutilators should be divested of every metaphysical prejudice; that they should have a detailed knowledge of the fundamental powers. Where is the physiologist, where, the anatomist, who has been able to follow this direction and who has not wished to find generalities and abstractions?[4]

[1] See Zangwill, 1961.                    [2] Quoted in Olmsted, 1953, p. 291
[3] Flourens, 1846, pp. 70–4. Quoted above, pp. 24n–25n.
[4] Gall, 1835, III, 99.

Flourens granted this point in principle,[1] but there is no evidence that it influenced his research.

It should be acknowledged that Gall's concepts of function may have been inadequate and that his faculty psychology begged the interesting questions which his studies of human and animal behaviour had raised. However, his psychological categories had the merit of relevance and were certainly an advance over the medieval faculties of perception, memory, judgement, imagination, etc. Gall was quite right to point out that Flourens' doctrine could not explain the marked differences among individuals and among species.[2] He was also right to object that, while Flourens may have advanced the study of the vital functions, he had completely ignored the 'special animal functions'—the different propensities, instincts, talents, sentiments, and determinate intellectual faculties.[3]

Flourens' criticism of Gall's faculty psychology is valid in its own right, but it is more interesting for the evidence it provides of the real basis of his objections. He grants that men and animals show very different propensities, talents, etc.

No doubt of it. But what sort of philosophy is that, that thinks to explain a fact by a word? You observe such or such a penchant in an animal, such or such a taste or talent in a man; *presto*, a particular faculty is produced for each one of these peculiarities, and you suppose the whole matter to be settled. You deceive yourself; your *faculty* is only a *word*—it is the name of the fact—and all the difficulty remains just where it was before.[4]

The authority with which he supports this point leads us to the basis of Flourens' objections.

There are in us as many faculties as there are truths to be known. . . . But I do not think that any useful application can be made of this way of thinking; and it seems to me rather more likely to be mischievous, by giving to the ignorant occasion for imagining an equal number of little entities in the soul.[5]

The quotation is from Descartes, to whom Flourens turned for the arguments which support his objections to Gall. The book is dedicated to the Memory of Descartes.[6] In the preface, Flourens says,

Each succeeding age has a philosophy of its own.
The seventeenth century enthroned the philosophy of Descartes; the

---

[1] Flourens, 1842, pp. 250–1.  [2] Gall, 1835, VI, 173–4.  [3] Ibid., VI, 1, 165.
[4] Flourens, 1846, p. 39.  [5] Quoted in Ibid., p. 41.  [6] Flourens, 1846, p. xi.

eighteenth that of Locke and Condillac; should the nineteenth enthrone that of Gall?[1]

I frequently quote Descartes: I even go further; for I dedicate my work to his memory. I am writing in opposition to a bad philosophy, while I am endeavouring to recall a sound one.[2]

Later, in the body of the work, he expresses his supreme contempt for Gall: 'Descartes goes off to die in Sweden, and Gall comes to reign in France.'[3]

Flourens' rejection of Gall's psychology is wholly based on Cartesian dualism and the doctrine of the unity of the soul.

'I remark here, in the first place,' says Descartes, 'that there is a great difference between the mind and the body, in that the body is, by its nature, always divisible, and the mind wholly indivisible. For, in fact, when I contemplate it—that is, when I contemplate my own self—and consider myself as a thing that thinks, I cannot discover in myself any parts, but I clearly know and conceive that I am a thing absolutely one and complete.'[4]

Now here is the sum and the substance of Gall's psychology. For the understanding, essentially a unit faculty, he substitutes a multitude of little understandings or faculties, distinct and isolate.[5]

Gall reverses the common philosophy. . . . According to common philosophy, there is one general understanding—a unit; and there are faculties which are but modes of this understanding. Gall asserts that there are as many kinds of peculiar intelligences as there are faculties, and that the understanding in general is nothing more than a mode or attribute of each faculty.[6]

Flourens joins Gall in rejecting sensationalism. Faculties are derived from the soul, not the senses.[7] However, he goes farther and rejects Gall's argument for the plurality of the faculties by analogy from the fact that each of the senses has its proper, distinct organ.[8] He does not contest the innateness of the faculties. In fact, he points out that although Locke opposed innate ideas, he did not doubt that our faculties are innate. He maintains that the innate faculties are, after all, only the unitary soul itself, 'viewed under different aspects'.[9]

Flourens' view of the hemispheres is a consequence of his psychological assumptions.

Gall's philosophy consists wholly in the substitution of *multiplicity* for *unity*. In place of one general and single brain, he substitutes a number of small

---

[1] Flourens, 1846, p. xiii. (Translation corrected.)   [2] Ibid., p. xiv.   [3] Ibid., p. 96.
[4] Ibid., p. 53. Cf. p. 57.                              [5] Ibid., p. 38. Cf. p. 45.
[6] Ibid., pp. 53–4. Cf. p. 41.                           [7] Ibid., p. 27.   [8] Ibid., p. 70 ff.
[9] Ibid., p. 52.

rains: instead of one general sole understanding, he substitutes several individual understandings.[1]

If the understanding is a unit, its organ must also act in a unitary fashion. He repeats his experimental evidence in support of the thesis that 'the cerebral hemispheres concur, by their whole mass, in the full and entire exercise of the intelligence'.[2] Any qualification of the unity of the soul or its organs is, as Flourens sees it, equivalent to denying the existence of the mind or soul.[3] To divide the functions of the soul among different parts of the brain is equivalent to materialism. He cannot allow Gall's tendency toward the position that 'Organization explains every thing'.[4] He is especially opposed to Gall's contention that our awareness of God is dependent on material conditions.[5] Flourens maintains that the activities of the soul 'are not *results*—they are *powers*, and primary powers of thought'.[6] His opposition to the materialist tendencies in Gall's thought are connected with his belief that division of the soul entails fatalism. He will allow no hint of limitation of free will: 'Liberty is precisely the power to determine against all motive'.[7]

Flourens is explicitly opposed to Gall's naturalistic methods and his willingness to look upon 'the outer man' and construct 'the inner man after the image of the outer man'.[8] He ridicules Gall for going out among men and questioning them. He is unwilling even to transcribe some of Gall's conclusions which offend his view of the dignity of man's soul. 'The pen refuses to transcribe such things, which fortunately, however, are pure extravagances.'[9] Thus, Flourens' advocacy of physiological experimentation is complemented by a complete unwillingness to apply the scientific method to the study of mental phenomena, and his philosophical assumptions dictate the interpretation which he puts on his physiological findings. He immensely improved standards of research on the physiological side but relied solely on introspection for his psychological views. It is his consciousness (supported by Descartes') which provides evidence of unity to oppose Gall's observations on multiplicity, and his consciousness which supports his spiritualism and doctrine of moral liberty against Gall's alleged materialism and fatalism.[10] He cites Descartes' *Meditations* as authority

---

[1] Flourens, 1846, p. 47.  [2] Ibid., p. 34.  [3] Iid., p. 58.
[4] Ibid., p. 63.  [5] Ibid.  [6] Ibid., p. 42. Cf. pp. 45, 59.
[7] Ibid., p. 42.  [8] Ibid., p. 76.  [9] Ibid., p. 65. Cf. pp. 62-3.
[10] Ibid., pp. 123-4.

for turning all the senses aside and closing off all contact with his memo
ries and the external world in order to learn about his true nature.
He has nothing but ridicule for the methods which would eventuall
transform behavioural studies.

Men will always be looking out for external signs by which to discove
secret thoughts and concealed inclinations: it is vain to confound the
curiosity upon this point: after Lavater came Gall; after Gall someone els
will appear.[2]

Flourens was not prepared to submit the human character, the min
or its organ to analysis. Their unity was a necessary basis of his belie
about man's dignity and freedom. On the other hand, he was prepare
to subject sensory-motor functions to close analysis, as long as the orga
of mind was kept entirely separate from this analysis. Thus, the hemi
spheres were the seat of perception, will, and intellect, but played n
role in sensation and motion. How the will acted upon the lower centre
which caused muscular contractions, and how sensations reached th
organ of perception and higher functions, remained a mystery, for ther
were supposed to be no nerves connecting them. This separation is, c
course, anatomically false and physiologically absurd. Also, havin;
granted that the brain is the organ of the mind, one would expect tha
Flourens would have no reason to hold back from accepting the im
plications of this view. However, he could go this far and no farther
The pattern which was set in his research remained characteristic o
investigations on the hemispheres for several decades. However, hi
methods and his research on sensation, motion, and irritability pro
vided the basis for the eventual extension of the sensory-motor paradigr
to the hemispheres. The success of his methods in some areas gave stron;
support to his other findings and to his assumptions. However, later us
of the methods would eventually lead to the setting aside of Flourens
assumptions and conclusions. His technical contributions, when free
of the essentially theological context in which he used them, woul
serve other assumptions equally well and, in fact, better.

*Magendie, the Experimental Method, and the Spinal Nerve Roots*

Gall described himself as a naturalist who waited patiently for th
results of observation, and opposed this approach to philosophica
speculation. Flourens coupled a view of himself as an experimentalis

[1] Flourens, 1846, p. 95.  [2] Ibid., pp. 95–6. Cf. Bergmann, 1956.

'with a probe in his hand', with a strong penchant for defending preconceived philosophical dogmas. François Magendie gave the following description of his work:

Every one is fond of comparing himself to something great and grandiose, as Louis XIV likened himself to the sun, and others have had like similes. I am more humble. I am a mere street scavenger (*chiffonnier*) of science. With my hook in my hand and my basket on my back, I go about the streets of science, collecting what I find.[1]

He had no use for philosophy. In fact, he discussed it only once—in his first publication. When Magendie qualified in medicine in 1808 (aged 24), physiology and biological sciences generally were not counted among the exact sciences. They lacked both the foundations and the prestige of the Newtonian sciences of physics and astronomy.[2] His first paper attributed the unsatisfactory state of physiology to the influence of the theory of vital properties of Xavier Bichat,[3] which separated physiology from physico-chemical analysis. Vitalism led to despair over the stability and dependability of vital phenomena, and Magendie opposed this. Bichat maintained that

The instability of the vital powers, is the quicksand on which have sunk the calculations of all the Physicians of the last hundred years. The habitual variations of the living fluids, dependent on this instability, one would think should be no less an obstacle to the analyses of the chemical physicians of the present age.[4]

He argued that vital phenomena were not reducible to the laws of physics and chemistry, considered these sciences 'wholly strangers to physiology',[5] and even opposed such obviously useful analogies as that between hydraulics and the study of the circulation of the blood.[6] Magendie had no quarrel with Bichat's distinction between vital and physico-chemical phenomena. In fact, he remained a believer in vitalism throughout his career. Rather, he rejected the counsel of despair which Bichat had linked with his vitalism. It was the belief that vital phenomena were *not* stable which had been quicksand to previous investigators. Magendie insisted that physiologists should believe that their phenomena were law-like and that the *only* way of showing this was by the experimental method.

[1] Quoted in Foster, 1899, p. 40.    [2] Olmsted, 1944, pp. 20–2.
[3] See Bichat, new ed., 1962: Rosen, 1946; Nordenskiöld, 1928, pp. 344–51; Temkin, 1946.
[4] Bichat, n.d. p. 82; cf. pp. 81–4.    [5] Ibid., p. 83.    [6] Ibid., p. 91.

After he had made his position clear, Magendie never published another paper which did not contain reports of experiments or observations.[1] In fact, the sterile discussions of vitalism and other doctrines of the day so repelled him, that 'he was driven towards the other extreme, and arrived almost at the position of substituting experiment for thinking'.[2] He did not use experiments to test hypotheses. 'He so to speak thrust his knife here and there, to see what would come of it.'[3]

The extremity of his reaction, coupled with the success of its fruits, led to Magendie's recognition as the founder of the purely experimental school of physiology in France.[4] His career can be seen as the embodiment of growing acceptance of the experimental method in physiology.

Magendie's first experiments were concerned with the effects of strychnine. They were pioneer efforts in experimental pharmacology.[5] In 1813, he resigned his appointment in anatomy, abandoned his prospects in surgery, and turned exclusively to experimental physiology. His first physiological experiments were on the mechanisms of swallowing and vomiting.[6] He gave the first course in the science of physiology as an autonomous discipline, 'not as a mere adjunct to anatomy or medicine'.[7] In the period between 1813 and 1822, he came to be known as 'the only professional exponent of experimental physiology'.[8]

In 1816–17 Magendie published *Précis Élémentaire de Physiologie*, which 'set a new fashion in text-books by calling the attention of students of medicine to experiment as a source of scientific knowledge'.[9] It replaced Richerand's text, which adhered to Bichat's vitalism and made no attempt to provide an account of contemporary experimental work.[10] In the preface, he reiterated his purpose: to bring physiology to the stature of a natural science by doing what Galileo had done for astronomy.

It is not enough to IMAGINE or BELIEVE, as the ancients supposed, but to OBSERVE, and, above all, to INQUIRE by EXPERIMENTS.[11]
The object of this work is to endeavour to change the state of Physiology in this respect; to lead it back to positive facts; in one word, to impart to that beautiful science the happy renovation which has taken place in the physical sciences.[12]

Magendie was strongly advocating the experimental method in the same period that Gall was completing his life's work. The last volume of Gall's *Anatomie* was published in 1819, and the first volume of the

[1] Olmsted, 1944, pp. 20–1, 30–4.  [2] Foster, 1899, p. 39. Cf. Temkin, 1946, p. 35.
[3] Foster, 1899, p. 40. Cf. Nordenskiöld, 1928, p. 376.  [4] Merz, 1903, p. 384.
[5] Olmsted, 1944, pp. 35–44.  [6] Ibid., pp. 51 ff.  [7] Ibid., p. 51.
[8] Ibid., p. 75.  [9] Ibid., p. 66.  [10] Ibid.
[11] Magendie, translated Revere, 1843, p. v.  [12] Ibid., p. vi.

evised edition appeared in 1822. In 1821, Magendie began the first
journal devoted to experimental physiology, the *Journal de Physiologie
Expérimentale* (and, after Vol. II) *et Pathologie*. The journal was well
received, paid for itself, and appeared for ten years.[1] This success was
aided by Magendie's policy of accompanying articles on animal experiments with citation of hospital cases illustrating the principles involved.
Consequently, it was popular with physicians.[2]

In the same year (1821), the Academy of Sciences awarded its first
Montyon Prize in Experimental Physiology. Magendie received 'very
honourable mention', while one of his pupils won half the prize.[3]
When Corvisart, who had been Napoleon's physician and a supporter of
Gall, died in the same year, it is significant of the changing climate that
his seat in the Academy of Sciences went to the young experimentalist,
Magendie, in preference to Chaussier, who had once helped Magendie
obtain a promotion and who was, at seventy-five, a venerable and
respected anatomist.[4] Magendie rapidly rose to the position of arbiter
of all things physiological, including the award of the Academy's prize.
In fact, according to a disputed account by Flourens, it was Magendie's
experiments that had led to the establishment of the prize.[5] In any
case, Magendie sat on the committee that awarded a gold medal to
Flourens in 1824 and the Montyon Prize in 1824 and 1825.[6] Beginning
in 1823 a rivalry seems to have developed between them, based on
supposed trespasses into each other's experimental domain. It recurred
until Magendie's death, and Olmsted suggests that 'it may have been
partly in pique that Flourens always gave first credit to Bell in regard
to the discovery of the functions of the roots of the spinal nerves'.[7]

Magendie's biographer reports that he was vain, stubborn, and rash.
His fiery temper made him unpopular and often stimulated criticism.
He was extremely jealous, and resented the work of others, especially
those who had anticipated his own discoveries. These traits were all
exemplified in the prolonged Bell-Magendie controversy over priority
in discovering the functions of the spinal nerve roots, which did no one
credit.[8] Nevertheless, he continued in a distinguished experimental

---

[1] Olmsted, 1944, p. 84.    [2] Ibid., p. 85.    [3] Ibid., pp. 87–8.
[4] Ibid., pp. 48–9.    [5] Ibid., p. 130. Cf. pp. 87–8.    [6] Ibid., pp. 124, 130.
[7] Ibid., pp. 127, 130. Cf. pp. 247–9.
[8] The role of Sir Charles Bell in the discovery of the functions of the roots of the spinal
nerves will be ignored in this presentation because it is irrelevant for present purposes and
because Bell, as has been shown, was not an experimentalist. It should be noted, however,
that both Flourens and Mueller give primary credit to Bell. (Flourens, 1842, p. 13; Mueller,
translated Baly, 1838, pp. 642–4.) A balanced view of the shares of credit is that of Merz:
Bell discovered the law on primarily anatomical evidence; Magendie verified it in living

career and had numerous honours bestowed on him. He made significan contributions to the study of neurophysiology, hydrophobia, the cere brospinal fluid, the circulatory system, goitre, cowpox, cholera, publi health, and (in collaboration with Bernard) respiration and digestion.

If one considers the names most prominently associated with th experimental method in physiology in France in the nineteenth centur they are all seen to be closely related: Flourens, Magendie, Bernard and Pasteur. Pasteur considered Bernard the master spokesman for th method. Bernard, in turn, was Magendie's pupil.[2] When Flouren died, Bernard succeeded to his Chair at the French Academy in 1868 and became Chairman of the Committee awarding the prize fo experimental physiology.[3] Thus, it can be seen that Magendie exertec a massive influence in establishing the experimental method in physi ology in the first decades of the century, and in training its mos eloquent exponent in the later decades. Concomitant with the rise o the experimental method, there was a decline in the prestige of correla tive and anecdotal and purely anatomical investigations.

## The Functional Division of the Spinal Nerve Roots

In the June, 1822, number of Magendie's journal, he published a short paper entitled 'Experiments on the Functions of the Roots of the Spinal Nerves'.[4] He reports that for some time he had wanted to try the experiment of cutting the posterior roots of the spinal nerves. Several attempts to do this had failed, because of the difficulty of open ing the vertebral canal. However, when someone gave him a litter o eight pups, six weeks old, he made a fresh attempt. He succeeded in reaching and cutting the posterior roots.

I at first thought the limb corresponding to the cut nerves to be entirely paralysed; it was insensible to pricking and to the strongest pressures; it also

---

animals. The thesis was not generally considered to be proved until after Mueller's experiments in 1831. (Merz, 1903, p. 384.) Liddell takes the same view (1960, pp. 48–54). For more adequate treatments of Bell's work see Gordon-Taylor and Walls, 1958; Carmichael, 1926. Concerning the controversy, see Olmsted, 1944, pp. 92–122, 130.

[1] See Olmsted, 1944, Chapters 8–13, and pp. 271–7.

[2] See Olmsted and Olmsted, new ed., 1961, p. 14 and *passim*; Vallery-Radot, translated Devonshire, 1960.

[3] Olmsted and Olmsted, 1961, p. 153.

[4] The paper is translated and reprinted in Olmsted, 1944, pp. 100–2. The experimental method was having spectacular successes on at least two important issues that summer. At the same meeting of the French Academy of Sciences, where Magendie communicated his classical findings on the spinal nerve roots, Cuvier delivered his laudatory report on Flourens' experiments on the cerebrum and cerebellum. It was on July 22, 1822. (Ibid., p. 124.)

seemed to be immobile; but soon, to my great surprise, I saw it move in a very obvious manner, although sensibility was still quite extinct in it. A second, a third experiment gave me exactly the same results; I began to regard it as probable that the posterior roots of the spinal nerves might very well have different functions from the anterior roots, and that they were more particularly destined for sensibility.[1]

He had great difficulty in reaching the anterior roots in order to conduct the complementary experiment, but he finally succeeded.

As in the preceding experiments, I made the section only on one side in order to have a means of comparison. One can imagine with what curiosity I followed the effects of this section: they were not painful, the limb was completely motionless and flaccid, whilst it preserved an unequivocal sensibility. Finally in order that nothing might be left undone, I cut the anterior and posterior roots at the same time; there was absolute loss of feeling and movement.[2]

After repeating these experiments on various kinds of animals, Magendie concludes:

I am content to be able to state positively today that the anterior and posterior roots of the nerves which arise from the spinal cord have different functions, that the posterior roots seem to be particularly destined for sensibility, while the anterior roots seem to be especially connected with movement.[3]

This discovery was made independently by Charles Bell on anatomical grounds and came to be known as the 'Bell-Magendie Law'. The importance of this single discovery for the subsequent history of research on the nervous system cannot be overestimated. Indeed, the remainder of this study is primarily concerned with tracing the progressive application of the functional division between sensory and motor nerves to successively higher parts of the central nervous system until it provided a uniform explanatory principle in both physiology and psychology.

The significance of this discovery was immediately appreciated by an international audience. The *Edinburgh Medical and Surgical Journal* reviewed Magendie's findings, along with the experiments of Flourens, and remarked, 'The discoveries of Magendie are not less important or less extraordinary, than those [of Flourens] we have hitherto been considering'.[4] Gall also ranked the discovery of Magendie with that of

[1] Olmsted, 1944, pp. 100–1.    [2] Ibid., p. 101.    [3] Ibid., pp. 101–2.
[4] Anon., 1824, p. 154.

Flourens; that is, he discounted it. He conducted a review of the evidence, found it hopelessly contradictory, and concluded that the relations between given nerves and the phenomena of sensation and motion, and like questions, 'I say, are as yet, beyond the reach of our knowledge'.[1] His only other references to the finding are slighting.[2] It can be seen just how far and how rapidly the methods and assumptions of physiological research were moving away from Gall's approach. His evaluation must be compared with the general concensus: 'Within ten years physiologists were to agree that the difference in function of the roots of the spinal nerves had been established, and that this discovery was second only to that greatest of all landmarks in the history of physiology, Harvey's discovery of the circulation of the blood'.[3] In 1842 Longet called it 'the most beautiful physiological discovery of modern times'.[4] Fifty years later, Meynert referred to it as 'the first fundamental thesis of neurophysiology'.[5] Although Magendie continued to lecture and to do experiments on the nervous system throughout his career, his later work and his discoveries in other areas are overshadowed by this single finding. Indeed, the subsequent history of neurophysiology and psychology have been dominated by it. However, in 1822, its full implications were far from being realized, as Magendie's own work shows.

## The Functions of the Brain

The Committee which had reviewed the 1808 memoir of Gall and Spurzheim issued the following summary of the state of knowledge of the nervous system:

Undoubtedly we cannot expect a physiological explanation of the action of the brain in animal life, like that of the other viscera. In these the causes and effects are of the same kind. When the heart causes the blood to circulate, it is one motion which produces another motion: when the stomach converts the food into chyle, it is the heat, moisture, gastric juice, and slow compression of its muscular coat, which unite to produce, at the same time, a solution and trituration, greater or less, according to the species of animal, and nature of its food.

The functions of the brain are of a totally different order. They consist in receiving, by means of the nerves, and in transmitting immediately to the mind, the impressions of the senses; in preserving the traces of these impressions, and in reproducing them with greater or less promptitude, distinctness, and abundance, when the mind requires them for its operations, and when

[1] Gall, 1835, VI, 184.    [2] Ibid., VI, 200, 206.    [3] Olmsted, 1944, p. 112.
[4] Quoted in Liddell, 1960, p. 53.    [5] Meynert, 1891, p. 166.

he laws of the association of ideas recall them; lastly, in transmitting to the muscles, always by means of the nerves, the desires of the will.

Now these three functions suppose the mutual, but always incomprehensible influence of the divisible matter and the invisible mind (moi); a hiatus in the system of our ideas never to be supplied, an eternal stumbling-block of all our philosophies. But there is another difficulty not necessarily connected with the former. We not only do not comprehend, and never shall be able to comprehend how any traces impressed on our brain can be perceived by the mind, and produce images in it; but however delicate our researches, these traces are in no way visible to our eyes, and their nature is perfectly unknown to us; although the effect of age and of disease upon the memory does not permit us to doubt of their existence, or of their seat.

It seemed, at least, that the action of the nervous system upon the organic life, would be more easily explained, as it is entirely physical, and we might expect, by means of investigation, to discover in this system some texture, some intermixture, or direction of parts which would render it more or less analogous to the vascular or secreting organs. There was especially no reason to doubt, that it would be possible to unfold their different portions, to assign their connections, their relations, and respective terminations, as easily as in the other systems.

This, however, has not happened. The texture of the brain, of the spinal marrow, and of the nerves, is so fine, so soft, that all that has been hitherto said of them is blended with conjectures and hypotheses; and the different masses which compose the brain are so thick, and have so little consistence, that the greatest dexterity is required to show all the parts of their structure.

In short, none of those who have examined the brain, have succeeded in establishing a rational and positive relation between the structure of that organ and its functions, even those which are most evidently physical; the discoveries hitherto made known with regard to its anatomy, are confined to some circumstances regarding the form, connections, or texture of its parts which had escaped the observation of preceding anatomists; and whenever any one has supposed that he had proceeded farther, he has only introduced, between the well known structure and its common effects, some hypothesis, scarcely capable of satisfying for a moment even the least sceptical minds.[1]

This view, held by Cuvier, Tenon, Pinel, Portal, and Sabatier, that is, by some of the most eminent scientists of the day, has been quoted in full because it provides an excellent statement of the position when Magendie began his researches on the nervous system. It should be recalled that Gall's work was primarily psychological and provided no basis for changing the prevailing opinion. Magendie, on the other hand, soon showed that something could be learned about the functions of the nerves by the experimental method. When he turned to the higher

[1] Tenon, *et al.*, 1809, pp. 38–9. Cf. below p. 208.

functions of the nervous system, it was legitimate to expect something
equally exciting to result from the combination of his positivist prin
ciples and his experimental skill, and his initial approach was extremely
promising.

The most sublime features of the human character are intelligence, thought
the passions, and that admirable faculty by which we are enabled to direc
our movements, and communicate by speech. These phenomena are
dependant upon the brain, and are designated by many physiologists as the
*cerebral functions*. Other physiologists, sustained and inspired by religiou
creeds, regard them as belonging to the soul, a being derived from the Divine
essence, of which immortality is one of the attributes. It would not be becom
ing in us to undertake to decide here between these two modes of contemplat
ing this important subject; our object is science, not theology. Besides, we do
not pretend to explain the acts of the understanding or the instincts; our
object is to study them, and to demonstrate the physiological connexion
they may have with the brain generally, or with certain of its parts.[1]

In this way he hopes to avoid the errors others have made. He considers
the phenomena of the human understanding in the context of the
physiology of the encephalon.

Whatever may be the number and diversity of the phenomena which pertain
to the human understanding, however different they may appear from the
other phenomena of life, and though they may be evidently dependent upon
the soul, it is indispensable to consider them as the result of the action of the
brain, and not to distinguish them, in any way, from other phenomena,
which are dependent on organic action. Indeed, the functions of the brain are
absolutely governed by the same general laws as the other functions.[2]

They develop with age and are modified by experience and disease.

In a word, like every other organic action, they are not susceptible of explanation by us, and in investigating them, laying aside hypothesis, we must be
governed by observation and experience alone. It is also necessary to guard
ourselves against the impression that the study of the functions of the brain
is more difficult than that of the other organs, and that it belongs exclusively
to metaphysics. By adhering rigorously to observation, and scrupulously
avoiding all explanations or conjectures, this study becomes purely
physiological.[3]

These statements appear to be the preamble to the studies which the
Committee considered impossible, and the realization of some of
the hopes which Gall clearly enunciated but could not himself fulfil: the

---

[1] Magendie, 1843, pp. 135–6.    [2] Ibid., p. 146.    [3] Ibid.

investigation of the physiological bases of mental and behavioural phenomena.

However, when Magendie goes on to specify what he means by the 'physiological' study of the understanding, it becomes clear that the 'hiatus' mentioned by the Committee is still very much in evidence.

Perhaps it is even easier than many of the other faculties, from the facility with which we are enabled to produce and examine its phenomena, inasmuch as we have only to turn our attention upon ourselves, to *listen* or *think*, so that the phenomena may be subjected to our observation.[1]

Granted, there are difficulties in this study, since we cannot directly know the thoughts of others.

But however this may be, the study of the understanding has not heretofore been considered as constituting an essential part of physiology. One science is specially devoted to this, and is called *ideology*. Persons desirous of examining this interesting subject *in extenso*, may consult the works of Bacon, Locke, Condillac, Cabanis, and, especially, the excellent work of M. Destutt de Tracy, entitled 'Elements of Ideology'. We shall confine ourselves to some of the fundamental principles of this science.[2]

Magendie considers mental phenomena to be functions of the brain in principle and argues that their study is, like the study of any other organ, part of physiology. However, in his actual analysis, he reverts to the sensationalism of Condillac, and his contemporary disciples, Cabanis and Destutt de Tracy.[3] 'Ideology' was a term invented by Destutt de Tracy.[4] The Idéologues argued that ideas were merely compounds of sensations and saw the end of their enquiries as the analysis of ideas into their constituent sensations.[5] This was supposed to supplant metaphysics.[6] Although de Tracy claimed that 'Ideology is part of zoology',[7] it is clear that its methods and assumptions were far from those that Gall had advocated for a biological science of psychology and which, suitably modified, would later be appreciated as important aspects of evolutionary biology.[8]

The experimental method which Magendie applies to the spinal cord is replaced by the introspective and analytic approach[9] which Gall had attempted to transcend by means of naturalistic observation of the behaviour of animals and men. The functions which he investigates and which he attempts to relate to the nervous system are the

---

[1] Magendie, 1843, p. 146.    [2] Ibid., p. 147.
[3] Cf. Temkin, 1946, pp. 13, 14, 16, 24.    [4] Boas, 1925, p. 24.    [5] Ibid., pp. 4–5.
[6] Ibid., p. 24.    [7] Quoted in Ibid., p. 25.    [8] Cf. Temkin, 1947, p. 291.
[9] See Rosen, 1946, p. 334.

7

traditional normative categories of philosophical analysis: sensibility, memory, judgement, and desire or will. He makes no attempt to consider whether or not these categories are adequate for the explanation of experience and behaviour. While he considers thought a function of the brain, he does not enquire into the functional role of thought in the lives of organisms. Thus, in practice, his psychology had stronger links with metaphysics than with biology.

Although the terms 'sensation' and 'motion' appear in both his work on the spinal cord and his discussion of the functions of the brain, he thought of these as two orders of phenomena and did not attempt to integrate them into a unified view. This was the task of the half-century which followed his initial discovery. Magendie's own work exemplifies the traditional analysis in one part of his work on the nervous system, while in another he provides the experimental finding which eventually transformed the philosophical sensationalism of the Idéologues into an experimental sensory-motor psychophysiology.

Magendie's treatment of Ideology was at least an advance on Condillac, who had made no attempt to specify the material basis of his sensationalism. Cabanis had set out to correct this omission, and investigated the structure of the sense organs and the physiological conditions of mental processes, including how they varied with age, sex, temperament, diet, and so on.[1] He had also stressed the importance of internal sensations in addition to the five external senses.[2] Magendie's treatment of the senses is an exposition of the ideas of Cabanis and involves no new findings.[3]

Magendie turns from an exposition of the senses to an analysis of the intellectual phenomena for which they were the sole source.

The innumerable phenomena which constitute the human understanding (the human understanding has been called the spirit, the faculties of the soul, intellectual faculties, cerebral functions, etc.) are but modifications of the faculty of perception. When we examine them with attention, we shall find no difficulty in confirming this observation, the truth of which is generally admitted by modern metaphysicians.

We may divide the faculty of perception into four principal modifications:

1st. Sensibility, by which we receive impressions from within or from without. 2nd. Memory, or the faculty of reproducing impressions or sensations previously received. 3rd. The faculty of perceiving the relation between sensations or judgment. 4th. Desire or will.[4]

---

[1] Cabanis, 1805; Boas, 1925, pp. 4–5. Cf. Lange 1925, II, 242–3; Merz, 1903, pp. 470–2.
[2] Temkin, 1946, pp. 25–6.        [3] Magendie, 1843, pp. 112–15.
[4] Ibid., p. 147.

hese four are the 'simple faculties of the mind'.[1] 'It is the combination
ad reaction of these faculties upon each other which constitutes the
nderstanding of man and the higher order of animals.'[2] Magendie
roceeds to explain each of them and to attempt to specify their
lations with the nervous system. In following the details of his dis-
ussion, one is struck by the vagueness of his analysis of the higher
nctions, compared with the elegance and simplicity of his classical
periment on the spinal nerve roots.

1. *Sensibility has two modes.* The first is unperceived and is the effect
a body impinging on the senses. 'In order for a perfect sensation to
ist, it is necessary that the brain should perceive the impression
ceived by it. An impression thus perceived is called, in ideology, a
rception, or *idea*.'[3] The parts of the nervous system with which sensi-
lity is most particularly connected are the posterior roots of the
mpound nerves and the superior branch of the fifth cranial nerve
rigeminal). 'I have shown, by experiment, that if these nerves are
vided, the sensibility of the parts to which they are distributed is
tinguished. Experiment has equally informed me, that if we divide
e posterior fasciculi of the spinal cord, the general sensibility of the
unk is abolished'.[4] Similarly, cutting the fifth pair of cranial nerves
olishes sensibility on the head, the face and its cavities.[5] The evidence
vailable to Magendie from his own experiments and those of others
ecluded the extension of the nervous basis of sensibility to the brain,
cept for the sense of sight. Ablation of the cerebrum abolishes sight,
Flourens and Rolando had shown, but ablation of the cerebrum or
rebellum involves no loss of odours, tastes, and sounds.[6] Thus,
hile he saw the brain as the organ of the understanding, it was a
ystery how it was related to most of the primary sensory modalities,
e supposed source of all its operations.

2. *Memory is the reproduction by the brain of recently acquired ideas, while
collection is the analogous function for more distant ideas.*[7] Magendie grants
all's thesis that there are different kinds of memory for words, places,
rms, music, and so on, and that these may manifest themselves
dividually to a striking degree and be selectively diseased. However,
e denies the implication Gall drew from this.

---

[1] Magendie, 1843, p. 151.    [2] Ibid.    [3] Ibid., p. 147.
[4] Ibid., p. 148.    [5] Ibid., p. 149.
[6] Ibid., cf. p. 145. It will be recalled that Flourens considered the brain the seat of per-
ption of all sensory modalities.
[7] Ibid., p. 149.

Generally, in these cases, after death, lesions are found to a greater or l«
extent in the brain or medulla oblongata. But morbid anatomy has n
established a direct and constant relation between the diseased part and t
kind of memory abolished, so that we are still ignorant if there exists a:
part of the brain which is more particularly destined to the exercise
memory.[1]

3. *The principle of association* was not explicitly recognized as an impc
tant factor in the psychological assumptions which Magendie adopt«
from the Idéologues, but the role played by association in the Engli
tradition is served by the faculty of judgement. 'There can be no dou
that judgement is the most important of the intellectual faculties. . . .
All our knowledge is the direct result of the faculty of judgemer
To form a judgement is to establish a relation between any two idea
or collections of ideas. . . . A series of judgements connected togeth
constitutes reasoning'.[2] The quality of one's judgement is 'the result
organization. It is impossible to change in this respect; we mu
remain as nature has formed us'.[3] 'We are ignorant of the part of tl
brain which is the particular seat of judgement. It has been lor
believed to be in the hemispheres, but nothing directly proves this.
In adopting this position, Magendie has hypostatized the law which tl
psychologists of the English school of associationism considered to l
the fundamental law of mind.

4. *Will is not an active agent or faculty.* Rather, it is the perception «
'desire'. 'We give the name of will to that modification of the facul«
of perception by which we experience desires.' Happiness or unhapp
ness depends on whether or not desires are satisfied.[5] The derivati\
nature of the concept of will in the philosophy of Ideology is consiste»
with the passive sensationalism which had characterized this approac
since Condillac.

It is characteristic of Magendie's separation of sensation and muscul:
motion from the analysis of the higher functions, that motor functio»
have no place in his exposition of the properties of the understan(
ing which he was attempting to explain as functions of the brain. Th
action of the nervous system which produces muscular contractio»
is a phenomenon distinct from the will. 'Desires have been generall
confounded with that cerebral action which presides over th

---

[1] Magendie, 1843, p. 50. Cf. Broca's findings: below, Chapter 4.
[2] Ibid., p. 50.          [3] Ibid.
[4] Ibid., p. 151. Once again, Magendie is less confident of the evidence for the role of tl
hemispheres than Flourens.
[5] Ibid.

contraction of the voluntary muscles. I think it advantageous to the student that this distinction should be established.'[1] In another place, he says,

From these considerations, it may be inferred that the *will* and the *action of the brain*, which produce directly the contraction of the muscles, are two distinct phenomena. But the direct experiments of modern physiologists, and what has already been said respecting the influence of the cerebrum and cerebellum on the movements, have clearly established this truth. These experiments have clearly demonstrated that, in man and mammiferous animals, the will more particularly resides in the cerebral hemispheres. The direct cause of the movements appears, on the contrary, to have its seat in the medulla spinalis. If we separate the spinal marrow from the rest of the brain by an incision near the occiput, we prevent the will from determining and directing these motions, though they are, nevertheless, executed. As soon, however, as the separation takes place, they become irregular in extent, rapidity, duration, and direction.[2]

Thus, Magendie concluded that will is a cerebral action which causes motion, but the production of the muscular contractions necessary to execute the motion is not cerebral but is instinctive and is associated with the following structures: spinal nerve roots, spinal cord, corpora quadrigemina, cerebral peduncles, thalamus, corpora striata, and cerebellum.[3] The quality of his evidence is not always high, and some of his findings were not supported by later research, but the important point is clear. There was no role for the hemispheres in the direct production of muscular motion, just as there was none for any of the senses except sight. The sensory-motor analysis of the spinal cord and its partial extension to structures higher up the neuraxis was a distinct topic from the analysis of the phenomena of the understanding. It employed different methods and assumptions and was part of a separate intellectual discipline. In fact, except for the vague correlations between sensibility, memory, judgement, and desire with the activity of the cerebrum, Magendie had nothing original to say about the higher ıunctions from either a physiological or psychological viewpoint. He was no more successful than Gall had been in relating his important new discoveries to the actual physiology of the brain, and his psychological conceptions were a reversion to the functions which Gall had attempted to replace with a naturalistic biological approach. Magendie's method and his work on the spinal cord provided the foundations of later important concepts and findings, but these could not be fully

---

[1] Magendie, 1843, p. 151.    [2] Ibid., pp. 252–3.
[3] Ibid., pp. 252, 243–6. Cf. Olmsted, 1944, pp. 125–6.

exploited until the hiatus which his own work exemplified was eliminated.

It would be artificial to propose a discussion of the relations between Magendie's work and phrenology. The only point to be made is that there was very little relation, except in the contrast between their methods, assumptions, and approach to the study of organisms. Magendie does mention Gall on anatomical topics several times.[1] He notes that phrenologists were particularly concerned with the topic of instinct but 'with little appearance of success'.[2] His only extended comment appears in a footnote, where he discusses cranioscopy and reveals that his passionate rejection of this aspect had prevented him from paying sufficient attention to Gall's work to understand or profit from his approach to the study of the functions of the brain.[3]

## Johannes Mueller's Handbuch

Johannes Peter Mueller was the third great exponent of the experimental method in this period. He received his doctorate at Bonn in the same year that Flourens and Magendie were publishing their most important findings (1822). He then moved to Berlin and was called to Rudolphi's Chair (1833) which thereby became the first chair of physiology in Germany. He is credited with introducing experimental physiology into that country. In the light of their similar roles in their respective countries, some interesting comparisons can be made between Magendie and Mueller. Magendie had begun his investigative career with a rejection of the counsel of despair of the vitalists in the name of the experimental method. Mueller had scornfully rejected

---

[1] Magendie, 1843, pp. 143, 247.     [2] Ibid., pp. 155–6.

[3] 'Phrenology, a *pseudo-science* of the present day; like astrology, necromancy, and alchemy of former times, it pretends to localize in the brain the different kinds of memory. But its efforts are mere assertions, which will not bear examination for an instant. Craniologists, with Dr Gall at their head, go even farther, they aspire to nothing less than determining the intellectual capacities by the conformation of the crania, and particularly by the local projections which they remark. A great mathematician presents a particular elevation about the orbit; this is said to be the organ of calculation. A celebrated artist has a large bump on the forehead; that is the seat of his talent. But, replies some one, Have you examined many heads of men who have not these capacities? Are you sure that you do not meet with the same projections, the same bumps? That is of no consequence, replies the craniologist; if the bump is found, the talent exists, only it is not developed. But here is a great geometrician, or a great musician, who has not your bump. No matter, replies the sectary, you must believe. But, replies the skeptic, the aptitude should always exist, united with the conformation, otherwise it will be difficult to prove that it is not a mere coincidence, and that the talent of the man depends really on the particular form of his cranium. Still, replies the phrenologist, believe! And those who delight in the vague and the marvellous, do believe. There is some show of reason in this, for they thus amuse themselves, while the truth would only cause them ennui.' (Ibid., p. 150.)

e experimental method, expecially the work of Flourens, in his early
ritings and had searched for 'divine life in nature'.[1] He remained a
oroughgoing vitalist but embraced the experimental method after
oving to Berlin. Thus, his writings contain precise findings, many of
ich remain valid, while their theoretical context is less appealing to
e modern reader. Magendie eschewed such theoretical embroidery
. his empirical work. On the other hand, Magendie did his experi-
ents in the context of medicine and with constant reference to its
nical applications, while Mueller's career marks the emancipation
physiological research from such practical demands and its estab-
hment as an autonomous discipline.[2]

Mueller's original work will be considered in the light of the influence
s specific findings exerted on later workers.[3] For the present it is
iportant to stress the general influence of his major writing in physi-
ogy. Where Magendie had written an excellent textbook for students,
ueller provided the first exhaustive compendium since Haller's.
is Handbuch der Physiologie des Menschen (1833–40) brought together
l the notable results of physiological, anatomical, and psychological
search and brought to bear on these the results of comparative
atomy, chemistry, and physics. It thus became the international
thoritative source. It was translated into many languages and re-
ained pre-eminent until the advent of Darwinism.[4]

After writing the Handbuch Mueller turned to research in comparative
atomy, specializing in marine research. Nordenskiöld reports that
had a strong tendency to overwork and that he suffered from proud
oism, fits of melancholy, and hallucinations. He is believed to
ve ended his own life as his worries increased and his powers
clined.[5]

Mueller was extremely influential as a teacher. The list of justly
mous pupils who worked under him has few parallels in the history
science: Schwann, Virchow, Henle, Remak, Kölliker, Du Bois-
eymond, and Helmholtz.[6] It is apparent that Mueller's vitalism was
ot imparted to his students with the same success as was his method-
ogy and technical expertise, since these men were the main instru-
ients of the spread of somaticism and the experimental method in
iology. Their applications of these approaches extended from work

[1] Nordenskiöld, 1928, p. 384.        [2] Murphy, revised ed., 1949, p. 92.
[3] See below, Chapter 3.
[4] Nordenskiöld, 1928, p. 384; Murphy, 1949, p. 96; Boring, 1950, pp. 33–5, 46; Singer,
d ed., 1959, p. 393.
[5] Nordenskiöld, 1928, pp. 382–3.        [6] Ibid., pp. 382, 388.

on cells and tissues to the consideration of physiology, optics, and th conservation of energy.

The three major exponents of the experimental method in neur physiology had much in common in addition to their commitment to method. Flourens, Magendie, and Mueller all contributed to th application of sensory-motor analysis to the functional organizatic of the nervous system. There were minor variations in how far up th neuraxis they applied it, but they all refrained from including th cortex in the direct initiation of muscular movements. They share the view that the cerebrum was inexcitable. Their respective views c sensory functions defy neat summary, but they joined in rejectir cortical localization. They explicity opposed Gall's concepts of functio and his organology, though their reasons were diverse. Flouren opposition was in the name of a Cartesian view of the unity and in dependence of the mind and a belief in free will, both of which he fe to be threatened by Gall's analyses and his tendency toward materialism He was equally opposed to the sensationalism of Condillac and th Idéologues.[1] Magendie, on the other hand, followed the Idéologue and was led from their philosophical position to his own experimenta work.[2] The result of this adherence was the exclusion of the study c the higher functions from what is usually seen as the domain of exper mental physiology, and its discussion in terms of introspective an philosophical analysis.

Mueller rejects Gall's divisions and localizations of intellectua functions in favour of a single faculty of 'attention',[3] and his views o the passions in favour of a single striving 'appetitus'.[4] He does not clair that such localizations have been disproved, but he believes them to b unlikely, given his view of the functions themselves.

The conception of ideas, thought, and emotion, or the affections, are mode of consciousness. There is no sufficient reason for admitting the existence c special organs or regions set apart in the brain for the different acts of th mind, or for regarding these as distinct powers or functions. They are, i fact, as we shall presently show, merely different modes of action of the sam power.[5]

The other basis of his objection to phrenological faculties and organ is an associationist view of mentation.

---

[1] Flourens, 1846, pp. 26-7.     [2] See Temkin, 1946.     [3] Mueller, 1842, p. 1345.
[4] Ibid., pp. 1368-9.     [5] Ibid., p. 1345.

It is true that the mind is rendered conscious of external impressions only through the medium of the nerves of sense, and their action on the brain: but the retention and reproduction of mental images of external objects of sense, exclude altogether the notion of particular orders of ideas being fixed in particular parts of the brain; for example in the ganglionic corpuscles of the grey substance. For the thoughts accumulated in the mind become associated in the most various manners, in a chronological succession, according to the relation of simultaneous occurrence, or according to their similarity or contrariety; and these relations of the ideas or thoughts to each other change every moment.[1]

From these diverse arguments a uniform result emerged: discussions of the higher functions have a vagueness that effectively precluded their experimental exploitation. The experimental techniques available at the time could only lead to equivocal results which allowed Mueller to conclude in favour of his own views. For example, he reports negative results from various experiments designed to elicit muscular contractions from irritation or injury of the hemispheres, corpora striata, optic thalami, and the corpus callosum. He also reports the ablation and stimulation experiments of Flourens and others in some detail. However, he does not feel compelled to adhere to Flourens' views of the functions of the hemispheres. He only reports the data and reaches the following weak conclusion, which he turns to his own purpose:

It is evident from these experiments, and from the effects of pressure on the cerebral hemispheres in man, that they are the seat of the mental functions; that in them the sensorial impressions are not merely perceived, but are converted into ideas; and that in them resides the power of directing the mind to particular sensorial impressions—the faculty of attention.[2]

Beyond this he does not go, and his views would thus be irrelevant to the debate on cerebral localization if he did not follow this discussion with a firm rejection of Gall's psychology as well as his organology. Once again, vague findings, vaguely reported, allow him to draw the conclusion he pleases. He argues that there are 'no facts calculated in the slightest measure to prove the correctness of the hypothesis generally, or the correctness of the details of the doctrine founded upon it'.[3]

---

[1] Mueller, 1838. Cf. p. 837, where Mueller repeats Napoleon's comment that Gall's faculties are not fundamental but are merely conventional results of living in society. In rejecting this as a bad psychological foundation for concepts of function, Mueller reveals his inability to appreciate the fact that the relation of such faculties to living in society was precisely Gall's point in formulating a set of functions which were relevant to the life of organisms in their natural environments.

[2] Ibid., p. 836. Cf. pp. 834–6.     [3] Ibid., p. 837.

He rejects Gall's faculties, 'a part of which are totally unpsychological' and feels that 'we may at once exclude from the forum of scientific researches these arbitrary dogmas, which can never be proved'.[1]

With regard to the principle, its possibility cannot, *a priori*, be denied; but experience shows that the system of organs proposed by Gall has no foundation, and the histories of injuries to the head are directly opposed to the existence of special regions of the brain destined for particular mental faculties. Not only may both the higher and lower intellectual faculties—as, reflection, imagination, fancy, and memory—be affected by lesion of any point on the surface of the hemispheres; but it has been frequently observed that different parts of the hemispheres can aid the action of other parts in the intellectual functions, and frequently where the removal of portions of the surface of the hemispheres has become necessary in the human subject, no change in their moral and intellectual powers has ensued. M. Magendie is very right in placing cranioscopy in the same category with astrology and alchemy.[2]

The fact that Mueller rejected Gall's faculties and reverted to the philosophers' faculties of memory, imagination, and so on, is a regressive step from the point of view of a biological approach to psychology. However, for the moment, the main point is not the particular form which conceptions of the higher functions took. It is, rather, that the analysis of higher functions and their cerebral bases was neglected. It was making no progress, and attention was increasingly turned elsewhere.

The contrast between the vagueness with which higher functions were discussed and the new approach suggested by the Bell-Magendie law is striking. The study of sensory-motor functions was at once philosophically safe and precise. The result is that sensory-motor interpretations increasingly fill the conceptual void left by the muddled approach to higher functions. The contrast between Mueller's treatment of Gall and Flourens and his treatment of the Bell-Magendie law reflects this radical change of emphasis. He refers to the doctrine of the functional division of the spinal nerve roots as 'one of the most important truths of physiology'.[3] He attributes the view, to Bell, and its partial experimental confirmation to Magendie. After reviewing the evidence, he retained doubts about how completely proved the theory was and conducted his own experiments on frogs.[4] He concludes that 'The foregoing experiments leave no doubt as to the correctness of Sir C. Bell's theory'.[5]

[1] Mueller, 1838, p. 837.    [2] Ibid., pp. 837–38. Cf. above, p. 88n.
[3] Mueller, 1838, p. 642.    [4] Ibid., pp. 640–6.    [5] Ibid., p. 644.

In reviewing these developments over a century later, one can still
el some sense of the significance of this finding for students of the
rvous system. When one encounters it after all the vague, confused,
d contradictory results of previous investigators there is a quickening.
: last! A clear, unambiguous, replicable experimental fact about the
ysiology of the nervous system: something on which to build. To
e modern physiologist it may seem comically exaggerated that the
nctional division of the spinal roots was ranked second only to Harvey's
scovery of the circulation of the blood. In its historical context,
wever, it is not difficult to share this evaluation. One of the dis-
ppointing facts about the scientific method as compared with specula-
n is that it permits the investigation of only those problems which are
nenable to rigorous testing. In return for this emotional disappoint-
ent, science gives relative intellectual certainty. Consequently, some
' the most important and elegant findings within science have not
en very significant when considered in terms of their value to human
'e. Astronomy provides many notable examples. The excitement
gendered by the Bell-Magendie law was because it was the first
ep in making an area of central interest to man amenable to scientific
vestigation. Since science advances only where its method allows,
is not surprising that the sensory-motor analysis of the nervous system
me increasingly to replace the older systems of analysis which, though
ore subjectively appealing and relevant, were not amenable to
perimental testing.

The functional division of nerves and physiological phenomena in
rms of sensation and motion was obviously not a novelty in the nineenth century. A cursory and unsystematic search for earlier uses
nds that Aristotle gives it as a distinguishing criterion for animal life.
is as old as Greek medicine (Hippocrates), anatomy (Herophilus),
d physiology (Erasistratus).[1] It is fundamental to Galen's view of the
ervous system,[2] to Vesalius',[3] and to many others'. In all these instances
e sensory-motor view coexisted with some form of faculty psychology.
he significance of the nineteenth-century analysis lay first in its
perimental demonstration in the central nervous system and second
 the progressive extension of the concept as the fundamental explana-
ry principle in both physiology and psychology.

What was required for the full exploitation of the Bell-Magendie
w was a suitable theoretical context for bringing it into contact with

[1] Singer, 1957, pp. 20, 28–32. Cf. Liddell, 1960, p. 48.
[2] Riese, 1959, pp. 26–7.       [3] Singer, 1952, pp. 2, 3, 39.

psychology. One aspect of this context had been available since Lock and Hartley in the psychology of sensation and association. It onl remained to bring about the synthesis of the physiological with th psychological concepts of sensation in the first instance. Second, th sensationalist bias of the Lockean tradition had to be overcome b the provision of an adequate theory of muscular motion. The resultin balanced sensory-motor psycho-physiology could then, perhaps, tran form the old epistemological psychology into a unified theory of know ing, feeling, and doing which, through its links with physiolog might constitute a natural science. These developments took over fift years after the public statement of the Bell-Magendie law in 1822, an their story takes one back, in the first instance, to the associatio psychology itself. This tradition had to take on new interests which mov it from preoccupation with the philosophical and introspective analysi of the subject-object relationship in knowing, to the psychologica process of learning by doing. Finally, this change of approach had t be related to the nervous system in a new, evolutionary context.

*The Association Psychology*

In order to understand the union of the Bell-Magendie view of th nervous system with a psychology of sensation and motion, it is necessar to have some idea of the psychological developments which occurre prior to the emergence of the unified view. This history is that of th Lockean tradition of associationist psychology.[1] The major figures i the history of the association psychology are Hobbes, Locke, Hume Hartley, Condillac, Thomas Brown, James Mill, J. S. Mill, Alexande Bain, Herbert Spencer, and G. H. Lewes. Bain and Spencer develope the sensory-motor psycho-physiology which was adopted by Hughling Jackson and David Ferrier in their clinical and experimental studie of the nervous system. The following remarks are concerned with

[1] The following exposition of the associationist psychology owes much more to its secondar sources than its primary ones. In every instance the primary sources have been consulted but the order of study has been largely guided by histories and articles so that I can claim little originality for the result. My heaviest debts are to Warren, 1921, and J. S. Mill, new ed. 1867, but I have also consulted the following works: Aaron, 1955; Albee, reprinted, 1962 Baldwin, 1905, 1913; Boring, 1950; Brett, Ed. Peters, 1953; Cassirer, 1955; Dennis, 1948 Flugel, 1951; Halévy, translated Morris, 1952; Hamlyn, 1961; James, 1890, 1892; Lange 1925; Lewes, 1857; Mackintosh, 1860; Merz, 1896, 1903; Murphy, 1949; Pillsbury, 1929 Rand, 1912; Ribot, translated Fitzgerald, 1873; Robertson, 1875; Smith, new ed., 1962 Stephen, new ed., 1962; Stewart, 1860; Stout, 1898; Willey, new ed., 1962; Wolf, 1952. For the present I only want to mention the major figures and indicate that, as far as integra tion of associationism with empirically supported physiological concepts is concerned, n important contributions were made until the work of Alexander Bain.

associationism itself from the viewpoint of its eventual synthesis with experimental sensory-motor physiology and the concept of cerebral localization in the work of Ferrier.

The analysis of mind undertaken by the associationists grew naturally from their philosophical empiricism. Beginning with the sensationalism of Hobbes and explicitly formulated by Locke in opposition to *a priori* reasoning and the Cartesian doctrine of innate ideas, this *a posteriori* psychology sought to demonstrate that all knowledge and all experience could be accounted for by combinations of sensations and perceptions, caused in the first instance by external stimuli. True, Locke had postulated two sources of ideas—sensation and reflection. But the vagueness of his concept of reflection gradually led to the explanation of complex mental phenomena in terms of the relations among simple sensations, and the ideational complexes which they formed. The single explanatory principle which was eventually extended to account for all mental processes was the 'association of ideas'. Locke was not responsible for the systematic use of the principle of association. He only provided the phrase in a section added to the fourth edition of his *Essay*. 'At first a mere incident in the sensationist theory, it at length became the sole means of explaining all the great variety of experience that lies beyond sensation.'[1] Thus, two principles defined the view: (1) the complex is formed from the simple by means of (2) the law of association.[2] It can be seen immediately that associationism was to be the historical opponent of faculty psychology, and that its explanatory task was to reduce faculties to aggregates of elementary sensory units. The union of these basic units was accounted for in terms of mechanical connection, or a chemical analogy of compounding or fusion.

With the publication of David Hartley's *Observations on Man—His Frame, His Duty, and His Expectations* (1749), the association psychology first assumed a definite form and a psychological character not wholly derived from epistemological questions. Hartley was the first to apply the association principle as a fundamental and exhaustive explanation of all experience and activity. Hartley's interest in association was stimulated by an essay by a Reverend Mr Gay, who had written a dissertation in which he attempted to explain morality and all affections in terms of pleasure-pain and association.[3] Gay claimed to be a disciple of Locke, and has been credited with the first clear statement of

---

[1] Warren, 1921, p. 155.    [2] Mill, 1867, p. 107.

[3] For a fuller treatment of Gay's theory and his reaction to explanations in terms of instincts and innate ideas, see below, p. 176.

utilitarianism, and the effective founding of the association psychology.[1] Prior to this, the principle of association was applied only in the context of the phenomena of intellect and knowledge. Locke's sensationalism was an epistemological view in opposition to innate ideas as a source of knowledge. The principle of association was a relatively unimportant corollary of this position. Gay used Locke's general approach for very different purposes. He was concerned with primarily psychological issues: the origin of the moral sense and the passions. He also opposed innately given mental contents, but his opposition was to innate instincts. The principle of association became his central thesis for explaining the psychological experiences of the feelings of right and wrong, of love and hate, and of other passions. Gay and Hartley converted associationism from a view about the suffering of experience, whereby our ideas about the natural connections of things can be led astray by chance or custom, to a general psychological theory including affections and motions (both voluntary and involuntary). Associationism was not free from an epistemological bias after Gay and Hartley, but its centre of interest had shifted to the investigation of psychological processes. In concerning himself with the phenomena of motion, Hartley went beyond either Locke or Gay.[2] Moreover, he joined his psychological theory with postulates about how the nervous system functions. His sensations were paralleled by vibrations (derived by analogy to Newtonian mechanics) of 'elemental' particles in the nerves and brain. Although he says that sensations are occasioned by the vibrations of small particles of the white medullary substance of the nerves, spinal cord, and brain, which are caused by the effects of external objects, he eschews consideration of causal relations among these and attempts to avoid the materialist (though not the fatalist) implications of his theory by means of a belief in psychophysical parallelism. Psychophysical parallelism remained characteristic of the association psychology up to and including its union with physiology in the formulations of Bain, Spencer, Jackson, and Ferrier.

The relations among sensations, ideas, and muscular motions as well as the faculties of memory, imagination, fancy, understanding, affection, and will are accounted for by Hartley in terms of repetitive

[1] Halévy, 1952, p. 7; Albee, 1962, pp. 86, 90.

[2] Hartley's interest in motion did not significantly influence the main line of the associationist tradition until the work of Bain, who drew his concept of activity from the German physiologist Johannes Mueller. This topic had been virtually ignored by the psychologists of association in the interim but had been kept alive in physiological writings. Mueller's theory was drawn from Erasmus Darwin and J. C. Reil, *both* of whom, in turn, had adopted it from Hartley. See below, Chapter 3, and Lewis, 1958, p. 160. See below pp. 114–21.

ssociations. In relating the phenomena of sensation, ideation, and
notion to the nervous system he lays down the principles of physio-
ogical psychology which Ferrier would later combine with the concept
f cerebral localization. Although Hartley did no experiments on the
rain, his principles constituted the first physiological psychology of
ie associationist school. In fact, if one discounts Descartes' speculations
1 *Traité de l'Homme* (published posthumously in 1662), Hartley can
ay claim to being the founder of the physiological psychology of higher
unctions.[1]

The spectre of materialism raised by Hartley's view (in spite of his
isclaimers) combined with the scepticism of Hume's philosophy to
rovoke a reaction in the Scottish 'common sense' philosophers, Reid
nd Stewart, who returned to a form of innate ideas in their faculty
sychology. Their successor, Thomas Brown, attempted a reconciliation
with associationism and drew heavily on Cabanis and de Tracy for his
iews on the role of the muscle sense and touch in revealing the external
world. His posthumous *Lectures on the Philosophy of the Human Mind*
1820) is an eclectic work with elements of Reid, Stewart, and the
French sensationalists. Its major contributions lie in his emphasis on
he muscle sense (and thereby on the role of motion in sensation and
earning) and his elaborations of the secondary laws of association.
He follows Reid and Stewart in their reaction against Hartley and
herefore rejects the physical aspect as materialistic, while employing
he metaphor of 'mental physiology'. Brown's reintroduction of some
associationist principles in his view of 'suggestion' and his recognition
of the importance of physiology, even though he would not actually
elate his views directly to the nervous system, were both indications of
more explicit developments that were to follow.

James Mill's *Analysis of the Phenomena of the Human Mind* (1829),
returns to the main line of the tradition of Locke and Hartley. He accepts
Hartley's concept of mental phenomena rather than that of his teacher,
Stewart, or Brown's intermediate position. He applies himself to extending and completing Hartley's doctrine. Hartley had been concerned
to prove the validity of the associationist view. Mill assumed it, and
later writers in the school could extend a doctrine which was taken as a
settled starting point. All experiences, affections, and will are resolved
into sensations and ideas. The elements of his analysis are the five

---

[1] Hartley certainly deserves a more careful study than any which I have seen. The most
useful recent source is Oldfield and Oldfield, 1951. For Harley's views on cerebral localization, see Hartley, 1749, I, 39, 40, 61, 63, 68, 73, 121, 162, 212, 272.

senses, the muscle sense, alimentary sensations, and the pleasure-pain principle. Since James Mill's associationism served as a foundation for later extensions of the doctrines of the school, it may serve as a yard stick for measuring later developments. First, its aims: the philosophic bias was still strong in his work. He saw the analysis of the mental powers as a necessary preliminary to a valid logic, a new (Utilitarian) morality, and sound pedagogical principles. He was not concerned with psychology for its own sake. The relevant context for Mill's psychology is his interest in legislation and teaching. His Utilitarian allegiances insured that his psychology would be concerned with a theory of action.[1] However, these same interests effectively precluded any pursuit of comparative observations. As for relations with physiology he went all the way back to Locke, whose position is quoted at the head of Mill's first chapter:

> I shall not at present meddle with the physical consideration of the mind, or trouble myself to examine wherein its essence consists; or by what motions of our spirits, or alterations of our bodies, we come to have any Sensation by our organs, or any Ideas in our understandings; and whether those ideas do in their formation, any or all of them, depend on matter or no. These are speculations which, however curious and entertaining, I shall decline, as lying out of my way in the design I am now upon. *Locke*, i. 1, 2.[2]

The psychology of J. S. Mill is secondary to his logical and epistemological interests. What he has to say about psychology proper is included in his *Logic* (1843), his *Examination of Sir William Hamilton's Philosophy* (1865), his notes to the edition of his father's *Analysis* which he edited with Bain and others (1869), and an article which he wrote on 'Bain's Psychology' (1859).

The last of these provides an excellent indication of J. S. Mill's views on the association psychology.

> The great problem of this form of psychology is to ascertain not how far this law extends, for it extends to everything; ideas of sensation, intellectual ideas, emotions, desires, volitions, any or all of these may become connected by association under the two laws of Contiguity and Resemblance, and when so connected, acquire the power of calling up one another. Not, therefore, how far the law extends, is the problem, but how much of the apparent variety of the mental phenomena it is capable of explaining; what ultimate elements of the mind remain, when all are subtracted the formation of which can be in this way accounted for; and how, out of those elements,

---

[1] See Halévy, 1952, pp. 455–78.     [2] James Mill, 1829, I, 2.

and the law, or rather laws, of association, the remainder of the mental phenomena are built up. On this part of the subject there are, as might be expected, many differences of doctrine; and the theory, like all theories of an uncompleted science, is in a state of progressive improvement.[1]

However, Mill does not himself contribute much to the development of the theory. For the execution of this task he defers extravagantly to Alexander Bain, who

has stepped beyond all his predecessors, and has produced an exposition of the mind, of the school of Locke and Hartley, equally remarkable in what it has successfully done, and in what it has wisely refrained from—an exposition which deserves to take rank as the foremost of its class, and as marking the most advanced point which the *a posteriori* psychology has reached.[2]

In later editions of his *Logic*, Mill adds the following note to his discussion 'Of the Laws of Mind':

When this chapter was written, Professor Bain had not yet published even the first part ('The Senses and the Intellect') of his profound Treatise on the Mind. In this the laws of association have been more comprehensively stated and more largely exemplified than by any previous writer; and the work, having been completed by the publication of 'The Emotions and the Will', may now be referred to as incomparably the most complete analytical exposition of the mental phenomena, on the basis of a legitimate induction, which has yet been produced.[3]

---

[1] J. S. Mill, new ed., 1867, pp. 108–9.    [2] Ibid., p. 99.
[3] Mill, 8th ed., 1872, p. 557. Mill's faith in Bain's work had a more practical aspect. He persuaded his own publisher to print Bain's *The Senses and the Intellect*. It lost money, and when Bain was having difficulty getting the second volume published, Mill and Grote guaranteed the publisher against loss to the extent of £100. Thus, *The Emotions and the Will* appeared in 1859, and Mill's review in the *Edinburgh Review* furthered its success. (Packe, 1954, p. 410.) Similar generosity was extended by Mill to Comte and to Spencer when their work was threatened by financial difficulties. (Ibid., pp. 282, 433–4.) Bain was still a student at Aberdeen when he first met his hero in 1842. Bain was twelve years younger than Mill, but he was immediately asked to read the proofs of Mill's *Logic*, for which he provided many valuable suggestions and examples. (Ibid., pp. 289, 271.) Bain walked home with Mill from India House every day during the next five summers and thereafter all year round until Mill married in 1851. (Ibid., pp. 291, 359.) Bain had started out as Mill's protégé but rapidly became his friend and colleague, and they maintained close relations until Mill's death in 1873. Bain assisted in major revisions of the third edition of the *Logic* and in preparing the 1869 edition of James Mill's *Analysis*. Bain also wrote a biography of James Mill and *John Stuart Mill, a Criticism with Personal Reflections* (1882). See also Mill, edited Elliot, 1910, and Mineka, 1963, for correspondence with Bain. The Mill-Bain letters have not been published or even located, and we have only the excerpts which Bain included in his biography of J. S. Mill.

8

Bain's education in psychology was drawn from the standard works
Locke, Hume, Hartley, Reid, Stewart, Brown, James Mill, and J. S
Mill.[1] However, it will be seen that he shifted the whole direction of the
association psychology.[2]

[1] J. S. Mill taught Bain personally and presented him with James Mill's *Analysis* as
gift (Bain, 1904, p. 112).

[2] For further thoughts on the associationist tradition, see Young, 1966, pp. 20–4; Young
1967a, pp. 123–4.

# 3

## ALEXANDER BAIN: TRANSITION FROM INTROSPECTIVE PSYCHOLOGY TO EXPERIMENTAL PSYCHOPHYSIOLOGY

Like art, science is born of itself, not of nature.
There is no neutral naturalism. The artist, no less than the writer, needs a
vocabulary before he can embark on a 'copy' of reality.
E. H. Gombrich, 1962.
. . . no less than the scientist

To understand events as experienced by actual men and institutions we
must be concerned with the history of errors and false starts as well as
successes—although we make this distinction on the basis of what we now
know of the tradition of success. As we go back in time the uncertainty of
the outlook and of the objectives of scientific inquiries increases. The essence
of the scientific movement is research. The answers to the essential question,
what to *do* in scientific research—what questions to put to nature, by what
methods to get answers, what to count as satisfactory answers—became
clear only by the accumulation of successes and the marking of failures.
A. C. Crombie, 1963.

### *Synthesis of Associationism and Sensory-Motor Physiology*

Alexander Bain was probably the first modern thinker whose primary
concern was with psychology itself. He has been credited with writing
the first 'comprehensive treatise having psychology as its sole purpose'.[1]
His two-volume systematic work, *The Senses and the Intellect* (1855) and
*The Emotions and the Will* (1859), was the standard British text for almost
half a century, until Stout's replaced it.[2] He also founded *Mind* (1876–),
the first psychological journal in any country. His work requires close
attention, because it is the meeting-point of experimental sensory-
motor physiology and the association psychology. His influence on the
conceptions of later workers was direct and extremely important.
Ferrier studied classics and philosophy under Bain at Aberdeen (first
class honours, 1863). When he and Jackson acknowledge their intellectual debts or make references to psychology, the names most often
mentioned are Bain and Spencer—the figures whose work was the
culmination of the association psychology in its traditional form.
Ferrier and Jackson strongly influenced each other, and together they

[1] Murphy, 1949, p. 107.  [2] Boring, 1950, p. 235.

provided the sensory-motor psychophysiology for the new research o
cerebral localization.

Bain's work provided a completely novel approach in Englis
associationist psychology. Locke had disclaimed any interest in phys
ology in the second paragraph of his *Essay*.[1] Like Locke, Hume ha
elected not to enquire into the causes of the phenomena of association
He regarded association as a 'gentle force' arising from the qualiti
of resemblance, contiguity, and cause and effect.[2] The basis of associatio
was

a kind of *attraction*, which in the mental world will be found to have as extra
ordinary effects as in the natural, and to show itself in as many and a
various forms. Its effects are everywhere conspicuous; but, as to its cause
they are mostly unknown, and must be resolved into *original* qualities c
human nature, which I pretend not to explain.[3]

He had decided 'that we must in the end rest contented with experience
and not indulge in 'specious and plausible' physiological hypothese
involving 'imaginary dissection of the brain'.[4] When he does depar
(apologetically) from this maxim, his speculations involve 'ideas
which the powers of the mind excite or 'rouse up'. The mind despatche
the 'animal spirits' running into 'traces' and 'rummaging the cell
which belongs to the idea, while incidentally exciting contiguous an
related ones.[5] Hartley's theory of vibrations, while more detailed, wa
also pure speculation, and such speculations frightened away Reid
Stewart, and Brown. Returning to the main line of the associationis
tradition, it will be remembered that James Mill echoed Locke'
agnosticism about the brain.

It is against this background that Bain's psychology must be viewed
In 1851, he wrote to J. S. Mill from Paris as follows:

I have been closely engaged on my Psychology, ever since I came here.
have just finished rough drafting the first division of the synthetic half of th
work, that, namely, which includes the Sensations, Appetites and Instincts
All through this portion I keep up a constant reference to the materia
structure of the parts concerned, it being my purpose to exhaust in thi
division the physiological basis of mental phenomena. I have been able t
attain a pretty level explanation of the whole of the phenomena thu
included, and that to a greater depth than I could have supposed attainabl
in the present state of our knowledge. And although I neither can, nor a

---

[1] Locke, 1961, I, 5. Quoted by James Mill, above p. 98.
[2] Hume, new ed., 1911, I, 19.      [3] Ibid., I, 21.      [4] Ibid., I, 65.
[5] Ibid.

present desire to, carry Anatomical explanation into the Intellect, I think that the state of the previous part of the subject will enable Intellect and Emotion to be treated to great advantage and in a manner altogether different from anything that has hitherto appeared. There is nothing I wish more than so to unite psychology and physiology that physiologists may be made to appreciate the true ends and drift of their researches into the nervous system, which no one man that I have yet encountered, does at the present moment. . . . In fact I feel pretty confident of being up with the nervous physiology in its Psychological bearings, as it stands at present, although I am satisfied that if I had that familiar and perfect grasp that belongs to a professional Anatomist, I might do a vast deal more in the way of pushing forward my own subject.[1]

Four years later, in the Preface to the first edition of *The Senses and the Intellect*, he says,

Conceiving that the time has now come when many of the striking discoveries of Physiologists relative to the nervous system should find a recognised place in the Science of Mind, I have devoted a separate chapter to the Physiology of the Brain and Nerves.[2]

J. S. Mill is lavish in his praise of this new departure.

Mr. Bain possesses, indeed, an [sic] union of qualifications peculiarly fitting him for what, in the language of Dr. Brown, may be called the physical investigation of mind. . . . Having made a more accurate study than perhaps any previous psychologist, of the whole round of the physical sciences, on which the mental depend both for their methods, and for the necessary material substratum of their theories. . . . This is especially true of the science most nearly allied, both in subject and method, with psychological investigations, the science of Physiology: which Hartley, Brown, and Mill had unquestionably studied, and knew perhaps as well as it was known by any one at the time when they studied it, but in a superficial manner compared with Mr. Bain.[3]

The chapter on the nervous system which so impressed Mill is about fifty pages long, and consists mostly of lengthy quotations from Sharpey's contributions to the fifth edition of Quain's *Anatomy* and from Todd and Bowman's *Physiology*. In the first three editions of Bain's work (*i.e.* up to 1868) the section on the functions of the cerebral hemispheres echoes Flourens and denies cerebral excitability.

---

[1] National Library of Scotland. MS. 3650, ff. 165–6. I am indebted to Samuel Greenblatt for informing me of the existence of this letter, and to Thomas I. Rae, Assistant Keeper of Manuscripts, National Library of Scotland, for making copies of Bain's MS. letters available to me.

[2] Bain, 1855, p. v.    [3] Mill, 1867, pp. 116–7.

Bain does not seem to have thought at all carefully about cerebral localization, and his statements on the subject are confused and even contradictory. In the first edition of *The Senses and the Intellect* he does not mention the issue at all. Six years later, in his discussion of phrenology, he grants the phrenological localization of a number of cerebral organs, including sex,[1] language,[2] benevolence,[3] colour,[4] and tune. He has various objections to details of the phrenological faculties themselves, but he accepts their cerebral localization. His statement about the faculty of music or tune is a fair example.

Phrenology has very naturally laid hold of this faculty, and has, with confidence, assigned its local habitation. Musicians are found to agree in an enlargement of the lateral parts of the forehead. The analysis of the musical faculty has been made with great care, and we believe with success, by the leading phrenologists. . . . No objection can be taken to the tracing out of a cerebral conformation agreeing with this peculiar sensibility.[5]

Throughout his book on *Character*, Bain accepts not only the principle of cerebral localization but also the validity of the cranioscopic method, if rigourously applied. Although he grants some of the phrenological localizations, he is more interested in localizing the cerebral bases of his own classification of functions. 'It would be interesting to know if the different modes of the mental manifestations—feeling, will, intelligence—have different seats or portions of the cerebral mass assigned to them.'[6] The psychological doctrine of the book will be considered below. For the present, attention should be confined to Bain's statements about cerebral localization. His argument parallels his attempted transformation in the psychology of phrenology in order to bring it into conformity with his own associationist view and his three basic categories of Intellect, Feeling, and Will.

The most carefully considered discussion of cerebral localization in his writings is concerned with the cerebral basis of feeling and will.

Thus while the modes of FEELING—the pleasures, pains, emotions, sentiments, affections, passions—are *many*, the WILL may be considered as *one*. We may regard it as the collective muscular machinery of the system controlled by a certain portion of the cerebrum; having a character peculiar to itself, disposed to operate of its own accord, but practically at the service of whatever feelings are uppermost in the mind. If this view be correct,

---

[1] Bain, 1861, p. 222.    [2] Ibid., p. 165.    [3] Ibid., pp. 111–12; 298.
[4] Ibid., p. 155. Cf. Bain, new ed., 1875, p. 98.    [5] Bain, 1861, p. 162.
[6] Ibid., p. 21. He offers some tentative speculations on this issue in Bain, 11th ed., 1910, p. 103.

there ought to be in the development of the head a region of Will and a region of the various Emotions—the one indivisible, the other containing many sudivisions. For, although there are a variety of phenomena, or different aspects of Volition, constituting different subjects of consideration—such, for example, as desire, conflict of motives, deliberation, resolution, effort, ability and inability, belief—they would not properly occupy distinct centres, but would be merely the various modes and circumstances under which the one power shows itself. We should then convert the phrenological propensities and sentiments into one common group of emotions, abstraction being made of those that imply pure Activity, which last, if they could be concentrated into one locality, would represent the Will. There is nothing in the views of phrenologists essentially repugnant to this amendment. They admit that the present classification is only provisional. Combe says—'It appears impossible to arrive at a correct classification until all the organs, and also the primitive faculty or ultimate function of each, shall be definitely ascertained, which is not at present the case.' The foregoing doctrine of the multiplicity of emotion and the unity of volition is the view of the present writer, expounded at great length in the treatise on the *Emotions and the Will*. In the detailed criticism of the organs, and in the succeeding expositions, it will prominently reappear.[1]

It should be noted that Bain had made no observations on brains or on the behaviour of individuals (or, for that matter, on crania). His views on localization are deductions from his associationist principles and from introspection.

In other parts of the book Bain speculates about the localization of centres for muscular movements, spontaneous energy, and sensory modalities.

We must here, as in other cases, carry the explanations as far as the brain, and imagine some endowment in the centres in immediate relation to the muscular movements; something in the quantity or the quality of the part of the brain that actuates the larger masses of muscle.[2]

If we were to venture, after the manner of Phrenology, to specify more precisely the locality of the centres of general energy, I should say the posterior part of the crown of the head, and the lateral parts adjoining—that is, the region of the organs of Self-Esteem, Love of Approbation, Cautiousness, Firmness, and Conscientiousness—must be full and ample, if we would expect a conspicuous display of this feature of character. The fore-part of the head would not appear to have the same bearing upon the active disposition as the hinder parts.[3]

In his discussion of the senses of taste and smell, he says,

Without local organs in the scheme of Phrenology, they must still be conceived as having each a relation with a definite mass of the cerebrum, on

---

[1] Bain, 1861, pp. 46–7.    [2] Ibid., p. 221.    [3] Ibid., p. 195.

whose quantity or quality the energy of their discriminating function is dependent.[1]

At one point in the book, Bain came very close to a conception that was not fully appreciated until nine years later. It was a corollary of his attempt to make phrenology conform to his own view. The faculty of Weight had not been included in Gall's classification and was introduced by Spurzheim to account for ideas of weight, resistance, consistency, density, softness, and hardness.[2] George Combe, the leading exponent of phrenology in Britain, had restricted its domain to the appreciation of small variations in weight and exquisiteness of touch.[3] Bain set out to transform the faculty into a general sense of movement and voluntary activity.

We have no difficulty in admitting the susceptibility to different degrees of expanded energy—whether in raising weights, in resisting moving bodies, or in putting tools in motion,—as an ultimate power of the human mind, and unequally manifested among individuals. We consider it as related to the so-called 'muscular sense', or the feeling connected with muscular exertion.[4]

The faculty involves the muscularity of 'the hands, arms, and the body generally'. It includes all muscular regions except 'the eyes, features, jaw, and voice'. It is also involved in coordination, and amounts to a 'general endowment of our voluntary activity'.[5] Having transformed the phrenological faculty of weight in this manner, Bain felt that the phrenological localization of its cerebral organ did not do justice to the importance of the altered conception of the faculty. It was

dependent physically upon the cerebral centres that give origin to the anterior, or motor, roots of the spinal nerves taken collectively. That a high development of those centres should be apparent merely as a small swelling in about one-fourth part of the extent of the eyebrow, is exceedingly improbable.[6]

He notes that what is known about the cerebellum goes part-way towards explaining the mechanical skills and coordination associated with the faculty but goes on to say that

We must not, however, stop short of the hemispheres in our explanation of the control of the voluntary muscles, and it is not consistent with other facts to locate an energy so extensive and complicated in such a limited mass. . . .

---

[1] Bain, 1861, pp. 303–4.  [2] Spurzheim, 2nd ed., 1815, pp. 361–2.
[3] Bain, 1861, p. 150.  [4] Ibid., p. 151.  [5] Ibid., p. 151–3.
[6] Ibid., p. 153.

It would be an exceedingly interesting result, if we could allocate with certainty the cerebral centres whence emanate the impulses to our voluntary movements, and which, when largely developed, give sensibility and delicacy of graduation to those movements; but we cannot say that phrenology has even started a plausible conjecture on this matter.[1]

The above passage might have provided the key to developments which occurred in the next decade, but in all his other writings Bain did 'stop short of the hemispheres' in his explanation of the control of voluntary movements. His book on *Character* is the only place where he makes extensive remarks on cerebral localization. If he had developed his views on the localization of centres for sensations, movements, and other functions, his work might have played a significant part in the history of cerebral localization. What happened, though, was that Bain never pursued many of the ideas raised in this work and, perhaps more important, the book itself sank rapidly into oblivion. When Bain next refers to the topic of cerebral localization, he expresses the orthodox position of the experimental physiologists of the time.

The attempt to localize the mental functions in special portions of the cerebral mass, has been thwarted by observations of a remarkable kind. The phrenologists noticed cases where the destruction or disease of one hemisphere was unaccompanied with the entire loss of any function; the inference being that the hemispheres were duplicate bodies performing the same office, like the two eyes, or the two halves of the nostrils. But cases have been recorded of disease of large portions of the brain in both hemispheres at once, without apparent loss of functions; which would require us to extend still farther the supposition of a plurality of nervous tracks for a single mental aptitude.[2]

However, four years later he shows that the topic still intrigues him and that, on the whole, he thinks that cerebral localization is a reputable hypothesis.

It would be interesting, if we could assign distinct mental functions to different parts of this large and complicated organ [i.e., the cerebral hemispheres]; if we could find certain convolutions related to specific feelings, or to specific intellectual gifts and acquirements. This Phrenology attempted, but with doubtful success. Yet, it is most reasonable to suppose that, the brain being constituted on a uniform plan, the same parts serve the same functions in different individuals.[3]

Bain's remarks on cerebral localization are significant in two ways. First, they show that the associationists were beginning to evolve some

[1] Bain, 1861, p. 153.    [2] Bain, 1868, p. 46.    [3] Bain, 1875, p. 10.

sort of working relationship between their own views and those aspects of phrenology which were useful. The phrenologists themselves were extremely polemical and used their journals as a platform for launching a ferocious attack upon anyone who deviated from loyalty to all their views. They knew only two reactions: refutation and incorporation. If a man was not a wholehearted phrenologist he was either a fool or was saying something that the phrenologists had said all along.[1] Bain's work on character and his sympathetic remarks about cerebral localization show that orthodox scientists were beginning to defy this reaction. His treatment of the subject is symptomatic of the growing importance of the concept of cerebral localization in the psychological and physiological thinking of the period. It was being applied to neurology by Broca (in the same year that Bain's book on character was published), and formed the basis of his conception of speech pathology.[2] It had already been transformed by Spencer and used in his psychology of evolutionary associationism.[3] The concept of cerebral localization was being dissociated from the excesses of phrenology and applied to more orthodox conceptions in psychology, neurology, and physiology. However, Bain's failure to pursue his earlier speculations about cerebral localization in his major treatise, and his easy acceptance of the orthodox view show equally well the timidity with which scientists approached anything that could be construed as advocacy of phrenology in the 1850's and 1860's. One suspects that the failure of Bain's book on character to sell well enough to justify a second edition, and the silence about it in his own writings and the work of others, indicate that he had gone farther toward accepting phrenology than the climate of opinion in the 1860's would allow.

Bain's scattered remarks on cerebral localization do not seem to have had any direct influence on the work of the main figures in British localization research, Jackson and Ferrier. The concept of cerebral localization which they employed was also ultimately derived from phrenology, but the specific version which influenced them will be seen to come from Spencer. Although Bain remained friends with his former pupil and visited with him on his last trip to London,[4] he reacted against the findings of the experimentalists. He upheld the older methods in the face of Ferrier's new, objective approach involving direct experimentation on animal brains. For Bain, introspection was 'the alpha and the omega of psychological inquiry: it is alone supreme,

---

[1] See the early volumes of George Combe's *Phrenological Journal.*
[2] See below, Chapter 4.    [3] See below, Chapter 5.    [4] Bain, 1904, p. 415.

everything else subsidiary. Its compass is ten times all the other methods put together, and fifty times the utmost range of Psycho-physics alone'.[1] He was also sceptical about the significance for psychology of the findings of Ferrier and others on cerebral localization.

A considerable amount of scientific interest has been aroused by these laborious inquiries; but they have added nothing to the explanation of our intellectual workings; while in Physiology the interest is purely theoretical. Possibly, they may be the beginning of great results on both sides; but, if we were to insist on the ideal of the subjective purists, we should make no mention of them in Psychology proper.[2]

These remarks were written in 1891, thirty-five years after the appearance of his own seminal work. It is surprising that Bain took so little interest in the localizing work on cerebral physiology which drew so heavily on his psychological conceptions. He neither grasped its significance nor attempted to integrate it with his own thought. This is even more remarkable in Bain than it might be in others. Two of his main theses were the importance of integrating physiology and psychology, and the central significance of will and movement in psychology. Yet the third edition of *The Emotions and the Will* (1875), which appeared five years after the discovery of the electrical excitability of the motor areas of the cerebral cortex by Fritsch and Hitzig, made no mention of their work or that of Ferrier. This is in striking contrast to William Carpenter, who had added a special appendix on 'Dr Ferrier's Experimental Researches on the Brain' to his *Principles of Mental Physiology* (1874). The whole treatise was in type when Ferrier's first results appeared, and Carpenter held up publication in order to take account of these important findings.[3] The fourth edition of *The Senses and the Intellect* (1894) contained a new chapter on the nervous system which included a general picture of the results of localizing studies on the brain, but Bain did not undertake to write it. It was contributed by Dr W. Leslie Mackenzie.[4]

Bain's failure to appreciate the significance of the findings of his former pupil is the more remarkable because the conception of cerebral functions which Ferrier put forward was so obviously a confirmation of Bain's earlier speculations. In fact, the statement which Mackenzie included in the chapter he contributed to Bain's own work bears a

---

[1] Bain, 1903, p. 242.    [2] Ibid., pp. 187–8. Cf. Bain, 1894, p. x.
[3] Carpenter, 1874a, p. 709. See below, pp. 214–5.    [4] Bain, 1894, p. vii.

striking similarity to the passages on localization of sensory and moto functions in *Character*.

In its simplest and most practical form the Doctrine of Localisation may b stated as follows: Certain limited areas of the Cortical Grey Matter ar associated with certain definite movements; certain other areas are associate with certain sensations. The movements concerned are roughly name 'voluntary', a designation that indicates a 'variable spontaneity' of occurrenc and marks them off from movements due solely to the lesser grey centre In like manner the sensations, being sensations proper, are marked off from mere excito-motor afferent impressions.[1]

In other respects Bain had revised his treatise meticulously. Fo example, he had attempted to bring his own views into close harmon with the theory of evolution. He responded to Spencer's criticism (1860) that he had ignored evolution, by keeping back the second edition o *The Senses and the Intellect* as long as possible in order to be in possessio of Spencer's latest utterances in the *Principles of Biology*.[3] He include a postscript on Darwin's studies on emotional expression in later print ings of the third edition of *The Senses and the Intellect* (1868; Postscript 1873), and a chapter on mental evolution in the third edition o *The Emotions and the Will*.

Bain's major influence on Jackson and Ferrier lay in his juxtapositio of associationism with sensory-motor physiology, and in his view of th elements of mind. Jackson says,

To Prof. Bain I owe much. From him I derived the notion that the anatomica substrata of words are motor (articulatory) processes. (This, I must mention is a much more limited view than he takes.) This hypothesis has been o very great importance to me, not only specially because it gives the bes anatomico-physiological explanation of the phenomena of Aphasia *when al varieties of this affection are taken into consideration*, but because it helped me very much in endeavouring to show that the 'organ of mind' contains processes representing movements, and that, therefore, there was nothing unreasonable in supposing that excessive discharge of convolutions should produce that clotted mass of movements which we call spasm.[4]

Ferrier, in turn, drew his sensory-motor view of brain and mind, as well as his theory of volition, from Bain and Jackson.[5]

---

[1] Bain, 1894, p. 50.     [2] See below, pp. 183–6.
[3] Spencer, edited Duncan, 1908, p. 115.
[4] Jackson, edited Taylor, 1931, I, 167–8. Jackson's emphasis is irrelevant to my point.
[5] Ferrier, 1886, pp. 425–6, 443.

The theories of Bain which had these effects on clinical and experimental findings which he himself discounts are the result of a union
of association psychology with the sensory-motor physiology of Magendie
and Mueller. J. S. Mill's review of Bain's work indicates the significance
of the Bell–Magendie law both for Bain and for the associationist
tradition.

What may be called the outward action of the nervous system is twofold,—
sensation and muscular motion; and one of the great physiological discoveries
of the present age is, that these two functions are performed by means of two
distinct sets of nerves, in close juxtaposition; one of which, if separately
severed or paralysed, puts an end to sensation in the part of the body which
it supplies, but leaves the power of motion unimpaired; the other destroys
the power of motion, but does not affect sensation. That the central organ
of the nervous system, the brain, must in some way or other co-operate in
all sensation, and in all muscular motion . . . [except for reflex responses]
is also certain; [for if continuity with the brain is interrupted, sensation and
motion in that part cease to exist].[1]

Mill's last sentence reflects the prevailing confusion over how far the
sensory-motor analysis should be extended up the neuraxis. Bain was
quite clear about the functional division of the spinal nerve roots and
of higher centres as far up as the medulla oblongata.[2] In the first
edition of *The Senses and the Intellect* he considered the functions of the
lesser grey centres of the brain undetermined (except for the association
of the corpora quadrigemina with vision). 'The thalami optici and
corpora striata, from their size, and the amount of grey matter they
contain, are likely to be influential bodies, but what precise purpose
they perform is a subject of uncertain speculation.'[3] By 1868 he had
satisfied himself that the thalamus was primarily a sensory ganglion,
while the corpora striata were 'believed to contain principally the
motor fibres'.[4]

The collective reflected fibres of all the ganglia at the base of the brain,
together with the cerebellum, are considered as making up a department
or region, which is the seat of reflex acts, and of a large number of grouped
or associated movements, involved alike in voluntary action and in emotional
expression. It is not unlikely that consciousness accompanies the reflected,
as well as the transmitted, currents of this whole region.[5]

This view had been put forward by Todd and Bowman in 1845.
Their work on *The Physiological Anatomy and Physiology of Man* was one

[1] Mill, 1867, p. 117.     [2] Bain, 1855, pp. 40–7.     [3] Ibid., p. 53.
[4] Bain, 1868, p. 44.     [5] Ibid., pp. 44–5.

of the two main sources of Bain's information on physiology. In present-
ing their conclusions on the functions of the corpora striata and optic
thalami, they made it clear that their conception was an extension of
the Bell–Magendie law.

> The corpora striata and optic thalami bear to each other a relation analogous
> to that of the anterior to the posterior horn of the spinal gray matter. The
> corpora striata and anterior horns are centres of motion; the optic thalami
> and posterior horns, centres of sensation.[1] And it must be admitted that the
> intimate connexion of sensation and motion, whereby sensation becomes a
> frequent excitor of motion,—and voluntary motion is always, in a state of
> health, attended with sensation,—would à priori lead us to look for the
> respective centres of these two great faculties, not only in juxtaposition, but
> in union at least as intimate as that which exists between the corpus striatum
> and optic thalamus, or between the anterior and the posterior horns of the
> spinal gray matter.[2]

William Carpenter, who shared their view, credits Todd and Bowman
with being the first to point out this important analogy.[3] Thereby,
the sensory-motor analysis of the nervous system was extended one step
further up the neuraxis. It had been applied to the peripheral nerves
since the beginning of the study of anatomy and physiology. Bell and
Magendie had demonstrated its applicability to the spinal nerve roots,
Flourens and Mueller applied it as far rostral as the medulla oblongata,
and Todd and Bowman extended it into subcortical structures. However, it stopped there and was extended no further until just before
1870. Todd and Bowman provide a convenient summary of the orthodox
position.

> It is quite established as a result of all the experiments upon the cerebral
> convolutions and the white matter of the centrum ovale, that mechanical
> injury to them occasions no pain, nor disturbance of motion. The endow-
> ments of the nerve-fibres which form the fibrous substance of the cerebral
> convolutions appear to be quite distinct from those of sensitive or motor
> nerves. They are internuncial between parts which are beyond the *immediate*
> influence of the ordinary physical agents, and which have no direct con-
> nections with muscular organs. And if, under the influence of morbid
> irritation, they do excite pain or convulsion, which is frequently the case in
> disease of the cerebral meninges, this is effected through a change produced
> in the corpora striata or optic thalami propagated to the origins of motor and
> sensitive nerves.[4]

---

[1] Todd and Bowman, 1845, p. 350.    [2] Ibid., p. 351.
[3] Carpenter, 1855, p. 490; Carpenter, 1846, p. 505. Cf. below pp. 210–20.
[4] Todd and Bowman, 1845, p. 364.

They say nothing beyond this except to provide an elaborate version
of Gall's second and third postulates, that the moral and intellectual
faculties depend on organic supports, and the brain is the organ of
the mind.

It may be laid down as a just conclusion that the convolutions of the brain
are *the centre of intellectual action*, or more, strictly, that this centre consists in
that vast sheet of vesicular matter which crowns the convoluted surface of
the hemispheres. This surface is connected with the centres of volition and
sensation (corpora striata and optic thalami), and is capable at once of
being excited by, or of exciting them. Every idea of the mind is associated
with a corresponding change in some part or parts of this vesicular surface.[1]
   The actions of the convoluted surface of the brain, and of the fibres
connected with it, are altogether of the mental kind. The physical changes
in these parts give rise to a corresponding manifestation of ideas; nor is it
likely that any thought, however simple, is unaccompanied by change in
this centre.[2]

Though they grant these major premises of phrenology, they are
careful to dissociate themselves from its organology. Nothing specific
could yet be said with any certainty about the functions of the hemispheres or about cerebral localization.

In considering the truth or falsehood of Phrenology, it is absolutely necessary
to separate the metaphysical question—as to the existence of certain faculties
of the mind—from what has been admitted as a physiological fact before the
foundation of the phrenological school, that the vesicular surface of the
brain is the prime physical agent in the working of the intellect. A physiologist
may hold the validity of this latter doctrine, and yet think as we do, that
many of the so-called faculties of the phrenologists are but phases of other
and larger powers of the mind; and that the psychologist must determine
what are, and what are not, fundamental faculties of the mind, before the
physiologist can venture to assign to each its local habitation.[3]

This was the state of physiological thinking when Bain set out to
unite physiology with the association psychology. His brief discussion
of the functions of the hemispheres is a straightforward expression of the
orthodox position. He says that 'Mind is . . . pre-eminently associated
with the cerebral hemispheres'.[4] At the same time, experimental evidence
excludes them from the sensory-motor paradigm.

When irritation is applied to the hemispheres, as by pricking or cutting, we
find a remarkable absence of the effects manifested in the other centres.

---

[1] Todd and Bowman, 1845, p. 365.     [2] Ibid., pp. 365–6.     [3] Ibid., pp. 366–7.
[4] Bain, 1855, p. 54.

Neither feeling nor movement is produced. This marks a very great distinction between the hemispheres and the whole of the ganglia and centres lying beneath them.[1]

His position did not change from the one he expressed to Mill in 1851 He neither could, nor wanted to, specify any details for the physiologica basis of intellect. Only one thing was certain: it was not sensory-motor This view has already been met in the work of Flourens and Magendie. It was still orthodox in 1868. The inconsistency between an otherwise thoroughgoing sensory-motor analysis and a vague treatment of the hemispheres was a constant feature of psychophysiological writings at least until 1870. Although Bain adhered to it in his own work, his conceptions provided much of the basis for its eventual abandonment. The only place Bain departs from this view is in his aberrant work on *Character*. The remarks he made there remained undeveloped by him or by those he influenced, even though they pointed the way later research actually took.

### *Bain, Mueller, and the Place of Motion in Pyschology*

Bain provided a discussion of motor phenomena which gave the association psychology a balanced sensory-motor view. The bias of the Lockean tradition had been toward the sensory side, and ran the risk of a passive sensationalism. Neglect of spontaneous activity, motor phenomena, and overt behaviour was a natural consequence of the epistemological interests of the empiricists and their commitment to sensation as the primary (ultimately the *only*) source of knowledge. Condillac's radical sensationalism had led his followers to criticize his almost total neglect of motion. The Idéologues, Erasmus Darwin, Brown, and James Mill had included one aspect of motion in their analyses—the sensory aspect of movements or the so-called 'muscle sense' and its role in our knowledge of extension.[2] Of the main figures in the associationist tradition Hartley was the exponent of a more balanced view, but he had no empirical knowledge of sensory-motor physiology to support it. Bain's analysis of motor phenomena was the first union of the new physiology with a detailed association psychology in the English, tradition and he thereby laid the psychological foundations of a thoroughgoing sensory-motor psychophysiology.

Bain's emphasis on movements was a new departure for the associationists and is in striking contrast to James Mill's views. Brett argues

---

[1] Bain, 1855, pp. 53–4.        [2] Halévy, 1952, pp. 441–5.

hat after James Mill, British psychology turns from passivity to activity. Bain and J. S. Mill disagreed with James Mill's whole treatment of mind.

Their fundamental protest against the imputation of 'passivity' is only saved from being a rejection of James Mill's whole work by being diplomatically adapted to the neutral and colourless parts of the work. The new note in the school was activity, combined with an extension of the physiological groundwork that is strikingly in contrast with Mill's perfunctory notes on the sense-organs.[1]

Bain prefaces his work with an explicit statement of how far his analysis goes beyond the doctrine of the muscle sense.

In treating of the Senses, besides recognising the so-called muscular sense as distinct from the five senses, I have thought proper to assign to Movement and the feelings of Movement a position preceding the Sensations of the senses; and have endeavoured to prove that the exercise of active energy originating in purely internal impulses, independent of the stimulus produced by outward impressions, is a primary fact of our constitution.[2]

He begins by arguing for the fundamental importance of the muscle sense and of movement: 'Action is a more intimate and inseparable property of our constitution than any of our sensations, and in fact enters as a component part into every one of the senses, giving them the character of compounds while itself is a simple and elementary property.'[3] Spontaneous movements are a feature of nervous activity prior to and independent of sensations.[4] The acquired linkages of spontaneous movements with the pleasure and pains consequent upon them, educate the organism so that its formerly random movements adapted to ends or purposes. Bain defines volition as this compound of spontaneous movements and feelings.[5] The coordination of motor impulses into definite purposive movements results from the association of ideas with them.

Bain argues that no previous 'writer on the human mind' had advanced the concept of spontaneous actions nor their connection with voluntary actions; 'but the following interesting extracts from the great physiologist, Mueller, will show that he has been forcibly impressed with

---

[1] Brett, 1953, p. 441. The epistemological issues involved in the introduction of muscular motion into sensationalist philosophy are discussed by Hamlyn, 1961, Chapter 9.
[2] Bain, 1855, pp. v–vi.      [3] Bain, 1868, p. 59.      [4] Ibid., pp. 64–73.
[5] Ibid., pp. 296–306.

9

both the one and the other of these views'.[1] Mueller traces the develop
ment of volition from the spontaneous movements of the foetus an
infant and the consequent sensations.

*Thus a connection is established in the yet void mind between certain sensations an
certain motions.* When subsequently a sensation is excited from without in an
one part of the body, the mind will be already aware that the voluntar
motion which is in consequence executed will manifest itself in the lim
which was the seat of the sensation; the foetus in utero will move the lim
that is pressed upon, and not all the limbs simultaneously. The voluntar
movements of animals must be developed in the same manner.[2]

Mill calls this passage from Mueller 'the germ of' Bain's theory.
It is more than that. The context of the quotations which Bain too
from Mueller is most remarkable, for it shows that Mueller, thinkin,
primarily as a physiologist, had worked out a full-fledged motor viev
on associationist lines and related this to his understanding of th
functional organization of the nervous system.

Mueller's motor theory[4] is a synthesis of the sensory-motor physiolog
of Bell-Magendie and Flourens, with a view of the laws of associatio
of voluntary movements taken from Erasmus Darwin's *Zoonomi,*
(1894–6)[5] and J. C. Reil. Following Flourens, Mueller held that th
medulla oblongata was the highest motor centre,[6] the seat of the actio
of the will, and 'the source of all the voluntary movements'.[7]

The fibres of all the motor, cerebral, and spinal nerves may be imagined a
spread out in the medulla oblongata, and exposed to the influence of th

---

[1] Bain, 1868, p. 296. Cf. Bain, 1855, p. 289. Boring (1950, p. 238) says of Bain that 'It is als
probable that he did not know Johannes Mueller's psychological physiology'. He bases thi
allegation on Bain's ignorance of German. It is, of course, Baly's translation of Mueller tha
Bain quotes and explicitly makes the basis of his motor theory—the central argument o
his work on the will and his most important contribution to the association psychology
There are innumerable references to Mueller in both volumes of Bain's treatise, beginnin
with the table of contents. Although Bain's discussion of spontaneous energy is drawn from
Mueller, he reports in his *Autobiography* that the concept occurred to him while he wa
attending Professor Sharpey's lectures on the brain and nervous system in April, 1851
Sharpey discussed some speculations of Faraday on the character of the nerve force a
illustrated by his electrical researches. 'I did not preserve the exact tenor of the speculation
but it operated upon my mind in the way of suggesting the doctrine of Spontaneity as a
necessary supplement to the recognized circle of the nervous current from sense to movement
I had not embodied this addition in any previous sketch of either Sense or Instinct, but intro
duced it somehow into the draft that was in my hands at the time.' (Bain, 1904, pp. 218–9.
Sharpey also revised the chapter on the nervous system for the first edition of *The Sense
and the Intellect* (Ibid., p. 240).

[2] Mueller, 1842, pp. 936–7. Quoted in Bain, 1855, pp. 290–1. (Bain's italics.)

[3] Mill, 1867, p. 121.        [4] Mueller, 1842, pp. 931–50.

[5] Erasmus Darwin's views were in many respects derived from those of Hartley. Se
E. Darwin, 1794–6, sect. XXXIX and vol. II.

[6] Mueller, 1838, p. 828.        [7] Mueller, 1842, p. 934.

will like the keys of a piano-forte. The will acts only on this part of the nervous fibres; but the influence is communicated along the fibres by their action, just as an elastic cord vibrates in its whole length when struck at any one point. It is in the present state of our knowledge—and perhaps always will be—impossible to determine how by an exertion of the will in the medulla oblongata the nervous fibres are excited to action. All that we can do is, to consider the fact in its greatest simplicity.[1]

The first voluntary movements of the foetus are produced by random action of the will on the medullary fibres. These movements give rise to sensations, and the association of effect with cause gradually leads to deliberate control of movements: 'an act of volition is nothing else than the voluntary and conscious direction of the nervous principle in the brain upon different cerebral apparatus'.[2] Complex finely coordinated voluntary motions are acquired through practice, 'and the more frequently certain groups of fibres are excited to action by the influence of the will, the more capable do they become of isolated action; this is exemplified in performers on the piano-forte, etc.'[3]

Compound voluntary movements were defined by Mueller as 'all combinations of movements in determinate groups, which the mind has a share in producing'.[4] His discussion of them is conducted in terms of the laws of association of movements as outlined by Erasmus Darwin. The relative lack of impact on association psychologists prior to Bain of Darwin's treatment of associations among movements, and of ideas with movements, highlights the sensory bias of earlier medical writers. Darwin's interests were primarily physiological and biological and thus naturally included behaviour and motion. These had an important influence on Mueller's physiological theories while they had had little on those of the English psychologists. Mueller acknowledges his debt to Darwin and notes that 'The laws of the association of voluntary movements have been so frequently explained, that they are now very generally recognized, even in writings on practical medicine'.[5] Prior to Bain this commonplace of physiology was ignored by psychologists. Though quarrelling with some of his examples, Mueller adheres to Darwin's view. The principle is: 'Practice diminishes or annuls the innate tendency to involuntary association of movements, while it renders the voluntary association of several muscles in action more easy'.

The law laid down by Darwin is, that 'all the fibrous motions, whether muscular or sensual, which are frequently brought into action together,

[1] Mueller, 1842, p. 934.    [2] Ibid., p. 938.    [3] Ibid., pp. 938–9.
[4] Ibid., p. 939.    [5] Ibid., p. 942.

either in combined tribes or in successive trains, become so connected by habit, that when one of them is reproduced the others have a tendency to succeed or accompany it.' (*Zoonomia*, p. 49.)[1]

Turning to the association of ideas and movements, Mueller holds that

The connection between ideas and movements is sometimes as close as that between different ideas; thus, when an idea and a movement have frequently occurred in connection with each other, the idea often excites the involuntary production of the movement. . . . It is a general rule that the more frequently ideas and movements are voluntarily associated together, the more prone are the movements to be excited by those ideas rather than by the will, or to be withdrawn from the influence of the will. This kind of association plays as important a part as the association of movements with each other in the production of mechanical dexterity and perfection in the mechanical arts.[2]

Finally, Mueller relates these motor and ideo-motor phenomena to the nervous system.

The association of movements with each other can only be accounted for on the supposition of a more ready path being developed in the brain for the communication of nervous influence in a certain direction, and the concatenation of ideas and movements seems to indicate that every idea in the mind gives rise to a tendency to action in the nervous apparatus of the movement which expresses that idea, and that this tendency to action is by practice and habit so exaggerated that the mere disposition which exists in ordinary cases becomes, each time that the idea occurs, a real action.[3]

The discussion closes with an argument for the coordination of the movements of locomotion being dependent on the functional organization of the spinal cord and cerebellum as indicated by the experiments of Bell-Magendie and Flourens.

Although the movements of locomotion are dependent on the will, the appropriate combination of the separate muscular acts necessary for them appears, nevertheless, to be rendered more easy by some internal disposition of the nervous system, and there seems to subsist between the nervous centres, the groups of muscles and their nerves, a harmony of action dependent on original structure. This idea is suggested by the experiments on the functions of the cerebellum and spinal cord . . . it appears, therefore, that there is some organic arrangement in the central organs which favours the co-ordinate action of certain nervous fibres.[4]

To the twentieth century observer, the above theory and its detailed exposition seem to be painful elaborations of the obvious. This reaction

---

[1] Mueller, 1842, p. 243.    [2] Ibid., p. 944.    [3] Ibid.    [4] Ibid., p. 949.

helps to make the important point about the significance of Mueller's work for the association psychology. These were new topics for the major figures in the associationist tradition. Movement, the nervous system, and the importance of inborn patterns of coordination had largely been ignored or given cursory treatment by associationists prior to Bain. His ideas were far from original, but their introduction into the context of associationist psychology was almost completely novel. Hartley had stressed them, but his followers had not.

With the incorporation of Mueller's motor theory into Bain's psychology, the union of sensory-motor physiology with associationism is, in principle, complete. After Bain, associationism turned directly to physiological experiments. Warren points out that the linking of motor phenomena to the traditional issue of sensation by Bain 'justifies the investigation of physiological processes by association psychologists. In Hartley the reference to brain activity is rather an analogy brought in from another science. With Bain it admits of translation into psychological terms, and thus interpreted it forms an integral part of psychology'.[1] Murphy adds that 'In Bain we have for the first time physiological explanations sufficiently elaborate to be taken seriously. The psychologist was beginning to think of experimental physiology as fundamental to his science'.[2] In fact, Bain set a precedent with his chapter on the nervous system. Although the psychological sections of his *Logic* had little to say on the subject, Mill immediately grasped the importance of Bain's new departure and said that

. . . no rational person can doubt the closeness of the connexion between the functions of the nervous system and the phenomena of mind, nor can think any exposition of the mind satisfactory, into which that connexion does not enter as a prominent feature.[3]

No matter how little relevance it had to the rest of the work or how little it actually explained the psychological processes under discussion, future writers almost invariably included a chapter on the structure and physiology of the nervous system. By 1873 the force of this precedent was clear enough to lead Ribot to say,

Every study of experimental psychology, whose object is the exact description of facts, and research into their laws, must henceforth set out with a physiological exposition, that of the nervous system. Mr Bain has done this, and also Mr. Herbert Spencer (in his latest edition of the *Principles of Psychology*),

[1] Warren, 1921, p. 167.    [2] Murphy, 1949, p. 105.    [3] Mill, 1867, p. 110.

This is the obligatory point of departure, not resulting from a passing fashion, but from nature itself, because the existence of a nervous system being the condition of psychological life, we must return to the source, and show how the phenomena of mental activity graft themselves upon the more general manifestations of physical life.[1]

Almost to the present day, students of psychology have been encouraged to know something about the nervous system and have felt *vaguely* ignorant if they did not. Bain's integration gave psychology the sensory-motor paradigm that was later elaborated into the reflex basis for most psychological theorizing. It was not until the second quarter of the present century that some justification arose for a knowledge of physiology so that the student felt *specifically* ignorant if he knew nothing of its findings.

Boring rightly remarked that Bain 'represented the culmination of associationism and the beginning of its absorption into physiological psychology'.[2] The associationist tradition had moved from Locke's physiological agnosticism to a sensory-motor psychophysiology, and from a passive sensationalism (equivocal in Locke, explicit in Condillac) to an emphasis on activity as a primary psychophysiological fact. The nature of the association psychology had changed radically from an epistemological science to a psychophysical science of feeling, knowing, and willing. The early associationists had neglected motion because of an overriding interest in how we come to know. The assumption was that we learn through sensory experience. Bain showed that knowing was the result of experiences *consequent upon doing*. Once an important role had been found for motion in learning, interest in the topic naturally spread to behaviour itself. The new biological context for associationism (which was beginning to manifest itself in Spencer's work on psychology which appeared in the same year as Bain's first book and in Charles Darwin's work which appeared simultaneously with Bain's second book) greatly advanced the development of an interest in behaviour and the adaptation of organisms to their environments. Still, it is Bain who has been credited with being 'the principal agent in putting psychology among the natural sciences'.[3] Once it was there, it had to find its proper place, and the evolutionists supplied that.

In 1868 there was one major impediment to the full integration of the association psychology with sensory-motor physiology: the cerebral hemispheres. The intellect and its cerebral substrate were still set apart.

In Mueller, for example, the will somehow 'played on' lower centres.

[1] Ribot, 1873, p. 198.     [2] Boring, 1950, p. 236.     [3] Brett, 1953, p. 643.

The analysis of intellectual phenomena was not an extension of his motor theory. Instead, he devoted a separate part of his treatise to mind. Given his earlier analysis much of it was redundant, and the significant fact is that he did not grasp this. Nor did Bain, who attempts a much closer integration of psychology and physiology. He sets out to examine each fact of mental life from both its psychological and its physiological aspect, yet when he comes to the cerebral cortices he draws back.

In order to extend the sensory-motor view to the cortex, it was necessary to integrate the work of the associationists, as enriched by Bain, with clinical findings about brain diseases and to have available new experimental results which eliminated the anomaly whereby the cortex, alone among nervous structures, was unresponsive to irritation. Such findings would naturally combine easily with the groundwork laid by Magendie, Mueller, and Bain and eliminate the duality of sensory-motor function on the one hand and intellect and will on the other. In the decade 1860–1870, Broca and Fritsch and Hitzig provided the findings, and Jackson (basing his ideas on the conceptions of Spencer and Bain) provided their sensory-motor context in the cortex itself. Jackson's chief target would be the dualism in the theories of the major figures in experimental physiology beginning with Flourens.

## Bain on Phrenology and the Study of Character

The sources of Bain's specific doctrines should be clear from the foregoing analysis: his associationism came from Hartley and the Mills, and his physiology partly from French and German sources (primarily Flourens and Mueller) and partly from the English works of Carpenter, Sharpey, and Todd and Bowman. However, one would also like to know how he first became interested in psychology and how he arrived at the position that a close integration between psychology and physiology was of fundamental importance. Unfortunately, Bain is not very forthcoming about the development of his ideas. His *Autobiography* is concerned with dates and events more than with ideas and their significance. Nevertheless, the evidence that is available points to phrenology as an important source of his interest in psychology and in its integration with physiology. His first contact with psychology was through phrenology. He studied George Combe's *Constitution of Man* at the Mechanics' Mutual Instruction Class in Aberdeen for two or three years, beginning in 1835, when he was seventeen. Phrenology was then in full flower in Edinburgh and had some votaries in Aberdeen.[1]

[1] Bain, 1904, pp. 27–8.

Bain reports that he was involved in controversy about the supposed materialism of phrenology, but says no more. He also mentions George Combe and Robert Chambers[1] as members of his circle of acquaintances in Edinburgh between 1844 and 1850, and describes a visit with James Straton, a friend who was a phrenologist and was experimenting with head measurement.[2] This would be little evidence were it not for the fact that Bain also wrote a book on phrenology. The fact that he wrote the book attests to his continuing interest in the subject, and its contents provide useful information about Bain's development, and an excellent opportunity to contrast the position of associationism with that of phrenology.

One would like to have much more evidence before drawing a firm conclusion, but what is available suggests that phrenology provided the stimulus which led Bain to attempt an integration between psychology and physiology. He says in his work on character,

It is a fact not to be disputed that the systems of Reid, Stewart, Brown, and indeed of metaphysical writers generally, took little or no account of the nervous system and its connexion with our mental manifestations. It is also equally true that, notwithstanding occasional references on the part of physiologists and others to the connexion of mind with bodily members, the phrenologists were the first to bring forward in a prominent manner, and to defend against assailants of every kind, the doctrine that the mind is essentially dependent, in all its manifestations, on the brain, being more vigorous as that is more fully developed, and dwindling under cerebral deficiency or disease. They have marshalled an array of facts in support of this position so formidable and cogent as almost to silence opposition. When they began their labours, it was not, as now, 'admitted as the result of all observations, and a fact on which nearly all physiologists are agreed, that the brain is the part of the body by means of which all the powers or faculties of the mind are manifested'.[3]

It should already be clear that neither the psychology nor the physiology which he employed were those advocated by phrenology. In fact, they were the approaches which Gall vehemently opposed. Nevertheless, the importance of the relationship between the two disciplines does seem to have been appreciated primarily as a result of Gall's work and its popularization by Spurzheim and George Combe.

It would be extremely useful to know why Bain wrote *On the Study of*

[1] See below, p. 162; Chambers (1844) 1884; cf. Millhauser, 1959.
[2] Bain, 1904, pp. 28, 215, 237–8. He also read George and Andrew Combe's books on health. Ibid., pp. 50, 90.
[3] Bain, 1861, p. 16.

*Character, Including an Estimate of Phrenology* (1861). His *Autobiography* says only that his (very rigid) plan of work was to follow the volume n *The Emotions and the Will* with a study of the subject of character, to be discussed according to the psychological views set forth in my two volumes. This was begun at once, and carried on continuously during 859 and next year'.[1] He relates that 'a thorough criticism of phrenology' was part of his plan and that he consulted a phrenological library in Edinburgh. There is no hint about how he came to write the book. Instead, he reports the incidents surrounding the publication of half the study in *Fraser's Magazine*, its completion and publication in book form, its slow sale and his unwillingness to recast or reprint it.[2]

Haldane says that Bain was 'led by Mill to make a special study of the philosophy of George Combe',[3] but I have seen no explicit confirmation of this by Bain or J. S. Mill. However, it is not at all unlikely in the light of their relationship and the similarity of their views and aims. In his *Logic*, Mill calls for a science of character, to be called Ethology'. Its laws are to be derived from the 'Laws of Mind' as investigated by the associationists.[4] Mill did not attempt to spell out the details of such a science. As Roback says, 'it cannot be said that he contributed much in the way of furthering our knowledge about character, thus reminding us in this respect of Francis Bacon, who, with all his programmes for discoveries, was not able to bring out a single new scientific result'.[5] Since he deferred to Bain in matters of psychology, it would be natural for him to encourage his protégé to undertake a critical examination of phrenology from a psychological point of view. He praised William Carpenter for undertaking the same job with respect to the physiological claims of phrenology.[6] Mill's opposition to phrenology was also indicated in his *Logic* and later in his work on Comte.[7] It may be that Bain's interest in phrenology was reinforced by the interest which Mill had taken in the topic in his correspondence with Comte. Mill introduced Bain to Comte's writings (which contained an enthusiastic treatment of Gall), and Bain later met Comte in Paris.[8] However, Bain's references to Comte make no mention of phrenology. The only mention of the work I have seen in Mill's writings is a letter to Bain written in 1859. 'It is very pleasant to hear that you will be ready with the discussion of Phrenology and the science of character by next spring. . . . I expect to learn a good deal from it,

---

[1] Bain, 1904, pp. 256–7.    [2] Ibid., pp. 259–60.    [3] Haldane, 1912, pp. 79–80.
[4] See below, pp. 164–5.    [5] Roback, 3rd ed., 1952, p. 142.
[6] See below, pp. 164–5.    [7] Ibid.
[8] Bain, 1904, pp. 112, 145, 150, 153–7, 223–4, 241.

and to be helped by it in anything I may hereafter write on Ethology—
subject I have long wished to take up, at least in the form of Essay,
but have never yet felt myself sufficiently prepared.'[1] The brief historica
review with which Bain introduces the book concludes with a referenc
to Mill's proposal and points out that 'Such a science cannot be sai
to exist at the present time'.[2] A final piece of evidence linking th
conception of the work with Mill is the fact that Bain's approach to th
study of character follows almost exactly the programme laid down b
Mill—to deduce the laws of character from the laws of mind.[3]

Whatever the origins of the work, Bain is unequivocal in expressin;
the importance of phrenology in making the study of character a seriou
topic in psychology and in attempting to establish principles for i
understanding. He begins his preface with a tribute to phrenology.

The present work is intended, if possible, to reanimate the interest in th
analytical study of human character, which was considerably awakened b
the attention drawn to phrenology, and which seems to have declined witl
the comparative neglect of that study at the present time. . . . Our furthe
progress in the knowledge of character must proceed in great part from
more searching inquiries into the human mind. Phrenology, notwithstandin;
its onesidedness, has done good service, by showing with more emphasi
than had ever been done before, that human beings are widely different in
their mental tastes and aptitudes, and by affording a scheme for representin;
and classifying the points of character, which is in many respects an improve
ment upon the common mode of describing individual differences.[4]

He speaks of phrenology as 'the only System of Character hitherto
elaborated',[5] and sets out to examine it. His comments are based on a
careful reading of George Combe's *System of Phrenology*, on familiarit
with the writings of Gall and Spurzheim, and on some articles in th
*Phrenological Journal*.

What Bain proposes to do is extremely simple in conception. H
wants to show that the phrenological faculties are not the ultimat
determinants of character and that a true science of character can b
deduced from the laws of association, the pleasure-pain principle, and
his own primitive mental elements.

It is the aim of the present discussion to bring out . . . the necessity of a
distinct examination of the mind itself, by the methods of self-consciousness
observations, and physiology combined, in order to constitute a menta
philosophy. The affirmation to be proved is that phrenology, as hitherto

[1] Mill, 1910, I, 226.      [2] Bain, 1861, p. 13.      [3] See below, p. 164.
[4] Bain, 1861, p. v.        [5] Ibid., p. vi.

exhibited, is at best but a *science of character*, and NOT a *science of mind*, as pretended; and that even as a science of character it is essentially dependent upon the degree of improvement realized by the science of mind *independently* cultivated.[1]

The science of mind which he evisages is diametrically opposed to Gall's conception of psychology. It is concerned with mind in general.

The SCIENCE OF MIND, properly so called, unfolds the mechanism of our common mental constitutions. Adverting but slightly in the first instance to the differences between one man and another, it endeavours to give a full account of the internal mechanism that we all possess alike—of the sensations and emotions, intellectual faculties and volitions, of which we are every one of us conscious. By an effort of self-examination, the primary instrument of the psychological inquirer, we discriminate these, one from the rest, classify those that resemble, and find out which of them appear simple and which compound. We pay special attention to the distinction between the primitive and the acquired powers, and study with minuteness and care the processes of education and acquisition. We look at the laws whereby sensations are transformed into ideas, and thoughts give rise to other thoughts; in other words, the operations of Intelligence have a chapter devoted to themselves. The obscure processes of the Will can be divined only by laborious introspection; the observation of other minds (children and animals especially) although also an important instrument, needs a constant reference to self as the interpreter of what is indicated. Thus the elements of Feeling, and Intelligence, and Activity, common to us all, are laid out in systematic detail; and thereby we pave the way for that study of their various degrees of development in individual minds, constituting individual characters. Of course, while engaged in the complicated problem of the conscious states—the laws and processes—of *universal* mind, we are liable to drop out of view the *individual* differences, perhaps even to overlook them so far as to misstate their amount; and may hence incur just rebuke on that score from those who look specially at the neglected side of the case. Still, that part of the work has to be well done at the peril of leaving everything undone.[2]

This passage is an epitome of the argument of the associationists against the claims of phrenology.

Bain's approach to phrenology is quite methodical.

In proceeding now to criticize in order the thirty-five or thirty-eight faculties as laid out in the phrenological chart, the main object is to discover how far these are well-defined and separate principles of our nature, how far they are *ultimate* principles, and whether, taken as a whole, they render a complete account of the known powers belonging to our mental constitution. Unless a

[1] Bain, 1861, p. 29.     [2] Ibid., pp. 29–30.

faculty be definite in itself and distinct from every other, and be at the same time one of the primitive components of the mind, the observations alleged in favour of its connexion with a specific locality in the brain are nugatory.[1]

He proceeds to provide a more or less detailed commentary on each of the faculties in Combe's *System*. His remarks are far from systematic and a careful reading of the one hundred and twenty-five pages he devotes to the phrenological faculties involves no surprises. Almost every faculty can either be reduced to some feature of Bain's own system or some (usually purely verbal) agreement can be found between the respective points of view. Those which cannot be easily accommodated are considered not proven. Some of his transformations are very far-fetched indeed. For example, six or seven of the phrenological faculties, including the senses of Form, Size, Locality, and Order are reduced to some aspect of 'the *ocular* sensibility, optical and muscular'.[2] The possible participation of other sensory modalities or intellectual functions is simply ignored. Bain's general criticisms of phrenology are exactly those which would be expected: insufficient appreciation of the role of the senses;[3] too much stress on innate tendencies at the expense of experience, acquisitions, and environment;[4] and lack of rigour in applying the standards of evidence for correlative studies.[5]

Bain's attack on the respective phrenological faculties is sufficiently confident and deprecatory that one would expect him not to take the field unless he had something very much better to offer. The constructive side of the book begins promisingly.

Having criticised at considerable length the only scheme of Human Character that has hitherto been elaborated in a manner proportioned to the subject, I mean now to present another scheme, which appears to me more in accordance with the present state of our knowledge of the human constitution. The basis of what I propose is the threefold division of mind into Emotion, Volition, and Intellect; and for certain important reasons, the element of Spontaneous, or Innate Activity, characteristic of Volition or Will, will be taken first in order.[6]

Now, it appears to me that we cannot make a better start in classifying and describing the elements of character, than by taking note of the degrees and varieties of this inborn energy, the manner of its display, and the practical consequences flowing from it. Manifesting itself, as it does, in a certain definite amount, before either the feelings or the intelligence come in to modify the current, we ought to endeavour to characterize it in its purity, or isolation, so far as we are able. We shall then be prepared to appreciate

[1] Bain, 1861, p. 48.     [2] Ibid., pp. 147–50; 155–8; 177.     [3] Ibid., pp. 178–9.
[4] Ibid., pp. 189–90.     [5] Ibid., pp. 59–60.     [6] Ibid., p. 191.

he compound effects that arise, when feelings and purposes come in to
control it.[1]

Thus, Bain argues, each individual has as a basic determinant of his
character a given amount of spontaneous energy. He complains that
he phrenologists had 'broken up and dispersed in the most irregular
way the great fact of our spontaneous energy, which lies at the basis
of will, and determines the strength or weakness of our active impulses
generally. The consequence is, that nearly the very same language is
used in describing the faculties of organs lying apart from each other'.
The result was that they had obscured a fundamental feature of
character by spreading it among the faculties of Concentrativeness,
Combativeness, Firmness, Self-esteem, and Veneration.[2] Bain argues
that the direction of the spontaneous energy of the will is at the service
of feeling or emotion, which prompts the spontaneous energy to increased efforts and guides it into specific channels.[3] The basic determinants of the direction of activity are the experiences of pleasure and
pain. The 'most essential nature of a sentient being' is 'to move *to*
pleasure and *from* pain'.[4] He thus bodily transfers his theory of activity
from his earlier work and attempts to use it to account for more or
less 'energetic' individuals.

Bain's analysis of the emotions is extremely disappointing. His list
of the 'special emotions' is a pot-pourri of the psychological, philosophical, and physiological issues of the day, and any attempts to make
a coherent position from its disparate parts consistently fail. His
catalogue of primitive emotions is as follows:[5]

1. Muscular Exercise
2. Sex
3. Organic Sensibility
4. Special Senses: Taste, Smell, Touch, Hearing, Sight
5. Wonder
6. Terror and Courage
7. Tender Emotion: Affection
8. Self-Love, Self-Esteem, Self-Complacency, Egotism
9. Love of Power
10. Irascibility
11. Emotion of Pursuit—Plot Interest

---

[1] Bain, 1861, p. 192.    [2] Ibid., p. 117.    [3] Ibid., p. 204.
[4] Ibid., p. 292.    [5] Ibid., pp. 219–53.

12. Sympathy

13. Fine Art or Aesthetic Emotion

Even his most ardent supporters cannot find a good word for this aspect of Bain's work. Ribot considers it 'the weakest portion' of his doctrine.[1] The harsher opinions of Mill and Spencer will be considered below.[2] Bain approaches the classification by using what he calls the 'Natural History Method'.[3] However, the 'nature' which he consults is the writings of philosophers, the biographies of famous men, and his own experience. He admits that there is no sure basis of classification as there was with the senses[4] and argues that 'Our own consciousness, formerly reckoned the only medium of knowledge to the mental philosopher, must therefore be still referred to as a principal means of discriminating the varieties of human feeling'.[5]

As long as the association psychology continued to rely on individual experience and the subtleties of philosophical arguments it failed in its investigations of emotional phenomena. Where Bain was far in advance of Gall in his close attention to controlled experiments in physiology, he apparently ignored Gall's injunction that 'The most sublime intelligence will never be able to find in a closet, what exists only in the vast field of nature',[6] where mental phenomena were concerned. In fact the point was not clearly grasped until the work in animal psychology that followed Spencer's evolutionary biology, and it was not even tentatively applied to the subject of individual differences in humans until the appearance of Galton's work in 1883.[7] As long as psychology was conducted as mental philosophy it had no hope of obtaining the data necessary for the understanding of emotional phenomena. Bain's union of mental science with physiology might well have offered more, but it did not fulfil its promises. It was not until psychology began to be seen as a biological science (as a result of the work of Darwin and Spencer) that the 'Natural History Method' obtained a firm foundation and began to be applied to the domain of the behaviour of organisms.

The stronghold of the association psychology has always been the analysis of intellectual phenomena, and it is here that Bain sets out most confidently. Where Gall had rejected speculative, normative faculties only to substitute a faculty psychology of his own, Bain set out to dispose of faculties altogether. He introduced *The Senses and the*

---

[1] Ribot, 1873, pp. 225, 209.     [2] P. 182. Cf. pp. 183–6.
[3] Bain, 1859, p. iii.     [4] Ibid., p. 56.     [5] Ibid., p. 57.
[6] Gall, 1835, V, 317.     [7] See Allport, 1937, p. 94.

*Intellect* with the claim that 'In treating of the Intellect, the subdivision into faculties is abandoned. The exposition proceeds entirely on the Laws of Association, which are exemplified with minute detail and followed out into a variety of applications'.[1] Stewart had attempted a compromise and argued that the association of ideas is a faculty on an equal footing with the traditional ones. Bain's reply is that 'The Association of Ideas, if good for anything, is competent to supersede Memory, Reason, Imagination, etc., by explaining all the phenomena that they severally imply. It cannot, therefore, be co-ordinate with these powers'.[2] The phrenologists had also been remiss in their treatment of the association of ideas, 'That great fact of the mind, so unaccountably slurred over by Phrenology'.[3]

When Bain spells out his scheme to replace the faculties, he lays down an alternative division. 'The primary attributes of Intellect are (1) Consciousness of *Difference*, (2) Consciousness of *Agreement*, and (3) *Retentiveness*. Every properly intellectual function involves one or more of these attributes and nothing else'.[4] However, in the details of his analysis it becomes clear that he has not replaced faculties but merely amended their classification. Each of his properties of intellect functions as a power or faculty in his descriptions of character. (In his work on character, he refers to 'Difference' as 'Discrimination' and 'Agreement' as 'Similarity'.) 'It will be remembered that three great facts, or properties, are implied in our intellectual nature, viz., Discrimination, Retentiveness, and Similarity.'[5] Quotation of passages in which each of these is discussed as a power or faculty should serve to demonstrate the point at issue.

The first, Discrimination, is essentially local: no one has a power of discrimination in the general or the abstract; it is in some one or more departments of Sensation, etc., that we are remarkable in this respect. The two other powers are, in all probability, general.[6]

The principle named Similarity has long been known as a law of the human mind; but it is only of late that any one has adverted to it as constituting, by its variations of degree, a trait of character. It was seen by Aristotle that, in reviving ideas or experiences formerly possessed by us, one link, or medium of restoration, is a *likeness* of those past states to some one now actually present; as when a copy recals [sic] an original, or a child reminds us of the parent that it resembles. And when closely investigated, it

[1] Bain, 1855, p. vi.     [2] Bain, 1894, p. 696.     [3] Bain, 1861, p. 266.
[4] Bain, 1875, p. 82. Cf. Bain, 1861, pp. 254–280; 325 ff.
[5] Bain, 1861, p. 325.     [6] Ibid.

appears that the important instances of the operation of similarity, in resuscitating former experiences, are those where the likeness is accompanied with unlikeness, which unlikeness is a bar to the stroke of recovery. It is then seen, that some minds are distinguished by their power of breaking through this barrier, so as to make out an identity undiscoverable by other minds. The reach of the identifying stroke, which recovers from the past the whole range of objects having any resemblance to what is before the view, or in the mind, at the time, is a peculiarity of the intellect radically distinct from both Discrimination and Retention. When this is feeble, the principal power of recovery is what is called 'Contiguity', or proximity in place and time, a link forged purely by the plastic or retentive energy of the mind.[1]

. . . it will be found that it is in the *third* power of the intellect, and not in Discrimination or Retentiveness, that a tendency exists to break through the formulas of use and wont, and bring together for the first time things that lay far remote before.[2]

In discussing Pope's poetry, he says, 'We have here still a profuse employment of the power of Similarity in adducing lively illustrations, not only with very little force to instruct the mind, but with a tendency to distort the truth'.[3] He compares this with the more scientific mind of Bishop Butler, whose

method is to observe and compare human experiences, till he find what he thinks a consistent representation of the general character of each passion. His identifying faculty was employed to obtain truth, like a man of science in any other walk. Remove from his mind this as a foremost end; give him the local susceptibilities to colour and form, to words, cadence, and metre; and the same reach of the identifying faculty would have emerged in a poet.[4]

Bain's concept of Retentiveness is the most blatant faculty in his 'non-faculty' psychology. He constantly refers to it as a power,[5] and explicitly identifies it as the general faculty of memory which had been rejected by the phrenologists. He says, 'It is at this point that Phrenology and Psychology part company for good'.[6] He supposes a '*general* quality of retentiveness in each individual mind, affecting all its perceptions, whether more or less acutely discriminated'.[7] In his discussion of 'universal learners', individuals who excel at any learning task to which they apply themselves, he says,

The Phrenologists would assign to such a large and equal development of all the Perceptive Faculties—Tune, Time, Colour, Number, etc.—and thus avoid the recognition of the general property. In the mean time, however,

[1] Bain, 1861, p. 326.    [2] Ibid.    [3] Ibid., p. 344.    [4] Ibid.
[5] E.g. Ibid., pp. 121–2, 186 ff, 283, 285, 307–8.
[6] Ibid., p. 261.    [7] Ibid., p. 262.

I prefer the other view, as better calculated to keep a hold of all the known facts, and because the subject of acquisition is thereby put into its due prominence, as a department of the human mind.[1]

Retentiveness is no doubt greatest where local sensibility, as shown by discrimination, is greatest; but we have reason to believe that this may be a general characteristic of the mind, and when it is so, extent of *acquisition* is the consequence. In fact, it is the occasional existence of the tendency to large and various acquirements, that leads us to assume Retentiveness as a quality unequally manifested in different minds, and therefore a proper basis of classification of character. In its utmost developments, this power exactly corresponds to what we have named Talent, and put into contrast with Genius, being the power of taking on at all hands whatever is brought before us.[2]

Ribot argues that Bain succeeds in reducing intellectual phenomena to a single law; 'that to imagine, to deduct, to induct, to perceive, etc., is to combine ideas in a definite manner; and that the differences of faculties are only differences of association'.[3] It should be clear that Bain accomplishes nothing of the sort. The most that can be argued is that he reduces the list of faculties to three. Two are hypostatized laws of association, and the third is the faculty of memory conceived in a manner that is not essentially different from the medieval faculty.

One's judgement of Bain's attempt to build a science of character from the materials described above must be harsh. He argues that 'natural or spontaneous Activity, Feeling, and Intellect exhaust the mind,[4] and bases three fundamental character types on this classification: the active nature,[5] the emotional nature,[6] and the intellectual.[7] Various sub-characteristics and talents are based on his list of special emotions. The resulting descriptions are pale shadows of individual human beings and bear little relation to the complex attributes of real men. The original part of the work consists of rambling reflections and anecdotes about great personages who illustrate or 'prove' particular aspects of his characterology. If Bain could fairly criticize the phrenologists' standards of evidence, his own deserve contempt. The range of his data is restricted to the biographies of great men, anecdotes about nations and races, and his own introspections. There are no original observations of the behaviour of other men and no comparative data. The tone is moral and exhortative as much as descriptive.

When an extremely intelligent man whose other writings reveal a mind which is at home in careful analysis and systematic presentation

---

[1] Bain, 1861, pp. 262–3.    [2] Ibid., p. 325.    [3] Ribot, 1873, p. 212.
[4] Bain, 1861, p. 119.    [5] Ibid., pp. 192 ff.    [6] Ibid., pp. 204–18.
[7] Ibid., pp. 254–344. Cf. Ribot, 1873, p. 254.

writes a rambling and incoherent book, this fact must be explained and the explanation is likely to be very enlightening. Bain was certain that the phrenological analysis of character was inadequate. This i an unexceptionable judgement, but when he set out to improve on i he foundered. The analysis which he so confidently put forward in hi systematic treatise simply did not account for the facts of character One suspects that after he wrote *On the Study of Character*, he grasped this. Thus, the less said about the book the better. His own treatment c it certainly supports this suspicion. His later writings contain no refer ence to the book or to the subject of character. That his mentor probably shared Bain's evaluation may be inferred from Mill's failur to mention Bain's work on character in later editions of the *Logic* though he was generous in praise of Bain's work in logic,[1] in psychology, and in helping to edit a new edition of James Mill's *Analysis*.[3] It i precisely because the book was an abysmal failure that it points ou how woefully inadequate the association psychology was for providing the elements of a science of character and personality. When one set about resynthetizing the elements which result from the analyses o associationists, the product simply does not resemble the experienc and the individuals we know in our every day lives. As Bain himsel says, when we are preoccupied with '*universal* mind, we are liable t drop out of view the *individual* differences'.[4] This admission undermine the whole conception of a psychology of character: its domain *is* th explanation of individual differences. If its normative categories canno be translated into differential criteria, it has failed. Bain's debacl should have shown this conclusively, but the modern heirs of th association psychology have yet to learn it. The closer links with biology which were forged by Darwin, Spencer, and their followers promised a psychology of organisms, including man, as they live their lives ir their environments, but the modern associationists or behaviourist have departed considerably from this approach and reverted to ar attempt to deduce a science of character from the association of simple reflex elements. Condillac could not reproduce a real man from simple sensory elements, Bain did no better with his associated sensory and motor elements, and the best that can be said of current attempts is that the road ahead appears very long indeed.[5]

---

[1] Mill, 1872, p. vi.    [2] Ibid., p. 557.    [3] Ibid.    [4] Bain, 1861, p. 30.
[5] My conclusions about the science of character advocated by Mill and attempted by Bain closely parallel the judgements of Ward and Allport. As to its deductive approach: 'We may safely count it as one of the curiosities of speculation that an empiricist of so extreme a type as Mill, who cannot be sure that there is not a world somewhere where two plus two equals

Bain had a novel and far-sighted grasp of the importance of bringing the objective results of experimental physiology to bear on the laws of mind. His emphasis on activity and behaviour was also a very significant advance. The other aspects of his work, however, were an expression of traditional methods and conceptions which were being made obsolete in the same years that he first published them. Thus, his work points two ways: forward to an experimental psychophysiology, and backward to the method of introspection and opposition to the important applications of his own conceptions by the experimental physiologists whose work he had deliberately set out to influence.[1]

---

five, and a world, if so we may call it, somewhere else, in which causes have no place, should yet believe in the possibility of an *a priori* science of character that can deduce universal laws from the truths of psychology, originally ascertained, as he insists they must be, from observation and experiment'. (James Ward, quoted in Roback, 1952, p. 146.) As to its equipment for explaining character 'What causal principles did psychology at the time of Mill have to offer? When this question is asked it becomes clear immediately why Ethology made no advance for fifty years after Mill published his program. Associationism, the principle by which fragmentary states of consciousness aroused other fragmentary states, was the sole "explanatory" tool of psychology, and woefully inadequate to account for the galaxy of human interests, motives, conflicts, and passions which are the essential forces in the formation of character. Psychology in Mill's time was intellectualistic, Apollonian, and not until the influences of Schopenhauer, Darwin, Freud, and McDougall had altered its point of view radically, training its vision upon the irrational motives of men, were the premises sufficiently complete to permit a realization of Mill's proposal.' (Allport, 1937, p. 87.)

[1] Bain's role in the development of functional psychology and pragmatist philosophy deserves further study. C. S. Peirce said that pragmatism is 'scarce more than a corollary' to Bain's definition of belief (which, in turn, is based on Bain's emphasis on action). Peirce called Bain 'the grandfather of pragmatism'. (Wiener, 1949, p. 19, etc.) See below p. 195.

# 4

## PIERRE PAUL BROCA AND THE SEAT OF THE FACULTY OF ARTICULATE LANGUAGE

Problems as presented and explanations as offered in scientific documents of the past are more often than not made intelligible to us only by asking what their author thought he was doing: what he saw as a problem, how he conceived the method of finding a solution, what modes of explanation he regarded as satisfactory.

A. C. Crombie, 1963

It is ironic that the experimental psychophysiology which stood diametrically opposed to Gall's conception of the functions of the brain and which reverted to the psychological tradition which he opposed, should have derived its belief in cerebral localization from phrenology. To assert baldly that the view of cerebral localization which Jackson and Ferrier used was derived from phrenology is to speak very loosely and to convey a false impression. Such an assertion is not a simple truth, but a complex one. Ferrier used three sources of the concept of cerebral localization: Broca, Fritsch and Hitzig, and Hughlings Jackson. Ferrier was not faithful to the precise conceptions of any of them. The views of localization employed by two of them grew historically out of phrenology—those of Broca and Jackson.

Broca's localization of a centre for 'the faculty of articulate language' was the first localization of a function in the hemisphere which met with general acceptance from orthodox scientists. Consequently, Broca is usually credited with priority in initiating the modern doctrine of cerebral localization.[1] This citation has appeared with such regularity that this fact alone gains for it a species of historical truth. However, if one begins to examine his claim to priority, it is difficult to establish with any degree of certainty. His work is part of a continuous consideration of aphasia and cerebral localization that stems directly from Gall and was a live issue throughout the intervening decades. Neither the conception of a faculty of articulate language nor its localization in the frontal lobes was novel. It might be argued that Broca was the first to confirm this localization and to clarify it with clear-cut pathological evidence, but the fact is that the quality of the evidence of his original case was very dubious indeed. What Broca seems to have contributed

[1] E.g., Herrick, 2nd ed., 1925, p. 19; Walker, 1957, p. 104; Boring, 1950, p. 70.

was a demonstration of this localization at a time when the scientific community was prepared to take the issue seriously. Those who had advocated cerebral localization of speech functions prior to Broca were so tainted by their connections with phrenology that the debate on the issue had the character of a local (and partly political)[1] squabble in Parisian medical circles. It is not clear how this occurred, but somehow Broca's confirmation of a finding that had been made and contested repeatedly for thirty-five years elevated it from the local level to that of an important finding which was considered seriously on an international scale. Broca was certainly no more eminent than Bouillaud, who had been advocating the view since 1825. Without further investigation, it is not possible to explain the significance attributed to Broca's advocacy of cerebral localization. In any case, his main contribution seems to have been a propaganda victory rather than an original discovery.

A brief discussion of the background of his 'discovery' and of his first case should show the relation of his method and conceptions to those of phrenology, the difficulties involved in the clinico-pathological method, and the relations between these and the work of the experimental psychophysiologists which constitutes the main line of investigation under review.

Observations on diseases affecting speech were made as early as the Hippocratic corpus (c. 400 B.C.), and more or less identifiable descriptions of speech pathology are scattered through the history of medicine since then.[2] Accurate descriptions of motor aphasia were made at least as early as 1673 (Johann Schmidt) and again in 1683 (Peter Rommel).[3] However, no important ideas about localization of the lesion had been advanced prior to 1800,[4] and Gall is usually credited with 'the first complete description of aphasia due to a wound of the brain'.[5] The case on which this claim rests was that of a young man brought to Gall by Baron Larrey (another physician) who had been wounded by the point of a foil which entered at 'the middle part of the left canine region, near the nostril' and penetrated 'in a vertical direction and a little oblique from before backward, to the depth of five or six lines in the internal posterior part of the anterior left lobe of the brain, in such

---

[1] See Temkin, 1947, p. 306, and below pp. 145–6.
[2] Benton and Joynt, 1960.    [3] Ibid., pp. 209–10.    [4] Ibid., p. 220.
[5] Head, 1926, I, 9. The case Riese reports from Goethe (Riese, 1947, pp. 322–3) neither was the first (see Benton and Joynt, 1960, p. 205), nor was the lesion traumatic. Both it and that reported by Pinel were due to apoplexy. Riese's revelation (1947, p. 323) that Pinel described a (non-traumatic) case prior to Gall would not have surprised Gall, since he quoted it. (1835, V, 22–3.)

a manner to approach the anterior part of the mesolobe'.[1] The clinical description of his symptoms is excellent. The patient's 'memory of names' was wholly extinguished. For example, though he recognized Baron Larrey, he 'could not recall his name, and always designated him as Mr Such-a-one'.[2]

Although this claim for Gall is legitimate, it is less interesting than its context. It should be recalled that the 'Faculty of attending to and distinguishing Words; Recollection of Words, or Verbal Memory', was the first of Gall's discoveries. It was this ability which he correlated with 'large, flaring eyes' in those of his classmates who were better than he at learning by heart.[3] He had made this correlation long before he thought of relating external signs to the underlying brain. 'It was this which gave the first impulse to my researches, and which was the occasion of all my discoveries.'[4] Other external signs were sought by analogy from this one. Later, after he based his formerly physiognomical doctrine on the brain, he inferred that large, prominent eyes were the result of the size of the 'organ of verbal memory, that cerebral part which rests on the posterior half of the roof of the orbit'.[5] The form of the orbit was changed 'according as all the cerebral parts placed on the roof. . . .' When they are highly developed, 'the eyeballs are pushed forward, whence result large prominent eyes'.[6]

A false impression is conveyed by taking Gall's case of a localized lesion out of context. His method of discovering it, and his reasoning about the seat of the faculty give some indication of the subordinate role of cases of localized lesions in his investigations. In describing his methods, he explicitly said that inspection of brains and 'accidental mutilations' (pathological lesions) played a subordinate role in confirming localizations which he had discovered by his cranioscopic methods.[7] Correlation of cerebral injuries with disturbance of a given function consituted 'a new proof' only 'after the seat of an organ has been discovered by other means, and this discovery has been sufficiently proved. . . .'[8] In writing about loss of speech, Gall gave no more weight to the account of the sword injury than he did to the following 'evidence' from another patient: 'In his embarrassment, he points with his finger to the lower part of his forehead; he manifests impatience, and indicates by his gestures, that it is from that point, that his inability to speak comes'.[9]

[1] Gall, 1835, V, 16.    [2] Ibid., V, 18.    [3] Ibid., V, 7–8; Gall, 1835, I, 58–9.
[4] Gall, 1835, V, 8.    [5] Ibid., V, 11.    [6] Ibid., V, 4.
[7] Gall, 1835, III, 120, 128.    [8] Ibid., III, 128–9.    [9] Gall, 1835, V, 23.

Gall's evidence for localization of the seat of the faculty of verbal memory was no less confused than his conception of the faculty itself. While acknowledging that he did provide early descriptions of the symptoms of motor aphasia, one should realize that his conception of the faculty was a hodgepodge when considered from a modern point of view. He did separate the patient's apparent ability to understand questions from his ability to speak voluntarily. He also noted that ability to speak could be impaired when the ability to move the tongue and pronounce isolated words was intact. Finally, he observed that the ability to express ideas by gestures and to identify objects could remain intact while various modes of formal expression, speaking, and writing are impaired.[1] However, his first descriptions involved ability to learn school lessons easily and recite them well. Thus the functions involved were not solely those of forming propositions and articulating them. The responsible faculty also accounted for the desire to make collections, study meticulously, read, and for various aspects of learning ability or intelligence. The phenomena of verbal expression were, therefore, not clearly separated from those of learning, retention, and recall. It was from a mixture of accurate description, confused methods, and rank nonsense that the idea took root that the memory for words was situated in the frontal lobes.[2]

The link between Gall and Broca is through Jean Baptiste Bouillaud (1796–1881).[3] Bouillaud received part of his clinical training from Gall, and he was a founding member of the Société Phrénologique which was organized in Paris three years after Gall died.[4] In 1825, he published a paper in which he argued on the basis of clinical evidence that loss of speech corresponds to a lesion of the anterior lobes of the brain, and that his findings confirmed Gall's opinion on the seat of the organ of articulate language. He opposed Flourens' view that the brain exerted no immediate and direct influence on the phenomena of speech and argued on the basis of cases of his own and from the literature that the brain plays an essential role in many movements, and that there were special organs in the brain for definite movements. 'In particular, the movements of the organs of speech are regulated by a special cerebral centre, distinct and independent. This is situated in the anterior

[1] Gall, 1835, V, 22–4.    [2] Head, 1926, I, 9.
[3] I have not read Bouillaud's papers, since his role in the history of cerebral localization is that of a link, not a direct contributor to the development of concepts or new findings. The comments on his work in the text are drawn from the following sources: Head, 1926, I; Wilks, 1879; Bastian, 1880; Ferrier, 1890; Walker, 1957; Joynt, 1961; Jefferson, 1960; Ackerknecht and Vallois, 1956; Ombredane, 1951. Most of the discussion follows Head closely (1926, I, 13–20).
[4] Ackerknecht and Vallois, 1956, p. 34.

lobes of the brain. Loss of speech depends sometimes on lack of memory for words, sometimes on want of the muscular movements of which speech is composed.[1]

His investigations involved an important change of methodological emphasis from the work of Gall. The correlations which he made were between clinical symptoms and brain lesions. The method of clinico-pathological correlation replaced that of correlating striking behaviours with cranial prominences and occasionally checking these against the brain. Bouillaud insisted that observation of the brain was essential in all cases. He arrived at his support of Gall by comparing the results of pathological studies with the opinions of phrenologists on the general issue of localization and the particular issue of a cerebral organ for articulate language. He believed that Gall ' "had announced rather than demonstrated" the fact'.[2] He was at once more precise and more vague than Gall. He was concerned with speech itself and not with the other aspects of Gall's faculty of verbal memory. However, his localiza-tion was less clearly defined than Gall's, and he claimed only that its seat lay in the frontal lobes.

He continued to present pathological cases in support of cerebral localization involving paralyses, loss of sensation and especially speech. He published a treatise in the same year as his original paper which contained 114 observations of disease of the frontal lobes accompanied by loss or defect of speech.[3] His views on aphasia were applications of a general principle of cerebral localization of muscular movements.

It is evident that the movements of the organs of speech must have a special centre in the brain, because speech can be completely lost in individuals who present no other signs of paralysis, whilst on the contrary other patients have the free use of speech coincident with paralysis of the limbs. But it is not sufficient to know that there exists in the brain a particular centre destined to produce and to co-ordinate the marvellous movements by which man communicates his thoughts and feelings, but it is above all important to determine the exact situation of this co-ordinating centre. From the observations (cases) I have collected, and from the large number I have read in the literature, I believe I am justified in advancing the view that the principal lawgiver of speech is to be found in the anterior lobes of the brain.[4]

He distinguishes clearly between the two classes of loss of speech which Gall had noted but had not emphasized. 'It is important to distinguish

---

[1] Quoted in Head, 1926, I, 13-14.    [2] Quoted in Jefferson, 1960, p. 117.
[3] Bastian, 1880, p. 674.    [4] Quoted in Head, 1926, I, p. 15.

he two causes which may be followed by loss of speech, each one in its wn manner; one by destroying the organ for the memory of words, he other by alteration of the nervous principle which presides over the novements of speech.'[1]

Bouillaud kept cerebral localization a live issue in the ensuing years. His views were vigorously opposed, but his work gained him the place of a popular professor of medicine at La Charité, Paris. He defended his position in 1839, in a lecture to the Académie de Médicine, in which he defined the relation of his views to those of Gall. Gall had considered the 'sense of words' from an intellectual aspect, while Bouillaud was more concerned with its mechanism. 'I wish to apply to the brain, considered as agent or principle of coordinated movements, that system of plurality which Gall invented for the same organ in as far as it is the instrument of intellectual and moral phenomena.'[2] He proposed a view of the mechanism of speech production and reaffirmed his belief in its localization in the frontal lobes. His paper led to a lengthy discussion of confirmatory and contradictory cases. His opponents were obsessed by the bogey of phrenology, whilst Bouillaud failed to explain why speech was sometimes gravely affected although the lesion was not situated in the frontal lobes'.[3] A paper read to the Académie de Médicine on localization in 1848 led Bouillaud to open another full-dress debate on the subject, which covered the old ground yet again. In the heat of the discussion he offered a prize of 500 francs to anyone who could produce a case of severe lesion of the frontal lobes without speech disturbance.

By 1861, Bouillaud was Doyen of the Faculty, Membre de l'Institut, and head of La Charité. Once again the issue of cerebral localization was being hotly debated, but the conduct of the debate had passed into the hands of the next generation. Broca was the secretary of the Société d'Anthropologie, which he had founded only months before. In February, 1861, a primitive human skull was presented, and debate followed on the significance of the volume of the brain. The issue was immediately expanded from the value of volume or form in determining the cultural level of a brain, to include the related issue of whether the brain functions as a whole or is composed of more or less independent organs or centres. Gratiolet, who presented the original skull, said, 'In a general manner I agree with M. Flourens that the intelligence is one, that the brain is one, that it acts above all as a whole; but this does not exclude the idea that certain faculties of the mind stand in special

[1] Quoted in Head, 1926, I, 16.      [2] Ibid, I, 16–17.      [3] Ibid., I, 17.

relation, although not exclusively, with certain cerebral regions'. Ernst Auburtin, Bouillaud's pupil and son-in-law, rejected global measurements and unequivocally argued the case for cerebral localization. Broca, who had not discussed localization in the first debate reopened the issue in March. He had high praise for Gall's anatomical work and for the principle of cerebral localization 'which has been one may say, the point of departure for all the discoveries of our century on the physiology of the brain'. His advocacy of Gall's principle was carefully distinguished from their phrenological applications. 'I for my part, believe in the principle of localization,' he said, and supported his belief with facts from embryology and anatomy.[2] Auburtin opened the sitting of 4 April, with case reports drawn in part from Bouillaud's writings, and upheld the value of pathological observations against those of physiological experiment. The clinicians were not only following Gall's principles in opposition to those of Flourens, but also upheld the value of a modified form of his naturalistic approach and correlative method. Since the first empirical demonstration of the principle of cerebral localization followed from these discussions, it should be noted that it came from the examination of an 'experiment of nature'. It was not until nine years later that cortical localization was demonstrated by the experimental method, by direct intervention into nature and the production of effects.

More particularly, Auburtin followed Bouillaud in upholding the association of speech with the frontal lobes. In a grand gesture reminiscent of his father-in-law's prize offer, he promised to abandon his belief in cerebral localization if anyone could produce a case of loss of speech without a lesion in the anterior lobes of the brain. Conversely, Auburtin argued that the localization of a single faculty would suffice to establish the truth of the principle of cerebral localization.[3] It was in this highly charged atmosphere that the patient 'Tan' (whose real name, Leborgne, has been almost forgotten because of the characteristic and symptomatic utterance that became his nickname) was proposed by Broca as a test case and accepted by Auburtin.[4] The patient died within a week of admission to Broca's surgical service with diffused gangrenous cellulitis of the left leg. He had lost his speech 21 years before and had been a patient at the Bicêtre since then. When Broca demonstrated the brain to the Société d'Anthropologie the next day he offered

---

[1] Quoted in Head, 1926, I, 18.
[2] Ibid. Cf. Broca, 1861, pp. 56–7.
[3] Broca, 1861, p. 55.     [4] Ibid., p. 56.

is observations in support of the views of Bouillaud and Auburtin. However, the opponents of localization were not immediately aroused, and Broca himself was agnostic about particular localizations in his closing remarks. It was Broca's complete account of this case to the Société Anatomique de Paris four months later that brought the debate to a climax.[1]

There are two important aspects of Broca's presentation in addition to the evidence he gives: his conception of method and his view of the functions which are to be localized.

His methodological observations involve the final and complete rejection of cranioscopy in localizing research. He notes that 'the phrenological school placed the seat of the faculty of language in the anterior part of the brain, in one of the convolutions which rest on the orbital roof'.[2] Bouillaud's change in method was a fundamental advance. The phrenological localization of language,

would doubtless have disappeared with the rest of the system if M. Bouillaud had not saved it from shipwreck by making important modifications and by surrounding it by a series of proofs, mostly taken from pathology. Without considering the language as a simple faculty depending on only one cerebral organ and without trying to circumscribe within a few millimeters the place of this organ, as did the school of Gall, this professor has been led by the analysis of a large number of clinical facts, followed by autopsies, to state that certain lesions of the hemisphere abolish speech without destroying intelligence and that these lesions are always in the anterior lobes of the brain.[3]

Previous observations using the pathological method had not been incompatible with those reached by cranioscopy, but

It is enough to compare our observation with the preceding ones, to dismiss the idea that the faculty of articulate language resides in a circumscribed fixed point situated under a certain elevation of the skull. The lesions of aphemia have been found most often in the most anterior part of the frontal lobe, not far from the eyebrow and above the orbital roof, whereas in my patient they were much further back, much nearer to the coronal suture than the superciliary arch. This difference in the localization is incompatible with the system of bumps.[4]

Broca recalled that the phrenologists had neglected the study of the cerebral convolutions 'far too much'. 'One allowed oneself to be

---

[1] The original publication was 'Remarques sur le siège de la faculté du langage articulé; suivies d'une observation d'aphémie', and it appeared in *Bull. Soc. Anat.*, Paris. **6**, 330–57, 1861. All quotations are taken from the translation in von Bonin, 1960, and page references are to it.
[2] Broca, 1861, p. 49.    [3] Ibid., pp. 49–50.    [8] Ibid., p. 72.

dominated by the old prejudice that the cerebral convolutions are in no way fixed, that they are simply pleats made by chance, comparabl to the disorderly flexions of the intestinal loops'.[1] Broca pointed ou that the fundamental convolutions were constant and that it woul not be possible to attain an understanding of the limits within which the principle of cerebral localization could be applied until studie were made much more precise. Bouillaud had advanced methodolog by insisting on pathological observations. Many more of these wer needed to finally establish the principle of localization. But more wa required than pathological observation and specification of only th area of the lesion or its distance from familiar landmarks on the brain' surface. 'We have to investigate not only in what parts of the brain ar situated the regions of aphemia, but we also have to designate by thei name and by their rank the diseased convolutions and the degree o alterations of each of them. So far one has not proceeded in that way.' Broca followed his own advice and the further injunction that 'if th lesion is very large, to try to determine as much as possible by anatomica methods the point or rather the convolution where the disease seem to have started'.[3] It will become clear when the work of Fritsch and Hitzig and Ferrier is discussed that standard cerebral nomenclatur became an increasingly important aspect of cerebral research.

Although Broca's observations were made in favour of a more precis version of Bouillaud's view of the seat of the faculty of language, he differed radically from Bouillaud's conception of that faculty (Bouillaud was apparently not troubled by this difference and accepte Broca's work as confirming his own.)[5] Broca's discussion reflects th prevailing confusion about the role of the hemispheres in muscula motion. When he describes the impairment of speech involved in th aphemia,[6] he is sympathetic to Bouillaud's view.

What they lost is therefore not the faculty of language, is not the memor of the words nor is it the action of nerves and of muscles of phonation an articulation, but something else. It is a particular faculty considered b

[1] Broca, 1861, p. 59.     [2] Ibid., p. 58.     [3] Ibid., p. 72.
[4] Ibid., p. 49.     [5] Head, 1926, I, p. 28.
[6] The nomenclature of speech pathology is of no importance for present purposes. Broc called loss of speech 'aphemia'. In 1864 Trousseau proposed the term 'aphasia', and i became generally accepted. See Head, 1926, I, 27–8. For Broca's protest and his own classi fication, see Broca, 1869 and below p. 206n. It is also irrelevant for this study that the lesio of aphasia which Broca localized was characteristically found in the *left* hemisphere. Mar Dax had pointed this out in 1836, although this remained unknown until his son pressed claim for priority after Broca's findings, in 1864. See Head, 1926, I, 16, 28. The issue o cerebral dominance is extremely complex; however, its significance was not generall appreciated in the period under review. See Znagwill, 1960, for a recent exposition.

M. Bouillaud to be the faculty to co-ordinate the movements which belong to the articulate language, or simpler, it is the faculty of articulate language; for without it no articulation is possible.[1]

His conception of the function also included motion.

The nature of that faculty and the place to which it should be assigned in the cerebral hierarchy could give rise to some hesitation. Is it only a kind of memory and have the individuals who have lost it, lost only, not the memory of the words but the memory of the procedure which one has to follow in order to articulate the words?[2]

These gradual perfections of the articulated language in children are due to the development of a particular kind of memory, which is not the memory of words but those of movements, necessary to articulate words. And this particular memory is not in relation with any other memory of the rest of the intelligence.[3]

It might be argued, then, that speech was a motor function. Indeed this is the ground on which Jackson and Ferrier opposed Broca.

Broca discusses in detail whether speech is an intellectual or a motor function. He recognized two hypotheses for the nature of the special faculty of articulate language. 'In the first hypothesis this would be a superior faculty, and aphemia would be an intellectual disturbance. In the second hypothesis, this would be a faculty of much less elevated order and the aphemia would be only a disturbance of locomotion.' He correspondingly distinguishes 'the thinking part of the brain' from 'the motor centers of the central nervous system'.[4]

Although Broca accepted that it was an open question whether speech and aphemia involved intellectual or motor functions, he inclined to the former view. His argument reveals the prevailing assumptions. He believed that the pathological anatomy of aphemia strongly supported the view that speech is an intellectual function.

In fact, in almost all cases in which an autopsy could be performed, it was found that the substance of the convolutions is profoundly altered to a notable extent. In some subjects the lesions were even confined to the convolutions; from this one can conclude that the faculty of articulate language is one of the functions of the convolutional mass. But it is generally admitted that all faculties, called intellectual, have their seat in this part of the brain, and it seems therefore very probable, that all faculties that reside in the cerebral convolutions are of the intellectual nature.[5]

The assumption implicit in taking this evidence as deciding the issue in favour of the intellectual view rather than the motor, is made

[1] Broca, 1861, p. 52.    [2] Ibid., pp. 52–3.    [3] Ibid., p. 54.    [4] Ibid.
[5] Ibid., p. 57.

explicit in Broca's discussion of the other symptoms of the patient 'Tan'. 'Everybody knows that the cerebral convolutions are not motor organs.'[1] One sees that Flourens' separation of intellectual functions from motor functions and his exclusion of the latter from the cerebral lobes had gained general acceptance by 1860. Ten years after Tan had lost the faculty of speech, a progressive right-side paralysis set in, and Broca reflects the prevailing view in saying. 'The corpus striatum of the left hemisphere is of all the attacked organs the only one where one could look for the cause of the paralysis of the two right extremities.'[2]

It is clear that two prevailing dogmas prevented Broca from seriously entertaining the alternative position that aphasia is a motor disturbance. He could support cerebral localization, but he could not believe that the cerebral convolutions were involved in motion. They were set aside for the intellectual functions. If speech was impaired by lesions in the convolutions, it could not be a motor function. It had to be a special faculty whose nature was unspecified. It was this special status for intellectual functions—somehow different from sensory and motor functions by virtue of being intellectual—that Jackson will be seen to oppose. Nine years later Fritsch and Hitzig demonstrated experimentally that the cerebral convolutions were, in fact, motor organs.

Broca had no doubt that speech was a separate faculty.

The existence of a special faculty of articulate language—as I have defined it—can no more be doubted, because a faculty which can perish isolated without those which are in its neighbourhood is evidently a faculty independent of all others, i.e., a special faculty.[3]

If all cerebral faculties were as distinct and as clearly circumscribed as this one, one would finally have a definite point from which to attack the controversial question of cerebral localization. Unfortunately, this is not the case, and the greatest obstacle in this part of physiology comes from the insufficiency and the uncertainty of the functional analysis which necessarily has to precede the search of the organs which are coordinated to each function.[4]

The apparent discreteness of this faculty made it an ideal case for testing the question of cerebral localization. The pathological anatomy of aphemia could be used to decide if there was any localization in the brain at all and if so how discrete it was, by lobes or convolutions. If the existence of this one localization could be proved, the principle and its limits would be established.[5]

[1] Broca, 1861, p. 70.     [2] Ibid.     [3] Ibid., pp. 54–5.     [4] Ibid.
[5] Ibid., p. 58.

The second half of Broca's report is devoted to the case of 'Tan': 'Aphemia for twenty-one years produced by the chronic and progressive softening of the second and third convolution of the superior part of the left frontal lobe'.[1] Broca's description provides excellent data for consideration of the problems of the clinico-pathological method.[2]

The patient's history of aphemia was complicated by epilepsy since youth, diminished sensitivity and progressive paralysis of the right arm and leg over eleven years, weakened vision in the left eye, partial pharyngeal paralysis, and left-sided weakness in the extremities and face. The progressive nature of the symptoms would disqualify the patient from modern clinico-pathological studies, but Broca was prepared to infer at autopsy that the lesion began at the third left frontal convolution, where damage was worst. However, there was extensive damage, no part of the hemisphere was absolutely intact,[3] and there was generalized atropy. In fact, as Pierre Marie later pointed out from examining the patient's brain, the inference of the locus of the original lesion was highly speculative, the examination of the patient was inadequate, and the brain was not sectioned or carefully studied at all.[4]

Broca presented a second case of the same year[5] from which he concluded that 'the aphemia was the result of a profound, but accurately circumscribed lesion of the posterior third of the second and third frontal convolutions'.[6] In this case the aphasia was not complicated by other symptoms, and the lesion was strictly limited. Therefore the evidence was more trustworthy. By 1863 Broca and his colleagues had collected twenty cases, all showing some pathological change in the left half of the brain, and in nineteen of them it was in the third frontal convolution. Nevertheless, the presentation of a serious exception led him to reserve his opinion on the exact location of the cortical centre for articulate speech.[7]

Head reports the sensational effect of Broca's findings.

These communications produced the greatest excitement in the medical world of Paris. They were specially selected for comment by the Secretary of the Société anatomique, in his Annual Report for the year 1861. Bouillaud

---

[1] Broca, 1861, p. 60.
[2] For a presentation that concentrates more closely on the clinical description of the case and its place in the history of aphasia theory, see Head, 1926, I, 19–23, cf. Joynt, 1961.
[3] Broca, 1861, p. 66.      [4] Head, 1926, I, Ch. 5; cf. Bateman, 1890, pp. 345–6.
[5] Head, 1926, I, 23–5; Bateman, 1890, pp. 22–5.      [6] Quoted in Head, 1926, I, 25.
[7] Ibid., I, 26.

and his son-in-law, Auburtin, greeted Broca as a convert to their doctrines
Localization of speech became a political question; the older Conservative
school, haunted by the bogey of phrenology, clung to the conception tha
the brain 'acted as a whole'; whilst the younger Liberals and Republican
passionately favoured the view that different functions were exercised by
the various portions of the cerebral hemispheres. During the next few years
every medical authority took one side or other in the discussion.[1]

The impact of Broca's findings on the experimentalists was far less
than might be supposed from the reviews of the history of cerebral
localization which trace its development as a simple progression from
the thesis and antithesis of Gall and Flourens to the findings of Broca
and Fritsch and Hitzig which preceded Ferrier's detailed studies. Their
effect on Fritsch and Hitzig and on Ferrier was confined to the suspicion
it cast on Flourens' dogma of the functional equivalence of the cortex.
Fritsch and Hitzig do not mention Broca by name, though his work is
implied in their review of clinical studies which formed part of a slow
process of doubt about the findings of Flourens and those who confirmed
them. These conceptions

were modified only very gradually even by a number of well stated facts
which presupposed other notions. It was known for a long time, by Bouillaud,
that the complex of symptoms, now known as aphasia can be caused by
destruction of a small eccentric part of the brain. Recently, several authors
have contributed to define this more closely.[2]

Their only further mention of Broca's work is in acknowledging that
it was the only other example of localization in the hemispheres known
in 1870, and that it spoke in favour of their results.[3] However, they
point out that such findings were suspicious in themselves, since they
suffered from 'the faultiness and the difficult interpretations of post
mortems' as compared with 'the simplicity and clearness of vivisections'.[4]

Ferrier's reaction was similar. In his first publication he does not

---

[1] Quoted in Head, 1926, I, 25. The attention of the followers of Broca was concentrated
on cases illustrating anatomical localization, rather than the phenomena of the function of
speech and the changes it underwent. The concepts of aphasia and the schemes of localization
that developed from them did not *directly* provide significant contributions to experimental
localization research or to concepts of function until Head reinterpreted Jackson's work and
began his own studies on the phenomena of speech function and dysfunction. It is for this
reason, as much as because of my ignorance of the subtleties of clinical neurology, that I
have felt able to ignore the history of aphasia in the present work. Also, the next significant
step in aphasia research did not occur until 1874, when Wernicke presented his conception
of sensory aphasia based on Meynert's research on the projection systems of the cortex.
See Head, 1926, I, 61–3, and Freud, 1891.
[2] Fritsch and Hitzig, translated von Bonin, 1870, p. 78.
[3] Ibid., p. 91.    [4] Ibid., p. 78.

nclude Broca's work as part of the inspiration of his own. He does
mention Broca's finding, but only to quarrel with its interpretation.
He opposes the conception that the lesion destroys a centre for 'memory
of words' and suggests that only the motor channels for words are
destroyed.[1] He raises the same point in the paper which he read to the
Royal Society in 1874.[2] Although his original experiments were closely
followed by the application of his findings to clinical cases, it is clear
(as far as it can be from available manuscripts and published sources)
that investigations by Broca or those inspired by his work played
little part in the motivation of Ferrier's original experiments. Once he
had made his initial findings he was prepared to draw on Broca for
support, while mentioning their differences.

The researches of Broca and the numerous confirmations of his observations
which have been put on record, taken with the results of my experiments
on monkeys and lower animals, seem to me to establish the fact of a localization of the faculty of speech and to explain at least the broad features of the
pathology of aphasia. I have shown that the region which governs the
movements concerned in articulation is that which is the seat of lesion in
aphasia.[3]

The question of the physiological interpretation of Broca's finding
also enters into Ferrier's reference to it in his major work. He mentions
a number of cases where considerable loss of brain substance had not
involved 'apparent mental deficiency'.[4]

But the remarkable and frequent coincidence of aphasia, or loss of the faculty
of speech, with softening of certain parts of the frontal region of the left
hemisphere (vaguely indicated by Bouillaud and Dax, but definitely fixed
by Broca in the posterior part of the third frontal convolution, and corrobor-
ated by multitudes of since recorded cases), served to render the theory of
functional equivalence at least doubtful; though what aphasia really meant
in physiological language, or why in symmetrically-formed hemispheres a
faculty should be localized in one side to the exclusion of the other, remained
a matter of mystery and dispute.[5]

This passage was expanded in the second edition to include findings of
'Bouillaud, Andral, and others' involving 'many unquestionable facts
of clinical medicine, such as limited paralysis in connection with
limited cerebral lesions, which appeared wholly inexplicable except

---

[1] Ferrier, 1873, p. 74.    [2] Ferrier, 1874, p. 129.
[3] Ferrier, 1874b, pp. 54–5, cf. p. 56.    [4] Ferrier, 1876, p. 126.    [5] Ibid.

on the hypothesis of a differentiation of function in the cerebral hemi
spheres'.[1] His description of these cases—even with the knowledge c
hindsight—indicated that their significance was limited to the doub
they cast on the theory of functional equivalence.

These exponents of the new experimental physiology of sensation an
motion were suspicious of both the correlative method and the un
physiological conceptions of clinical workers. The method of correlatin
clinical and pathological phenomena was uncomfortably reminiscen
of the dangers of craniological correlations, even though they wer
based on direct observations of the brains. Experiment was the onl
trustworthy method. Ferrier's view of the dangers of clinical observa
tions as compared with the trustworthiness of animal experiments ha
been mentioned.[2] He remained quite cautious about the 'facts furnishec
by the experiments of disease in man'.[3]

These, however, require to be handled with the utmost caution, otherwis
they may be made to support almost any doctrine however absurd. Almos
every form of disturbance of the cerebral functions has been manifested i
conjunction with anatomical lesions of the utmost diversity as to character
size, and position; and likewise without any visible or demonstrable lesio
whatever. In the absence of any exact means of discrimination between th
direct and indirect effects of pathological lesions, or of the relation betwee
functional disturbance and structural alteration, little reliance can be place
on localisation of function founded on the positive facts of cerebral diseas
alone. Clinical cases are mainly valuable as confirmatory of physiologica
experiments, and more especially as supplying negative instances.[4]

A case of total destruction of an area without loss of function is signifi
cant, since it conclusively refutes a relationship between the area
and its supposed function, but otherwise, clinical cases offer little hel
to the physiologist. Gall had seen cases of 'accidental mutilation' a
useful only in confirming his cranioscopic findings. Bouillaud and Broca
made clinico-pathological correlations their basic approach, anc
Auburtin voiced their faith in this approach in favour of the experi
mental one of producing effects by controlled stimulation or ablation
Fritsch and Hitzig and Ferrier complete the change in methodologica
faith by subordinating clinical cases to a confirmatory role.

Looking backward from the vantage point of Ferrier's work it i
clear that the view of localization that was most closely akin to Gall'
in conception, though not in method of localization, was least influentia

---

[1] Ferrier, 2nd ed., 1886, p. 222.     [2] Above, pp. 52–3; cf. below, pp. 236–8.
[3] Ferrier, 1886, p. 270.     [4] Ibid., cf. Ferrier, 1890, pp. 15–17.

on the experimental work of the sensory-motor psychophysiologists. The terms in which Ferrier thought of localization were also derived in a circuitous route from phrenology by way of Spencer and Hughlings Jackson. It will become clear in reviewing the development of this work that Broca's role was that of a foil for the precise statement of Jackson's sensory-motor view. The other source of Ferrier's concept of localization was the finding of Fritsch and Hitzig, who were also indirectly indebted to Broca. However, their contribution involved use of the experimental method to disprove exclusion of the cortex from motor functions: the proposition that had been central to Broca's view of both aphasia and the functions of the hemispheres. In conclusion, Broca can be credited with having provided important pathological support for belief in some form of localization, in opposition to one of the prevailing doctrines of Flourens in cerebral physiology, while his conception of the 'faculty' perpetuated another. Any statement beyond this involves conceptions that can be related to Broca's views only by contrast.

# 5

## HERBERT SPENCER: PHRENOLOGY, EVOLUTIONARY ASSOCIATIONISM, AND CEREBRAL LOCALIZATION

It is very satisfactory to see how you and Bain, each in his own way, have succeeded in affiliating the conscious operations of the mind to the primary unconscious organic actions of the nerves, thus filling up the most serious lacuna and removing the chief difficulty in the association psychology.

John Stuart Mill, 1864.

To Spencer is certainly due the immense credit of having been the first to see in evolution an absolutely universal principle.

Add this sleuth-hound scent for what he was after, and his untiring pertinacity, to his priority in perceiving the one great truth, and you fully justify the popular estimate of him as one of the world's geniuses, in spite of the fact that the 'temperament' of genius, so called, seems to have been so lacking in him.

William James, 1904.

That the philosophical system of Spencer is an object of derision is one of the few points on which all philosophers seem now to agree.

Charles Singer, 1959.

### *Early Phrenological Work and* Social Statics

Bain represented the culmination of classical associationism and brought it into relation with sensory-motor physiology. Herbert Spencer's *Principles of Psychology* was published in the same year that Bain's *Senses and the Intellect* appeared (1855), yet the two works belong to different generations. Where Bain had enriched the association psychology with a new interest in motion and provided it with an important alliance with experimental neurophysiology, Spencer gave it a whole new basis in evolutionary biology. It was Spencer's psychology of evolutionary associationism and the conception of cerebral localization which he united with it, that Hughlings Jackson applied to the nervous system. The views of Jackson and Bain then provided the psychophysiological theory which David Ferrier developed experimentally after the localized electrical excitability of the cerebral cortex was demonstrated in 1870. It is only a slight exaggeration to say that the work of Jackson and Ferrier can be deduced from the theories of Bain and Spencer. Jackson's clinical work and Ferrier's experiments were acknowledged applications of the conceptions of Bain and Spencer. An historical study of the development of concepts of cerebral localization and its biological context should therefore pay close attention to the sources of these conceptions as a necessary prerequisite to an appreciation of their use in the clinic and laboratory.

Spencer's intellectual development shows the relations among associationism, phrenology, sensory-motor psychophysiology, cerebral localization, and the new basis for psychology in the theory of evolution. All of these approaches came together in his early writings, providing a unique opportunity to review previous work and to lay the foundations for the work of Jackson and Ferrier. A close study of this period will also afford an opportunity to indicate further developments of the conception of psychology as a biological science which were raised in connection with Gall and were significantly advanced by Spencer. These developments will be indicated, although in the present study they will not be pursued in detail beyond Spencer.

The connection between Gall's biological view of psychology and Spencer's is not merely conceptual. Like Bain, Spencer derived his initial interest in psychology from phrenology.[1] His biographer reports that 'His letters show that he approached the study of mental functions through the avenue of phrenology, his conclusions being reached, as he is more than once careful to mention, not theoretically only, but by observation'.[2] In his *Autobiography*, Spencer says,

Between 1820 and 1830, phrenology had been drawing attention; and there came over to England, about 1830 or after, Gall's disciple, Spurzheim, who went about the country diffusing knowledge of the system. Derby was among the towns he visited. Being then perhaps 11, or perhaps 12, I attended his lectures: having, however, to overcome a considerable repugnance to contemplating the row of grinning skulls he had in front of him. Of course at that age faith was stronger than scepticism. Accepting uncritically the statements made, I became a believer, and for many years remained one.[3]

In 1842, when he was twenty-two, Spencer had his head 'read' by a reputable phrenologist, Mr J. Q. Rumball. Firmness, Self-Esteem, and Conscientiousness were the largest prominences, and Mr Rumball commented that 'Such a head as this ought to be in the Church'.[4] The full delineation and commentary are worth studying, as they are, on the whole, unexceptionable. However, one friend ventured the suggestion that 'he might have arrived at the same conclusion without feeling your head at all'.[1] Spencer was not moved by his friend's scepticism, 'Papers yield evidence that at that time my faith in phrenology was unshaken.'[2]

Between 1842 and 1846, his interest in phrenology was very active indeed. He wrote memoranda on the faculties of Veneration, Self-Esteem, and Love of Approbation, and made a design for an ideal head.[3] He wrote to a friend in 1843, 'At present I am engaged in writing an article for *The Phrenological Journal* upon the new theory of Benevolence and Imitation, which we have talked over together'.[4] By this time Spencer's scepticism about phrenology was beginning to manifest itself. The heretical article, advocated a *new* view of the functions of the organs, and it was rejected by Combe.[5] However, it was accepted by a new periodical, *The Zoist*, founded by Dr John Elliotson for the propagation of mesmerism.[6] 'Phreno-mesmerism[7] was at that time the name of one class of the manifestations; and, by implication, Phrenology was recognized as an associated topic. Hence, in part, I suppose, the reason why Dr Eliotson [*sic*] accepted this essay of mine.'[8] The article was published in *The Zoist* of January, 1844. Two other heterodox articles advocating relocation of Amativeness from the cerebellum to the adjacent cerebrum and suggesting that the 'ultimate function' of the organ of Wonder was 'the revival of all intellectual impressions' or 'Revivisence' appeared in the July and October numbers.[9]

Spencer says of this period,

Partially dissentient though I was concerning special phrenological doctrines, I continued an adherent of the general doctrine: not having, at that time,

---

[1] Specer, 1904, I, 202.    [2] Ibid., I, 203.    [3] Ibid.    [4] Ibid., I, 225.

[5] This rebuff was later used by phrenologists to explain Spencer's subsequent hostility to their views, e.g. Hollander, n.d., I, 459. The members of the British Phrenological Society were still sensitive about Spencer in the 1960s.

[6] Elliotson had been President of the Royal Medical and Chirurgical Society, Lecturer at St Thomas' Hospital and Professor at the University of London. He introduced the stethoscope into London. He was a famous surgeon. However, his espousal of painless operations by mesmerism ended his academic career. Phrenologists were grateful for the new ally and especially for the aura of martyrdom which hung around him. The standard translation of Gall was dedicated to him. He founded the London Phrenological Society and lectured extensively on phrenology. (Hollander, n.d., I, 342, 354, 357, etc.) Cf. Spencer, 1904, I, 227, 246–7; Wallace, 1901, p. 180; Boring, 1950, pp. 119–23.

[7] This was the aspect of phrenology that had converted A. R. Wallace. See above, pp. 44–5.

[8] Spencer, 1904, I, 227.    [9] Ibid., I, 246–7.

entered on those lines of psychological inquiry which led me eventually to conclude that, though the statements of phrenologists might contain adumbrations of truths, they did not express the truths themselves.[1]

His active interest in phrenology can be traced as far as 1846, when he set out to improve on phrenological technology.

My interest in phrenology still continued; and thought, occasionally expended upon it, raised dissatisfaction with the ordinary mode of collecting data. Examinations of heads carried on merely by simple inspection and tactual exploration seemed to me extremely unsatisfactory. The outcome of my dissatisfaction was the devising of a method for obtaining, by graphic delineations, mechanically made, exact measurements, instead of the inexact ones obtained through the unaided senses.[2]

A description and drawings of the 'cephalograph' which he designed are appended to his *Autobiography*.[3] He intended to publish its description in *The Zoist*, but a trial model had been badly made. He did not pursue the matter then, and when he returned to it, he says, 'I had become sceptical about current phrenological views, and no longer felt prompted to employ a better instrument-maker'.[4]

Spencer began reading in preparation for his first book, *Social Statics* (1851) in 1846, and between then and 1848, he abandoned his career as a railway engineer and decided to earn a living as a writer. *Social Statics* sought to relate his views on the proper sphere of government with general moral principles[5]; his attempts to argue a consistent laissez-faire view of society were based on a biological theory of the structure of human communities, in which social bodies were made analogous to the somatic organization of men and other organisms. The argument of the book can be briefly given in context with its relevance to the development of Spencer's views on psychology and physiology.

It was written as an attack on Benthamism[6]—retaining the utilitarian standard of value but rejecting the active role of the state in attaining the greatest happiness for the greatest number. State regulation and legislation are seen as interference with Spencer's 'First Principle': '*Every man has freedom to do all that he wills, provided he infringes not the equal freedom of any other man.*'[7] Men would eventually come to do

---

[1] Spencer, 1904, I, 228.    [2] Ibid., I, 297.    [3] Ibid., I, 540–3.
[4] Ibid., I, 540.    [5] Spencer, 1908, p. 55.
[6] Characteristically, Spencer had not read Bentham's works; see Spencer, 1908, pp. 418, 538.
[7] Spencer, 1851, p. 103.

naturally what is best, even though a lengthy struggle would be necessary. His position, which provided the rationale for the individualist and ultra-conservative ideology of 'Social Darwinism',[1] leads him to oppose such things as poor laws, state-supported education, sanitary supervision, protection of the ignorant from medical quacks, tariffs, state banking, and government postal systems. He opposes anything which he feels would interfere with the free exercise of all of men's faculties. The duty of the state is to *protect* equal freedom but never to interfere with it. He claims that 'beyond its function of protector against external and internal enemies, the State has no function: and . . . when it assumes any other function it becomes an aggressor instead of a protector'.[2]

His argument is based on a distinctly phrenological view of man. The faculties are heterodox, but they are phrenological faculties none the less. Consistent with the optimism added to Gall's views by Spurzheim and Combe, they are extremely modifiable: 'The universal law of life is, that the exercise or gratification of faculties strengthens them; whilst, on the contrary, the curbing or inflicting pain upon them, entails a diminution of their power.'[3] Each faculty grows by exercise and dwindles from disuse.[4] Happiness results from 'the fulfilment of their functions by the respective faculties'.[5]

His conception of psychological phenomena departs radically from that of the Utilitarians. He accepts the pleasure-pain principle but not the normative psychology with which it had been traditionally linked by the associationists. James Mill had elaborated Hartley's psychology to serve as a rational basis for the legislative, economic, and social programme of the Philosophic Radicals. The psychological view which he developed implied that a common human nature led to a 'natural identity of interests' of the individuals in society. Pleasure and pains could be scientifically determined and made part of a 'felicific calculus'. From these calculations of a scientific psychology, a legislative programme could be devised which created an 'artificial identification of interests'[6] by means of the rewards and punishments which the state dispensed. These two aspects of the Utilitarian programme are contradictory; and Spencer's *Social Statics* was a symptom of this major weakness. Spencer argues that if there is a common meeting ground of the interests of individuals in society, it will manifest itself without

---

[1] See Hofstadter, 1955, especially Chapter 2.    [2] Spencer, 1904, I, 362.
[3] Spencer, 1851, p. 80.    [4] Ibid., p. 466.    [5] Ibid. Cf. pp. 75–89.
[6] Halévy, 1952, p. 514. See Part III, Chapters 3 and 4, especially pp. 485–514; Burrow, 1966, chs. 1–4, 6.

he artificial sanctions of rewards and punishments by the state.
Moreover, he claims that the belief that such sanctions can be effective
s based on an erroneous conception of human nature. Reasoning
bstractly about the 'greatest happiness' only makes sense when talking
bout the ideal man. Attempts at defining such a state are nonsensical
where real men are concerned. 'It is not then to be wondered at, if
Paleys and Benthams make vain attempts at a definition.'[1]

The source of his objection is a phrenological view of individual
differences based on a faculty psychology.

Man . . . consists of a congeries of faculties, qualifying him for surrounding
conditions. Each of these faculties, if normally developed, yields to him,
when exercised, a gratification constituting part of his happiness; whilst, in
the act of exercising it, some deed is done subserving the wants of the man
s a whole, and affording to the other faculties the opportunity of performing
n turn their respective functions, and of producing every one its peculiar
pleasure: so that, when healthily balanced, each subserves all, and all
subserve each.[2]

Complete happiness is the result of the exercise of all the faculties,

n the ratio of their several developments; and an ideal arrangement of
circumstances calculated to secure this constitutes the standard of 'greatest
happiness'; but the minds of no two individuals contain the same combina-
ion of elements. Duplicate men are not to be found. There is in each a
different balance of desires. Therefore the conditions adapted for the highest
enjoyment of one, would not perfectly compass the same end for any other.
And consequently the notion of happiness must vary with the disposition
and character; that is, must vary indefinitely.[3]

State action cannot take account of the myriad subtle differences among
ndividuals. It can only do harm to the happy, self-sufficient man or
prevent a man who has not achieved this state from doing so.[4] 'To do
anything for him by some artificial agency, is to supersede certain of his
powers—is to leave them unexercised, and therefore to diminish his
happiness.'[5]

Turning from individual psychology to social relations, Spencer
proposes two reasons why men will act for the good of others without
needing the artificial restraints of state action. The first is the existence
of the faculty of the 'Moral Sense'. In his argument for such a faculty,

---

[1] Spencer, 1851, p. 5. Cf. Albee, new ed. 1962.    [2] Spencer, 1851, p. 280.
[3] Ibid., p. 5. Spencer's opposition to belief in the constancy of human nature is spelled
out, pp. 32–8.
[4] Ibid., pp. 281–2.    [5] Ibid., pp. 280–1.

Spencer reveals the detailed influence of phrenology on his psychological thinking. Phrenological faculty psychology and craniology are now mentioned explicitly, and he makes no acknowledgement of the interest which had dominated his writing activity a few years earlier. However in attempting to uphold the Moral Sense doctrine in opposition to Bentham's condemnation of the principle,[1] Spencer uses a phrenological view of the nature of man, which he believes unequivocally establishe the existence of a Moral Sense. He also tries to show that the Utilitarian fall back on the moral sense for the foundation of their own doctrine. His phrenological argument is that nature does not leave the fulfilment of important needs to chance or to the care of the intellect. 'Answering to each of the actions which it is requisite for us to perform, we find in ourselves some prompter called a desire; and the more essential the action, the more powerful is the impulse to its performance, and the more intense the gratification derived therefrom.'[3] This is obviously true of 'creature needs' such as food, sleep, and the continuance of the race. He argues that it is also true of our social lives, where analogous impulses exist leading to love of praise and the sentiment of friendship. His argument for the moral sense is derived by analogy from these provisions of nature.

May we not then reasonably expect to find a like instrumentality employed in impelling us to that line of conduct, in the due observance of which consists what we call *morality?* All must admit that we are guided to our bodily welfare by instincts; that from instincts also, spring those domestic relationships by which other important objects are compassed—and that similar agencies are in many cases used to secure our indirect benefit, by regulating social behaviour. Seeing, therefore, that whenever we can readily trace our actions to their origin, we find them produced after this manner, it is, to say the least of it, highly probable that the same mental mechanism is employed in all cases—that as the all-important requirements of our being are fulfilled at the solicitations of desire, so also are the less essential ones— that upright conduct in each being necessary to the happiness of all, there exists in us an impulse towards such conduct; or, in other words, that we possess a 'Moral Sense', the duty of which is to dictate rectitude in our transactions with each other; which receives gratification from honest and fair dealing; and which gives birth to the sentiment of justice.[4]

The existence of an innate instinct or faculty of moral sense had been claimed by Hutcheson and the Scottish faculty psychologists but rejected by Gay, Hartley, Paley, James Mill, and Bentham, who argued that all

---

[1] Spencer, 1851, p. 28.    [2] Ibid., p. 23.    [3] Ibid., p. 19.
[4] Ibid., pp. 19–20.

moral feelings were the result of experience, association, and reasoning. The Utilitarian view held that moral judgements should be derived from calculations based on the utility of actions in leading to the greatest happiness for the greatest number and that they should be enforced by the dispensation of rewards and punishments by those in authority. Gall believed that there was an innate faculty which suited men for living in society, which he called 'Moral Sense, Sentiment of Justice and Injustice' (and, variously, 'Goodness', 'Benevolence', and 'Compassion').[1] Gall was cautious in his argument about this faculty. He had discovered it by his usual method of correlating a large cranial prominence with extreme benevolence in three individuals with identical cranial prominences. He inferred that these were manifestations of an exaggerated degree of activity of the 'organ of benevolence'.[2] He felt that he had made an insufficient number of observations to enable him to determine the 'fundamental original destination' of the organ and so, as he expressed it, 'resorted to reasoning'.[3] He concluded 'that goodness or benevolence is only a gradation of the moral sense',[4] which had as its primitive destination to 'dispose man to conduct himself in a manner conformed to the maintenance of social order'.[5] He was not prepared to acknowledge a separate, fundamental quality of conscience and viewed it as an 'affection of the moral sense or of benevolence'.[6] Spurzheim departed from Gall's view and argued for separate faculties of 'Goodness' (Gall's 'Benevolence') and of 'Conscientiousness' or 'Justice'.[7] Combe credits Spurzheim with the discovery of Conscientiousness,[8] but his own account is much fuller. He identifies the phrenological faculty with the Moral Sense doctrine of Cudworth, Hutcheson, Reid, Stewart, and Brown. Combe held that phrenology could settle the issue by providing observations demonstrating 'That a power or faculty exists, the object of which is to produce the sentiment of justice or the feeling of duty and obligation, independently of selfishness, hope of reward, fear of punishment, or any extrinsic motive'.[9] It is the source of feelings of right and wrong.[10]

There is no obvious direct textual link between the details of any of these phrenological formulations and Spencer's. Rather, his argument adopts the form of the phrenological position while the resulting conception of the moral sense is put in the service of his own social theory. Spencer makes the phrenologists' identification between natural needs,

[1] Gall, 1835, V, 156–200.    [2] Ibid., V, 156–7.    [3] Ibid., V, 167.
[4] Ibid., V, 173.    [5] Ibid., V, 167.    [6] Ibid., V, 182.
[7] Spurzheim, 1815, pp. 337–8, 346–52.    [8] Combe, 4th ed., 1836 I, 352.
[9] Ibid., I, 355.    [10] Combe, 2nd ed., 1825, p. 78.

instincts, and faculties, and in illustrating his argument mentions ter of the faculties which are characteristic of phrenology, e.g. parental affection,[1] geometric sense (sense of number),[2] and mechanical sense.[3] He reaches the conclusion that the Utilitarian psychology is inadequate as an account of men's propensities and that the Utilitarian morality can only fail in its attempts at calculation of right and wrong in terms of expediency and by means of reasoning about the greatest good for the greatest number. Instead, one should study the innate propensities of individuals and the environmental conditions to which they answer in order to arrive at a true science of 'Moral Physiology'.[4] The existence of the moral sense insures that the social behaviour which the Utilitarians would legislate for the public good will occur naturally if only the state does not interfere with its ill-conceived artifices.

Spencer's second reason why men will act for the good of others without the need for state action involves his view of the organismic relation between society and its members. Public interests and private ones are essentially in unison, and men have only to realize this. Spencer believes that they will if left alone to discover it.

When, after observing the reactions entailed by breaches of equity, the citizen contemplates the relation in which he stands to the body politic—when he learns that it has a species of life, and conforms to the same laws of growth, organization, and sensibility that a being does—when he finds that one vitality circulates through it and him, and that whilst social health, in a measure depends upon the fulfilment of some function in which he takes part, his happiness depends upon the normal action of every organ in the social body—when he duly understands this, he must see that his own welfare and all men's welfare are inseparable. He must see that whatever

---

[1] Spencer, 1851, p. 21.     [2] Ibid., p. 29.     [3] Ibid., p. 30.

[4] Spencer, 1851, p. 58. The phrenological work which corresponds most closely to Spencer's position is George Combe's *Essay on the Constitution of Man and Its Relations to External Objects* (1827). I have seen no evidence that Spencer read it, but over seventy thousand copies of the work were sold by 1838 (Temkin, 1947, p. 309; cf. pp. 310–12). Combe considers the relations between faculties and environmental conditions more explicitly than Gall had. His view lies somewhere between a radical separation of man from nature and the consistent naturalistic approach to man which came in the wake of the theory of evolution. Man's relation to natural laws was that he could choose to act in harmony with them or not. The relevant analogy is his relations with civil and moral laws, and the argument is conducted in terms of 'infringement' and 'obedience'. These bring rewards or punishments, and happiness or evil befall man in the measure that he obeys or disobeys the laws for which he has been fitted (Combe, 1827, pp. 6, 7, 39, 46). Combe recast phrenological principles in the light of natural theology, and his book should be read with Paley's earlier work and later Bridgewater Treatises of Chalmers and Kidd in mind. Combe is said to have complained that Chalmers' *On the Adaptation of External Nature to the Moral and Intellectual Constitution of Man* (1833) adopted the principles of his *Essay* without referring to it (Temkin, 1947 p. 312). However, it is more likely that they had a common debt to Paley and the tradition of natural theology.

produces a diseased state in one part of the community, must inevitably inflict injury upon all other parts. He must see that his own life can become what it should be, only as fast as society becomes what it should be. In short, he must become impressed with the salutary truth, that no one can be perfectly free till all are free; no one can be perfectly moral till all are moral; no one can be perfectly happy till all are happy.[1]

In spelling out the details of this remarkably optimistic conception, Spencer presents the view of organs and functions which he later argued was all that he retained from phrenology, and on which he based his view of cerebral localization.

A FUNCTION to each organ, and each organ to its own function, is the law of all organization. To do its work well, an apparatus must possess special fitness for that work; and this will amount to *unfitness* for any other work. The lungs cannot digest, the heart cannot respire, the stomach cannot propel blood. Each muscle and each gland must have its own particular nerve. There is not a fibre in the body but what has a channel to bring it food, a channel to take its food away, an agency for causing it to assimilate nutriment, an agency for stimulating it to perform its peculiar duty, and a mechanism to take away effete matter; not one of which can be dispensed with. Between creatures of the lowest type, and creatures of the highest, we similarly find the essential difference to be, that in the one the vital actions are carried on by a few simple agents, whilst in the other the vital actions are severally decomposed into their component parts, and each of these parts has an agent to itself.[2]

Reasoning by analogy from this physiological principle, Spencer argues an organismic view of economic and social relationships. He does this by means of a view of life borrowed from Coleridge, and examples taken from zoology. Life, says Coleridge, consists in the progressive realization of a '*tendency to individuation*'.[3] Spencer gives examples in the animal kingdom to support the thesis that 'By greater individuality of parts—by greater distinctness in the nature and functions of these, are all creatures possessing high vitality distinguished from inferior ones'.[4] Tissues are progressively individuated into separate organs adapted to separate ends.[5] The nervous system is a notable example, and as it becomes progressively individuated, other systems (such as the muscular, repiratory, and circulatory systems) are simultaneously forming separate parts with special functions.[6]

Higher organisms have greater powers and are more self-sufficient and more individual. In man the individuation is most complete, and

[1] Spencer, 1851, pp. 455–6.     [2] Ibid., p. 274.     [3] Ibid., p. 436.
[4] Ibid., p. 438.     [5] Ibid., pp. 438–9.     [6] Ibid., p. 439.

it is best manifested in the progressive evolution of his ability to recog
nize the moral law of equal freedom.[1] Yet this individuation require
mutual dependence in society.[2]

Just that kind of individuality will be acquired which finds in the mo
highly-organized community the fittest sphere for its manifestation—whic
finds in each social arrangement a condition answering to some faculty i
itself—which could not, in fact, expand at all, if otherwise circumstance(
The ultimate man will be one whose private requirements coincide wit
public ones. He will be that manner of man, who, in spontaneously fulfillin
his own nature, incidentally performs the functions of a social unit; and y(
is only enabled so to fulfil his own nature, by all others doing the like.[3]

The identity of personal and social interests leads Spencer to view
society in organismic terms.

We commonly enough compare a nation to a living organism. We speak (
'the body politic', of the functions of its several parts, of its growth, and (
its diseases, as though it were a creature. But we usually employ thes
expressions as metaphors, little suspecting how close is the analogy, and hov
far it will bear carrying out. So completely, however, is a society organize(
upon the same system as an individual being, that we may almost say ther
is something more than analogy between them.[4]

The historical development of society from its lowest to its highes
stages again exemplifies the close analogy to animal organization. 'I
the one extreme there are but few functions, and many similar agent
to each function: in the other, there are many functions, and fe\
similar agents to each function.'[5] There is an ever-increasing divisio
of labour as a result of the increasing subdivision of functions an(
separation of their agents.[6]

There are two justifications for considering these passages fron
*Social Statics* in such detail. The first is to demonstrate the influenc
of phrenological thinking on this seminal work of Spencer's. The facult
psychology which he uses in conducting his arguments and the belie
that different functions are served by different organs throughou
nature came naturally to a formerly ardent student of phrenologica
faculties and their organs. The second justification lies in the relation
of the above passages with his subsequent biological and psychologica
views. For present purposes the passages must be lifted from thei
context and their use in his social theory ignored.[7] Their importanc(

---

[1] Spencer, 1851, p. 440.    [2] Ibid., p. 441.    [3] Ibid., p. 442.
[4] Ibid., p. 448.    [5] Ibid., p. 451.    [6] Ibid., p. 453.
[7] He remained loyal to the organism-society analogy, repeated it in the *Principles (
Biology* (1864, I, 160, 163 ff) and defended it (1908, pp. 570–1). Cf. Albee, 1962, for an analysi
of Spencer's ethical theories in *Social Statics* and his later writings.

to his later thinking is pointed out in two notes to the revised edition in which he comments on the arguments quoted above:

Until now (1890) that [*sic*] I am re-reading *Social Statics* for the purpose of making this abridgment, the above paragraph had remained for these 40 years unremembered. It must have been written in 1849; and it shows that at that date I had entered on the line of thought which, pursued in after years, led to the general law of evolution.[1]

In the generalizations contained in the two above paragraphs, and in the recognition of their parallelism, may be seen the first step towards the general doctrine of Evolution. Dating back as they do to 1850, they show that this first step was taken earlier than I supposed.[2]

Spencer's general theory of evolution and the biological, evolutionary basis of his psychology grew out of the arguments for specialization of functions which he elaborated in the context of his phrenological interests. He later freed his evolutionary psychology from phrenology, and the belief in cerebral localization (which was all that he retained from his earlier allegiance), was based on the general theory of evolution. However, it should be noted that this new basis for a remnant of his phrenological interests had itself grown out of the theory it replaced. In what follows an attempt will be made to trace in detail the development of Spencer's biological view of psychology, its evolutionary basis, and its associationist form.

The development of Spencer's views subsequent to the writing of *Social Statics* involves three closely intertwined themes. The first is the abandonment of the faculty psychology of phrenology in favour of associationism. The second is a change in the foundations of his organ-function view.

He added this to other analogies borrowed from embryology and development to elaborate his general theory of evolution. The novel features of his psychology arise from the union of the concepts of association and evolution and lead to a conception of psychology as a biological science of adaptation. Third, when he returns to the consideration of phrenology, almost as an afterthought in his *Principles of Psychology*, he retains only two aspects of the theory which formerly held his intellectual loyalty. Certain of the phrenological faculties are present in shadow form as the names for complex emotions, but these are no longer fundamental faculties. They are the synthetic products

[1] Spencer, 1892, p. 120, commenting on the passage quoted in part from Spencer, 1851, p. 274. See above, p. 159.
[2] Spencer, 1892, p. 266, commenting on the passage quoted in part from Spencer, 1851, pp. 451–3. See above, p. 160.

of associated individual and racial experiences. The theory of cerebral localization is retained as a corollary of the general theory of evolution from homogeneity to heterogeneity and of the resulting physiological division of labour.

### Spencer's Interest in Psychology: From Faculties to the Association of Ideas

Before the publication of *Social Statics*, Spencer's writings were primarily concerned with engineering topics, education, and government. Shortly after the appearance of his book, he met George Henry Lewes (Spring, 1850). They walked home together discussing the 'development question' (evolution), and Spencer defended the mechanism of inheritance of functional adaptations against the view of the *Vestiges of the Natural History of Creation.*[1]

Their friendship and their many long walks together had important results, including the renewal of Lewes' interest in science and his liaison with George Eliot, to whom Spencer introduced Lewes.[2]

'One result of my friendship with Lewes was that I read some of his books.' A novel did not impress Spencer either way. 'A more important result, however, was that I read his *Biographical History of Philosophy*, then existing in its original four-volumed form. . . . Up to that time questions in philosophy had not attracted my attention.' He had ignored a copy of Locke's *Essay* on his father's shelf and rejected Kant's *Critique of Pure Reason* after reading a few pages in 1844.[3]

It is also true that though, so far as I can remember, I had read no books on either philosophy or psychology, I had gathered in conversations or by references, some conceptions of the general questions at issue. And it is no less true that I had myself, to some extent, speculated upon psychological problems—chiefly in connexion with phrenology. . . . Still, I had not, up to 1851, made the phenomena of mind a subject of deliberate study.[4]

I doubt not that the reading of Lewes's book, while it made me acquainted with the general course of philosophical thought, and with the doctrines which throughout the ages have been the subjects of dispute, gave me an increased interest in psychology, and an interest, not before manifest, in philosophy at large; at the same time that it served, probably, to give more coherence to my own thoughts, previously but loose. No more definite effect, however, at that time resulted, because there had not occurred to me any thought serving as a principle of organization.[5]

---

[1] Spencer, 1908, p. 541.    [2] Cross, n.d., p. 259.    [3] Spencer, 1904, I, 378–9.
[4] Ibid.    [5] Ibid., I, 379.

Just as the reading of Lyell's refutation of Lamarck turned Spencer owards belief in inheritance of acquired characteristics,[1] the reading of Lewes' positivist polemics seems to have turned him towards metaphysics. He wrote to his father in September 1851, that he was absorbed n the subject.[2] Between the autumn of 1851 and the beginning of 1852, Spencer decided to write a book on psychology.[3] He wrote to his father in March, 'I shall shortly begin to read up in preparation for my "Introduction to Psychology".' This was envisaged as the preliminary to a larger work and was to contain its general principles.[4] Within two weeks, he wrote 'I am just beginning to read Mill's Logic. This is my first step towards preparing for my "Introduction to Psychology" which I mean to begin vigorously by and by.'[5] Spencer does not specify the other sources of his psychological development. However, the reading of Mill's Logic[6] and his subsequent writings give ample evidence of the direction his thinking took.

A direct result of his reading of Mill was the formulation of what he considered to be a unifying concept for his psychology. In reflecting on Mill's objections to Whewell, he was led to the formulation of 'The Universal Postulate'.[7] This was Spencer's ultimate criterion of belief: the thesis that 'in the last resort we must accept as true a proposition of which the negation is inconceivable'.[8] First begun in October, 1852, and published as an essay a year later, this conception was expanded into Part I of his Principles of Psychology.[9] Although the connection between this part of his work and the rest is very tenuous indeed, it seems to have had the psychological effect of spurring him on.

Thus it appears that the general interest in mental phenomena . . . which I . . . inferred was increased by reading Lewes's Biographical History of Philosophy in the autumn of 1851, quickly under that stimulus, began to have results. It was there remarked, that some original conception in relation to the subject was needed to give me the requisite spur; and this requirement was, it seems, fulfilled much sooner than I supposed.[10]

[1] See below, pp. 167, 172, 186–90.     [2] Spencer, 1908, p. 67.
[3] Spencer, 1904, I, 391.     [4] Ibid.     [5] Ibid.
[6] The book was a gift from George Eliot. Spencer, 1908, p. 418.
[7] Ibid., p. 544; Spencer, 1904, I, 416.     [8] Spencer, 1904, I, 472.
[9] The article engendered a prolonged controversy with Mill which is not relevant here. However, from the viewpoint of strictly psychological issues Mill was quite right to apologize for this part of Spencer's Principles as 'the very essence of the a priori philosophy' while giving the remainder of the work a qualified recommendation. (Mill, 1867, p. 99.) Mill's opinions changed somewhat toward a more favourable view of Spencer's psychology, though not toward the first part. (Spencer, 1908, pp. 114–5. Cf. Packe, 1954, pp. 431–4; Mill, 1872, p. 557.)
[10] Spencer, 1904, I, 392.

12

Mill's conception of psychology[1] was firmly opposed to the possibilit of deriving a science of character from direct observation of comple behaviour.[2] Nor could it be deduced from physiology. The true 'Law of Mind' were to be found by introspective observation and experiment on actual 'mental successions' and were based on the principle o association.[3] 'The subject, then, of Psychology is the uniformities o succession, the laws, whether ultimate or derivative, according to whic one mental state succeeds another—is caused by, or at least is cause to follow, another.'[4]

In the edition of Mill's *Logic* which Spencer read, the major authoritie cited are James Mill and (to a lesser extent) Hartley, though Bain i given precedence in later editions, and Spencer himself is mentioned. The science of character which Mill proposed was to be called Ethology

The laws of the formation of character are, in short, derivative laws, resulting from the general laws of mind, and are to be obtained by deducing them from those general laws by supposing any given set of circumstances, and then considering what, according to the laws of mind, will be the influenc of those circumstances on the formation of character.[6]

In other words, Ethology, the deductive science, is a system of corollarie from Psychology, the experimental science.[7]

Mill's approach was opposed to phrenology by implication, and he wa also explicitly opposed to it in his writings and activities. He close his discussion of the relations between psychology and physiology by saying,

The latest discoveries in cerebral physiology appear to have proved that any such connection which may exist [between mental peculiarities and any varieties cognisable by our senses in the structure of the cerebral and nervous apparatus] is of a radically different character from that contended for by Gall and his followers, and that whatever may hereafter be found to be the true theory of the subject, phrenology at least is untenable.[8]

When William Carpenter published an extensive review of a phreno-logical work which was scrupulously fair but highly critical of phrenology, Mill wrote to him

I should have been truly vexed not to have heard immediately of such a valuable contribution to science as your paper. I have read it once with great care, but I must read it a second time before I can have completely incorporated it with my system of thought. I have long thought that you

---

[1] Mill, 1872, pp. 552–71.    [2] Ibid., pp. 552–4.    [3] Ibid., pp. 555–6.
[4] Ibid., p. 557.    [5] Ibid., pp. 557, 558.    [6] Ibid., p. 567.
[7] Ibid., p. 569.    [8] Ibid., pp. 561–2.

were the person who would set to rights the pretensions of present and the possibilities of future phrenology; but I did not venture to hope that I should see, so soon, anything approaching in completeness and conclusiveness to this.[1]

Finally, it has been mentioned that Mill is supposed to have convinced Bain to write his critical examination of phrenology as a possible science of character.[2]

The most important concomitant of Spencer's reading of Lewes and Mill is the change that occurred in his psychological views. Whether or not Spencer's change in allegiance can be directly attributed to the reading of Mill's work must remain, for the present, an open question.[3] What is clear is that Spencer's renewed interest in psychology took a form radically different from his earlier phrenological work. He turned from the faculty formulation of phrenology to a belief in associationism. This change can be chronicled with the aid of a remarkable document.

There was another essay written in Spencer's phrenological period. The same letter that mentions the article later rejected by Combe refers to an essay on 'The Force of Expression', which was duly rejected by *Tait's Magazine*. 'It was not without merit; for, ten years after, it was, with improvements, published in the *Westminster Review*, under the title of "The Philosophy of Style".'[4] Spencer revised and developed the original essay during the early autumn of 1852.[5] The result provides an excellent picture of his views in transition.

The aim of the essay was 'to explain the general cause of force in expression'.[6] Its relevance to the development of his psychological views results from the fact that he attempts an explanation in terms of the effect of various stylistic constructions on the mind of the reader. For present purposes the details of his arguments about style are incidental, but the language in which he writes is quite revealing. The essay has a single point, with positive and negative aspects. His positive view is that economy and vividness of verbal expression and arrangement promote ease of understanding; the converse is that there is a danger of fatiguing the reader which must be avoided by suitable variation and balance of verbal constructions. These aspects are illustrated by numerous examples. Were this all, the essay would be most uninteresting to the historian of science.

---

[1] Carpenter, 1888, p. 55. Cf. below, pp. 212–14.
[2] Haldane, 1912, I, 79–80. I have seen no support for this claim in primary sources.
[3] Spencer's MSS in the British Museum should be carefully examined with this question in mind. A brief inspection has not provided any help on Spencer's debt to Mill. Spencer was not generous in acknowledging his intellectual debts.
[4] Spencer, 1904, I, 225.      [5] Ibid., I, 405.      [6] Ibid.

However, there is a point at which the langauge of his argument changes abruptly to the faculty psychology of phrenology. It may even be possible to specify the last sentence that underwent revision, since the following one contains the first mention of faculties, and the whole of the remainder of the essay is expressed in terms of faculties and groups of faculties, their exercise and exhaustion.[1] The negative expression of Spencer's thesis is 'that the sensitiveness of the faculties must be husbanded'.[2] The emotions he refers to are those of reverence, approbation, beauty. The different effects of words is 'dependent on the different states of our faculties'.[3]

The language in which he makes the positive point is that of the association psychology. Force of expression is achieved by means of the greatest economy of mental 'energy', 'effort', 'power', or 'attention'. The mental law governing the effects of forms of expression is that of association. The mental contents to which he refers are images, ideas, and their respective elements. The mental functions involved are attention, imagination, memory, and concentration. Until near the end of the positive statement of his thesis the language is uniformly associationist.[4]

All Spencer's subsequent writings employ the language and assumptions of associationist psychology.

There is one further point to be made about this remarkable snapshot of a mind in transition. It is not the case that the last portion of 'The Philosophy of Style' was left untouched, for the closing paragraph reveals another manifestation of the development of Spencer's psychology: the first extension of his concept of evolution to superorganic phenomena.[5] In order to appreciate the significance of the union of association psychology and his theory of evolution it will be necessary to look further into the development of his view of evolution. For the

[1] The point of transition occurs at Spencer, 1901, II, 360. The last sentence in associationist language refers to 'mental energy' and 'strain on the attention'. The next sentence contains the first mention of 'perceptive faculties'.

[2] Ibid., II, 364.

[3] Ibid. The subsequent development of Spencer's views is reflected in the fact that, in commenting on this essay in his *Autobiography*, he uses neither the language of association psychology nor that of phrenological faculties. His review of the thesis of the article is given in terms of nervous energy and the sensibility of nervous structures. (Spencer, 1904, I, 405–6.)

[4] The MS of this essay which Spencer deposited in the British Museum neither supports nor detracts from my reading. In particular, it shows no break at the point where the language changes to that of faculty psychology (MS., p. 113), and faculty language does not appear to have been deleted or replaced in the earlier portions of the MS. Since the last sentence contains reference to a view which he did not hold until 1851, one may conclude that it was probably a recopy of the revised version.

[5] Spencer, 1901, II, 366–7.

present one should note the union of the old phrenological psychology with the new faith in associationism and an embryonic form of his concept of evolution in the revision of this essay from his phrenological period.

## The Development of Spencer's General Theory of Evolution

Spencer claimed that a belief in evolution had been latent in him since boyhood. He held that the view was implicit in the habit which his father had encouraged of seeking natural causes of phenomena. This entailed a disbelief in miracles, and therefore a relinquishment of the creed of special creation. This process was occurring during his early manhood. It was rather far-fetched for Spencer to claim retrospectively that the inevitable corollary of belief in the universality of natural causation was a belief in evolution, since this corollary had escaped so many scientists and philosophers for centuries.[1]

The first explicit convictions on evolution came from reading Lyell's *Principles of Geology* when he was twenty. The argument *against* Lamarck in Lyell's work led Spencer to a partial acceptance of both the transmutation of species and the mechanism of inheritance of acquired characters.[2] His belief in evolution never wavered, though the particular way he expressed and applied it underwent considerable development.

It has already been noted that Spencer later saw the remarks on progressive specialization of function in animals and in societies, which appeared in *Social Statics*, as 'the earliest foreshadowing of the general doctrine of Evolution'.[3] The examples used in that work were largely drawn from T. Rymer Jones' *A General Outline of the Animal Kingdom*. What he took from Jones was the idea of progression from simple creatures, where the duties of all structures are performed by one tissue, to more complex organisms where separate organs are adapted to separate ends.[4] Spencer had drawn from this the analogy of increasing subdivision of functions in the development of society.[5] However, in both cases the concept of development used in this work 'involving as it did the idea of function along with the idea of structure, . . . was limited to organic phenomena'.[6]

Spencer encountered two phrases in the next two years which consolidated his concept of evolution and freed it from this limitation.

[1] Spencer, 1904, II, 6–7.　[2] Spencer, 1904, I, 176–7. Spencer, 1904, II, 6–7.
[3] Spencer, 1908, p. 541.　[4] Spencer, 1851, pp. 436–40. Cf. pp. 274–5.
[5] Ibid., pp. 451–3.　[6] Spencer, 1904, II, 9.

The first of these came from 'a little book just published by Milne-Edwards' which Spencer and Lewes took with them on one of their excursions in 1851:[1] 'the physiological division of labour'. This succinct expression had the effect of sharpening the views of development he put forth in *Social Statics*.[2]

The second phrase was discovered in W. M. Carpenter's *Principles of Physiology* (1851), which Spencer was reviewing: von Baer's formula that 'the development of every organism is a change from homogeneity to heterogeneity'.[3] Though von Baer limited the concept to the development of individual organisms, it was felt by Spencer to provide a general formulation which could be applied to evolution beyond the organic world. The first extension of the general concept of evolution crept into the end of the essay on 'The Philosophy of Style'. He says that a perfect composition will 'answer to the description of all highly-organized products both of man and nature. It will be, not a series of like parts simply placed in juxtaposition, but one whole made up of unlike parts that are mutually dependent'. On the adjoining page it is suggested that progress in style 'must produce increasing heterogeneity in our modes of expression'.[4]

[1] Spencer, 1908, p. 542. Henri Milne-Edwards (1800–85) was a noted French zoologist and a pupil of Cuvier. He worked mainly on invertebrate comparative anatomy. See Nordenskiöld, 1928, p. 425. Spencer does not mention the title of the work he read, but it was probably *Outlines of Anatomy and Physiology* (1850) or possibly *Introduction à la zoologie générale* (1851). The work and the principle of the division of labour are considered, along with Milne-Edwards' career, in Russell, 1916, pp. 195–200. Milne-Edwards believed in a sort of descent theory but rejected any explanation in terms of natural causes (Ibid., pp. 244–5).

[2] Spencer, 1904, II, 166; Cf. Spencer, 1864, I, 160 and Spencer, 1908, pp. 570–1.

[3] Spencer, 1904, II, 8–9. Karl Ernst von Baer (1792–1876), a German zoologist, was the most distinguished and influential of the early nineteenth-century embryologists. His work was the culmination of previous embryology and 'the point of departure of all that was to follow'. It was he who converted embryology from philosophic speculation to a laboratory science. His embryological law of development of special heterogeneous structures from general homogeneous ones played an important, if confusing, part in the history of evolutionary theory, and Carpenter's exposition of his work was at the centre of the issue. Both Darwin and Spencer twisted Von Baer's work for their own evolutionary purposes. In fact, he was opposed to organic evolution 'root and branch' and devoted his last years to an attempt at destroying Darwin's work by removing the embryological supports which Darwin considered crucial. Darwin's use of von Baer's work to support recapitulation was diametrically opposed to the latter's conclusions. This story is exhaustively told in two excellent essays in Glass, *et al.*, 1959; Oppenheimer, Jane. An Embryological Enigma in the *Origin of Species* (pp. 292–322), from which the above evaluation is taken, and Lovejoy, Arthur O., 'Recent Criticism of the Darwinian Theory of Recapitulation: Its Grounds and Its Initiator (pp. 438–58). Lovejoy notes the similarity of von Baer's formulation in embryology to Spencer's doctrine of the evolution of the universe, but he is unaware of the direct link. He remarks, however, that Spencer's use of the formula was 'essentially different from and opposed to the ideas of his German predecessor'. (Ibid., p. 447.) Cf. Nordenskiöld, 1928, pp. 363–6, etc.: Russell, 1916, Chapter IX, etc.

[4] Spencer, 1901, II, 366–7. Spencer, 1904, I, 406; Spencer, 1904, II, 9.

He had explicitly declared for organic evolution several months before (March, 1852) in an essay on 'The Development Hypothesis',[1] where it was argued that evolution of species is a much less implausible hypothesis than special creation, and the persistence of the latter view was attributed to ignorance and prejudice. He does not claim that actual changes of species can be demonstrated or the modifying influences identified, but argues that analogies to such processes are all around us, for example, continuous series can be drawn between distinct geometrical shapes and the development of a man from a single cell.[2]

After writing 'The Development Hypothesis', 'the evolutionary interpretation of things in general became habitual'.[3] It was applied in various forms in essays written in 1853–4, and these applications led naturally to his treatment of psychology where it became the central concept of his *Principles*.

## The Writing of the Principles of Psychology in Terms of Evolutionary Adaptation and Correspondence

The simplest description of the *Principles of Psychology* is that it united the association psychology with the theory of evolution. However, it was not evolution itself but the view which Spencer took of the development of mind which 'originated the book and gave its most distinctive character'.[4] His expositor put the point more clearly than Spencer: 'Two fundamental ideas rule the psychology of Mr Herbert Spencer: that of the continuity of psychological phenomena; that of the intimate relation between the being and its medium. These two points virtually contain his doctrine.'[5] No psychologists except Gall and his followers had so emphatically made the connection of mind with life, and the adaptation of the mental functions to the environment, central to their views. Certainly no one in the associationist tradition had gone so far in substituting a biological approach for the traditional epistemological one. In fact, there is evidence that Spencer's phrenological interests played an important part in his conception of psychology as a biological science of adaptation.

Adaptation was a major issue in *Social Statics*, and Spencer's conception of it was derived directly from phrenology. In attacking the general formulation of the Utilitarians, he criticized its failure to take account

---

[1] Spencer, 1901, I, 1–7.
[2] This essay and the *Principles of Psychology* were recognized by Darwin as legitimate anticipations of his own view. (Darwin, 6th ed., 1928 p. 13.) He refers to 'your excellent essay on Development' in a letter to Spencer. (Spencer, 1908, p. 98.) Cf. below pp. 188–92.
[3] Spencer, 1908, p. 544.    [4] Ibid., p. 546.    [5] Ribot, 1873, p. 158.

of individual and racial differences. 'Adaptation of constitution to conditions' was the cause of all physical and mental differences among men.[1] The goal of his social theory was the attainment of 'congruity between the faculties and their spheres of action'.[2] This leads to fulfilment, gratification, and genuine happiness.[3] As long as the state does not interfere and try to create an artificial identity of interests based on an erroneous belief in a uniform human nature, 'this nonadaptation of an organism to its conditions is ever being rectified; and modification of one or both, continues until the adaptation is complete'.[4]

These views were at two removes from Gall. The popular phrenologists who had influenced Spencer, especially Spurzheim and Combe, had abandoned Gall's belief in fixed mental endowment and held that the faculties could be considerably altered by exercise. Spencer's meliorism went still further to a belief in the inevitability of progress:

Organs, faculties, powers, capacities, or whatever else we call them, grow by use and diminish from disuse, [and] it is inferred that they will continue to do so. And if this inference is unquestionable, then is the one above deduced from it—that humanity must in the end become completely adapted to its conditions—unquestionable also. Progress, therefore, is not an accident, but a necessity.[5]

This remarkable belief was the conclusion to his argument that all maladaptation and imperfection would disappear if only the excesses or defects of faculties could be allowed to correct themselves by natural intercourse with the appropriate conditions of existence.[6] Spencer alluded to these views in reviewing the development of his psychology.

An early-impressed belief in the increase of faculty by exercise in the individual, and the subsequently accepted idea of adaptation as a universal principle of bodily life, now took, when contemplating the phenomena of mind, an appropriately modified form.[7]

This modification was formulated in 1853, as he was accumulating memoranda and preparing to begin the book.[8] He had arrived at a definition of life as 'the co-ordination of actions'. In applying this to psychology it

---

[1] Spencer, 1851, p. 61.    [2] Ibid., p. 59.    [3] Ibid., pp. 466–7.
[4] Ibid., pp. 59–60.    [5] Ibid., p. 65; cf. Young, 1969, pp. 134–7, 141.
[6] Ibid., p. 64. Cf. pp. 457, 460–1.    [7] Spencer, 1904, II, 11.    [8] Spencer, 1908, p. 74.

equired to be supplemented by recognition of the relations borne by such
o-ordinated actions to connected actions in the environment. There at
nce followed the idea that the growth of a correspondence between inner
nd outer actions had to be traced up from the beginning; so as to show the
vay in which Mind gradually evolves out of Life. This was, I think, the
hought which originated the book and gave its most distinctive chararacter;
ut evidently, the tendency to regard all things as evolved, which had been
rowing more pronounced, gave another special interest to the undertaking.[1]

Thus, when Spencer began writing the *Principles* in August, 1854,
t was Part III, the 'General Synthesis' that he wrote first.[2] 'Progressive
daptation became increasing adjustment of inner subjective relations
o outer objective relations—increasing correspondence between the
wo.'[3] The adaptive view is unified with evolution from homogeneity
o heterogeneity.

Previous association psychologists had been concerned with the
onnections among mental phenomena. Natural scientists had con-
entrated on the connections between external phenomena. The
epistemological bias of the Lockean tradition connected these two
domains in terms of a knowing mind and its objects. The aim of
Spencer's psychology was neither the connections among internal
phenomena nor among external phenomena nor within knowledge
tself.

Hence, then, as in all cases we may consider the external phenomena as
simply in relation, and the internal phenomena also as simply in relation;
the broadest and most complete definition of life will be—*The continuous
adjustment of internal relations to external relations.*[4]
. . . not only does the definition, as thus expressed, comprehend all those
activities, bodily and mental, which constitute our ordinary idea of life; but
it also comprehends, both those processes of growth by which the organism
is brought into general fitness for those activities, and those after-processes
of adaptation by which it is specially fitted to its special activities.[5]

Mental phenomena are defined within this context as 'incidents of the
correspondence between the organism and its environment'.[6]
The correspondence between life and its circumstances is treated
in successive chapters as 'direct and homogeneous', as 'direct but
heterogeneous', as extending in space and time, as increasing in speci-
ality, generality, and complexity, as coordinated and as integrated.

[1] Spencer, 1908, pp. 545–6.    [2] Ibid., p. 546. Cf. Spencer, 1904, I, 460–1.
[3] Spencer, 1904, II, 11.    [4] Spencer, 1855, p. 374.    [5] Ibid., p. 375.
[6] Ibid., p. 584.

The degree of life varies with the degree of correspondence. Bodily and mental life are but species of life in general. Mind 'emerges out of bodily life and becomes distinguished from it, in proportion as these several traits of the correspondence become more marked'.[1]

In adhering to the principle of continuity (perhaps more completely and consistently than any previous writer except Leibniz), Spencer was bound to apply his evolutionary view to the various categories of physiological and psychological manifestations. He held that no truly valid demarcations could exist among simple irritations, reflexes, their compounding into instincts, the beginning of conscious life, and the highest manifestations of intelligence—memory, reason, sentiment, and will. Memory, for example, is dawning instinct, and instinct is organized memory.[2]

## Spencer's Evolutionary Associationism as an Advance on Gall and on Traditional Sensationalism

The foregoing story of Spencer's development provides the necessary foundation for understanding both the implications of his psychology for the associationist tradition, and its bearing on some of the issues raised by Gall. Spencer's concept of mental evolution was at once an integration of his view of adaptation with that of development from homogeneity to heterogeneity, and an expression of his adherence to the association psychology. It has been noted that the reading of Lyell had turned Spencer toward a Lamarckian view of evolution. In 'The Development Hypothesis' the only mention of a mechanism is the statement that animals and plants, when placed in new conditions, undergo changes fitting them for their new environment. In successive generations these changes continue 'until, ultimately, the new conditions become the natural ones'.[3] In reviewing his application of this view to psychological phenomena, Spencer says,

The familiar doctrine of association here undergoes a great extension; for it is held that not only in the individual do ideas become connected when in experience the things producing them have repeatedly occurred together, but that such results of repeated occurrences accumulate in successions of individuals: the effects of associations are supposed to be transmitted as modifications of the nervous system.[4]

[1] Spencer, 1904, I, 470.
[2] Ribot, 1873, pp. 149, 189. For a very clear exposition of Spencer see Ibid., pp. 124–93.
[3] Spencer, 1901, I, 3.     [4] Spencer, 1904, I, 470.

In the light of Spencer's development this extension presents itself as the natural next step. Its simplicity is deceptive. In fact, the application of evolution to psychology has consequences which are yet to be fully exploited, but the present analysis must be confined to its effects on psychological issues in the mid-nineteenth century. Spencer provided an evolutionary theory which mediated between the conflicting claims of Gall's psychology and the Lockean tradition of sensation-association.

The choice for Locke in explaining the origin of knowledge was between innate ideas and sensationalism. He opted equivocally for the latter, and Condillac unequivocally made the choice for a *tabula rasa* view of mind. The attempt to build a psychology on this epistemological thesis had been faced with serious limitations which centred around a vehement objection to any endowment that suggested that mental phenomena were innate. Evolutionary associationism was incompatible with a simple *tabula rasa* view of mind.

To rest with the unqualified assertion that, antecedent to experience, the mind is a blank, is to ignore the all-essential questions—whence comes the power of organizing experiences? whence arise the different degrees of that power possessed by different races of organisms, and different individuals of the same race? If, at birth, there exists nothing but a passive receptivity of impressions, why should not a horse be as educable as a man? Or, should it be said that language makes the difference, then why should not the cat and dog, out of the same household experiences, arrive at equal degrees and kinds of intelligence? Understood in its current form, the experience-hypothesis implies that the presence of a definitely organized nervous system is a circumstance of no moment—a fact not needing to be taken into account! Yet it is the all-important fact—the fact . . . without which an assimilation of experiences is utterly inexplicable.[1]

These are the same objections that Gall made to sensationalism: it could not explain individual and species differences, and it ignored the fundamental importance of the biological endowment of varying brain structures. In fact, Lewes credited Gall with settling the issue with which Spencer is concerned.

Gall may be said to have definitively settled the dispute between the partisans of innate ideas and the partisans of Sensationalism, by establishing the connate tendencies, both affective and intellectual, which belong to the organic structure of man . . . all the fundamental tendencies are connate, and can no more be created by precept and education than they can be abolished by denunciation and punishment.[2]

[1] Spencer, 1855, pp. 580–1.
[2] Lewes, 1857, p. 633. The edition of Lewes' book which Spencer read did not include the chapter on Gall. It was added in the second edition, which is quoted here. Cf. Young, 1966. p. 39 (fn. 77).

Although Spencer echoed Gall's objections and his emphasis on biological endowment and adaptation, he could accept neither the view of nature nor the faculty psychology on which Gall's arguments were based. Gall saw organic life in terms of the static chain of being. The cerebral endowments of species were part of an eternally fixed order of nature, and he believed that the organs were added in a stepwise fashion. The endowments of individuals were also given at birth, and the role left for experience was very meagre indeed. In his extreme reaction to the sensationalists in the name of biological endowment, Gall had moved dangerously close to a belief in innate ideas. In pursuing their epistemological interests the sensationalists had clearly committed biological absurdities. Similarly, Gall had pursued his biological and social interests faithfully and incidentally had talked philosophical nonsense. Much of the reaction to his psychology was the result of the supposed relation of faculties to innate ideas. In his zeal to show the continuity of human behaviour with that of animals he had collapsed the distinction between instincts and the most complex manifestations of human intelligence. Thus, the laws of various pure and applied sciences were supposed to be innately given as instincts in animals with striking talents and in human geniuses.[1] The charge against Gall that he adhered to belief in innate ideas was therefore not without foundation.

Others had noted the relations between biologically endowed instincts and innate ideas. For example, Johannes Mueller says, 'The expression of Cuvier with reference to instinct is very correct. He says, that animals in their acts of instinct are impelled by an innate idea,— as it were, by a dream'.[2] In sharing this view Mueller argued, 'That innate ideas may exist, cannot in the slightest degree be denied: it is, indeed, a fact. All the ideas of animals, which are induced by instinct, are innate and immediate; something presented to the mind, a desire to attain which is at the same time given. The new-born lamb and foal have such innate ideas, which lead them to follow their mother and suck the teats'.[3] However, he was not prepared to extend this equation to man. To the question, 'Is it not in some measure the same with the intellectual ideas of man?'[4] he replied with an emphatic denial and reverted to the arguments of the sensationalists. The general intellectual ideas of man result solely from 'the mutual reaction of allied perceptions amongst themselves'.[5] He believed in fixed endowment where

[1] Gall, 1835, V, 48, 51, 65–6, 82–3.    [2] Mueller, 1842, p. 947.
[3] Ibid., p. 1347.    [4] Ibid.    [5] Ibid., p. 1348. Cf. pp. 948–9.

animals were concerned, and in sensationalism in human intelligence. In addressing himself to this extremely confused set of explanations and assumptions, Spencer had first to answer the argument of special creation in the name of evolution, and then to mediate the conflicting claims of the sensationalists and those who employed the concept of instinct. His first attack was on the special creation hypothesis on which Gall had based his objections to the sensationalists. Gall had argued the innate endowment of a pre-established harmony between a faculty and its proper objects in the environment. Speaking of this adjustment of psychical cohesions to relations among objects in the environment, Spencer says,

Concerning their adjustment, there appear to be but two possible hypotheses, of which all other hypotheses can be but variations. It may on the one hand be asserted, that the strength of the tendency which each particular state of consciousness has to follow any other, is fixed beforehand by a Creator— that there is a pre-established harmony between the inner and outer relations. On the other hand it may be asserted, that the strength of the tendency which each particular state of consciousness has to follow any other, depends upon the frequency with which the two have been connected in experience— that the harmony between the inner and outer relations, arises from the fact, that the outer relations produce the inner relations.[1]

Spencer believed that there was no real evidence to support the special creation hypothesis. Speaking, though not directly, to Gall's view, he says,

That the inner cohesions of psychical states are pre-adjusted to the outer persistencies of the relations symbolized, is a supposition which, if taken in its full meaning, involves absurdities so many and great that none dare carry it beyond a limited range of cases.[2]

On the other hand, the supposition that the inner cohesions are adjusted to the outer persistencies by an accumulated experience of those outer persistencies, is in harmony with all our positive knowledge of mental phenomena.[3]

The evidence commonly cited to illustrate the doctrine of the association of ideas made the evidence for the 'experience hypothesis' overwhelming.[4]

However, he also took account of the fact that the major barriers to the rejection of special creation were the phenomena of reflex action,

[1] Spencer, 1855, p. 523.    [2] Ibid., pp. 527–8.
[3] Ibid., p. 528.    [4] Ibid., pp. 525–6.

instinct, and the 'forms of thought' in man. 'But should these phenomena be otherwise explicable, the hypothesis must be regarded as altogether gratuitous.'[1] Since Spencer's answer is the same for all three of these sets of phenomena—evolution and association—the present discussion will centre on the one which was historically most troublesome.

The concept of instinct had been the traditional enemy of both evolution and associationism. It had been cited as conclusive evidence of special creation and design.[2] Gall held this view. Indeed, animal instinct was chosen as the topic of one of the eight *Bridgewater Treatises* in which natural theologians defended design by showing God's handi work throughout creation.[3] Conversely, Darwin's *Origin*, published four years after Spencer's *Principles*, contained a chapter devoted to an attempt to explain how instincts could evolve by natural selection. He considered this issue one of the most formidable objections to his theory.[4] The antagonism between the association psychology and explanations in terms of instincts goes back to the inception of the school. The founding of the psychology of association occurred in the Rev. John Gay's assertion of the possibility of deducing the moral sense and all our passions from the pleasure-pain principle and association.[5] Gay's dissertation was written in explicit opposition to Hutcheson's claim that moral sentiments and disinterested affections are innately given to the mind as instincts.[6] Gay's answer to Hutcheson was:

Our approbation of Morality, and all Affections whatsoever, are finally resolvable into *Reason* pointing out *private Happiness*, and are conversant only about things apprehended to be means tending to this end; and that whenever this end is not perceived, they are to be accounted for from the *Association of Ideas*, and may properly enough be call'd *Habits*.[7]

Although Hutcheson's view may not in itself have been 'a-kin to the Doctrine of *Innate Ideas*, yet I think it relishes too much of that of *Occult Qualities*'.[8] Gay goes on to argue that 'as some Men have imagin'd *Innate Ideas*, because forgetting how they came by them; so others have set up almost as many distinct *Instincts* as there are *acquired Principles* of acting'.[9] The psychological aspect of Hartley's associationism is an elaboration of this opposition to explanation in terms of instinct.[10]

---

[1] Spencer, 1855, pp. 523–4.     [2] Baldwin, 1913, II, 87–8.
[3] Kirby, 1835. Cf. Gillespie, 1959, pp. 209–16, 244–5.
[4] Darwin, reprinted, 1950, Chapter VII, especially pp. 207–8.
[5] Gay, 2nd ed., 1732. Cf. Halévy, 1952, pp. 7–9; Albee, 1962, pp. 78–90.
[6] Gay, 1732, p. xxxi.     [7] Ibid., p. xxxii.     [8] Ibid.     [9] Ibid., p. liii.
[10] Hartley, 1749; Halévy, 1952, pp. 7–9; Macintosh, 1860, p. 380; Willey, 1962, pp. 134–7.

Five years later (1754) Condillac argued from his extreme sensationalism to the position that instincts were acquired habits which an individual derived from sensations and had ceased to reflect about. This explanation left no way of accounting for the identity of instincts within species and their marked differences between species. It is not surprising therefore to find that the judgement made on eighteenth century associationism was that, 'All attempts to explain instinct by this principle have hitherto been unavailing'.[1] The aim had been to explain them *away*. After attention was explicitly turned to the comparative study of instincts within evolutionary psychology, Romanes judged the major nineteenth-century associationists prior to Spencer as follows: 'Mill, from ignoring the broad facts of heredity in the region of psychology, may be said to deserve no hearing on the subject of instinct; and the same, though in a lesser degree, is to be remarked of Bain.'[2] It is with Spencer that Romanes begins the serious debate on instinct and opposes Spencer's view in favour of Darwin's.[3] J. S. Mill had granted the existence of instincts and admitted that the association psychology could not explain them.

No mode has been suggested, even by way of hypothesis, in which these [human and animal instincts] can receive any satisfactory, or even plausible, explanation from psychological causes alone; and there is great reason to think that they have as positive, and even as direct and immediate, a connexion with physical conditions of the brain and nerves as any of our mere sensations have.[4]

Nevertheless, both he and Bain persisted in the belief that moral feelings or the moral sense were acquired by each individual during his lifetime. Darwin was hesitant about quarreling with Mill but claimed that 'it can hardly be disputed that the social feelings are instinctive or innate in the lower animals; and why should they not be so in man? . . . The ignoring of all transmitted mental qualities will, as it seems to me, be hereafter judged as a most serious blemish in the works of Mr Mill'.[5] Of Bain's view, he said, 'On the general theory of evolution this is at least extremely improbable'.[6] Spencer wrote to Mill that the evolutionary theory could account for an innate moral sense.

I believe that the experiences of utility organized and consolidated through all past generations of the human race, have been producing corresponding nervous modifications, which, by continued transmission and accumulation,

[1] Macintosh, 1860, p. 379.    [2] Romanes, 1883, p. 256.    [3] Ibid., pp. 256–62.
[4] Mill, 1872, p. 561.    [5] Darwin, 2nd ed., 1874, p. 98.    [6] Ibid.

have become in us certain faculties of moral intuition—certain emotions responding to right and wrong conduct, which have no apparent basis in the individual experience of utility.[1]

The innate moral sense that Spencer had argued in *Social Statics* was thus retained, but its basis was changed from endowment in the form of a phrenological faculty to endowment in the form of accumulated species experience.

Where instinctual phenomena had effectively opposed the separate positions of evolution and associationism, Spencer believed that they could be explained by the unified view of evolutionary associationism. 'The doctrine that the connections among our ideas are determined by experience, must, in consistency, be extended not only to all the connections established by the accumulated experiences of every individual but to all those established by the accumulated experiences of every race.'[2] Given this general principle, all the phenomena of life and mind can be explained in terms of the experience hypothesis.[3] The application of this view to reflex and instinct disposes of their opposition to associationism and the basis of this objection in the belief in pre-established harmony.

Though it is manifest that reflex and instinctive sequences are not determined by the experiences of the *individual* organism manifesting them; yet there still remains the hypothesis that they are determined by the experiences of the *race* of organisms forming its ancestry, which by infinite repetition in countless successive generations have established these sequences as organic relations: and all the facts that are accessible to us, go to support this hypothesis. Hereditary transmission, displayed alike in all the plants we cultivate, in all the animals we breed, and in the human race, applies not only to physical but to psychical peculiarities.[4]

By replacing the *tabula rasa* of the individual with that of the race, Spencer was able to retain the basic position of sensationalism while recognizing the inherited biological endowments in the nervous system, and avoiding the risk of the rationalist belief in innate ideas. The term 'innate' thereby lost its Cartesian terrors for the empiricist. Baldwin puts the position succinctly by saying that he replaced 'Condillac's individual human statue by a racial animal colossus, so to speak'.[5] And, most important for the present purposes, he gave the statue an

[1] Quoted in Bain, 1875, p. 722. Bain has provided a very useful history of pre-evolutionary views on the moral faculty (1875, pp. 448–751).
[2] Spencer, 1855, p. 529.    [3] Ibid.    [4] Ibid., p. 526.
[5] Baldwin, 1913, II, 84.

evolving nervous system and thus avoided the other rationalist fallacy of referring mental endowments solely to an immaterial mind.

The reduction of all distinction between instinct and the highest intellectual operation of the human mind which Gall felt was required by his biological, anti-sensationalist view could be abandoned when it became appreciated that the higher operations could evolve out of simple reflexes and instincts, and that the primitive could co-exist with the more advanced. Finally, the analytic principle and the genetic method which had been the central thesis of the Lockean tradition (and its main contributions to philosophy, psychology, and science) were retained and extended to a much wider domain. Gall had found it necessary to fall short of a rigorous application of the principle of continuity in order to give some reality to the faculties which he felt to be the important variables in behaviour. Spencer made it possible to retain a consistent application of continuity in the evolution of relatively stable functions, while still granting their reality and efficacy for the individual. Psychology was freed from the static adaptations of Gall's innate faculties and the more general application of the pre-established harmony of the special creation view. All of this was achieved by the comparatively simple expedients of (1) placing the principle of continuity on a temporal basis for the race; (2) extending the principles of the psychology of sensation and association to include the dynamic interactions between an organism and its environment; (3) stabilizing the results of these interactions in the nervous systems of various species.

Having provided himself with a uniform explanatory principle, Spencer applied it to the evolution of mind from the contraction of a sensitive polyp on irritation, and through the development of specialized tissues—nerves for irritation and muscles for movement. The simple reflex is the transitional point of nervous differentiation from the merely physical.[1] Instincts are complex reflexes whereby a combination of impressions produces a combination of contractions.[2] This increasing complexity involves such phenomena as the recognition of prey or a predator, and the activities necessary for capture or flight.[3] Still more complex correspondences lose their indivisibility, become dissociated, and occur independently. The impression is freed from both the immediate presence of the stimulus and the requirement for immediate response.[4] This is the dawn of conscious memory. Reason is but one

[1] Spencer, 1855, pp. 533–8.    [2] Ibid., p. 542.    [3] Ibid., pp. 539–53.
[4] Ibid., pp. 555–63.

13

more step in the developing complexity of relations of inner to outer—a further part of the insensible evolution. Both memory and reasoned action tend to lapse into automatism.[1] As a last step, the 'forms of thought', the last bastion of the rationalist position, are absorbed into the sensationalist explanation. Space, time, causation, and so on, became explicable.

Finally, on rising up to human faculties, regarded as organized results of this intercourse between the organism and the environment, there was reached the conclusion that the so-called forms of thought are the outcome of the process of perpetually adjusting inner relations to outer relations, fixed relations in the environment producing fixed relations in the mind. And so came a reconciliation of the *a priori* view with the experiential view.[2]

In addressing himself to the issue which had exercised epistemologists at least since Plato, and which is one of the thorniest questions of modern philosophy, Spencer implicitly asserts that such questions must henceforth be seen as psychological and therefore as biological. The answer which Spencer gave to the old question of the origin of ideas came not from metaphysics but from heredity. At this point the development of psychology from a branch of speculative metaphysics to a biological science is, in principle, complete. However, it will become abundantly clear that what was conceived in principle in 1855 has yet to be thoroughly applied in practice.

### Implications of Evolutionary Associationism for Traditional Issues

Associationists had always been opposed to faculty psychology, but before their view had been joined to evolution they could offer no convincing alternative. For example, Bain merely asserted that the principle of association of ideas was adequate to supersede and explain all the phenomena formerly attributed to the faculties of the Lockean tradition.[3] In dealing with the phrenological faculties in *On the Study of Character*, he argued that these were not fundamental, that they could be reduced to one of the classes of his own theory, and that these, in turn, could be explained by the laws of association and the pleasure-pain principle. But he had no convincing explanation for the enduring features of mental experience and behaviour. Spencer could provide an explanation of the development of the various modes of manifestation of intelligence and grant their relative stability in the species without making them distinct mental agents. His evolutionary associationism freed him from the usual procedure of starting at birth with a

[1] Spencer, 1855, pp. 568–9.     [2] Spencer, 1908, p. 547.     [3] Bain, 1868, p. 693.

*tabula rasa* and explaining the development of the complex phenomena of instinct, emotion, and intellectual functions on the basis of individual experience alone.

Spencer grants that there are valid differences among the various 'modes of intelligence known as Instinct, Memory, Reason, Feeling, Will, and the rest'.[1] However, in their true nature they are only phases of correspondence, and their genesis is by insensible degrees. He considers the faculties and emotions neither fundamental nor distinct nor part of a fixed endowment. 'Intelligence has neither distinct grades, nor is constituted of faculties that are truly independent; but that its highest phenomena are the effects of a complication that has arisen by insensible steps out of the simplest elements.' There are no valid demarcations. Classifications of faculties

can be but superficially true. Instinct, Reason, Perception, Conception, Memory, Imagination, Feeling, Will, etc., etc., can be nothing more than either conventional groupings of the correspondences; or subordinate divisions among the various operations which are instrumental in effecting the correspondences. However widely contrasted they may seem, these various forms of intelligence cannot be anything else than either particular modes in which the adjustment of inner to outer relations is achieved; or particular parts of the process of adjustment.[2]

The phrenological faculties retained none of their independent status as mental agents in Spencer's psychology. After his conversion to associationism they were retained only as the names of the emotions.[3] The emotions are not included in the analytic chapters of the *Principles of Psychology*. Indeed, the whole analytic half of the work is singularly uninteresting for present purposes. The 'General Analysis' consists of an expanded version of his defence of realism and his criterion of belief—the Universal Postulate. The 'Special Analysis' is old-style epistemological psychology—analysis of the forms of reasoning, perceptions of external objects, space, time, motion, and so on, and various mental relations. The aim of this part of his work is the traditional analysis of complex mental phenomena into their elements, explaining their cohesions by means of the laws of association.[4] The interest which the work holds for the modern reader is confined to those parts in which the old-style associationism is recast in an evolutionary framework.

[1] Spencer, 1855, pp. 486–7.    [2] Ibid., p. 486.
[3] Ibid., pp. 601–2; Spencer, 1901, I, 251.
[4] This part is summarized in Spencer, 1904, I, 471.

The treatment which Spencer gives to the emotions in the *Principle of Psychology* is but one more application of his evolutionary associationism to the synthesis of complex mental phenomena.

The progress from the initial forms of feeling to those complicated forms of it seen in human beings, equally harmonizes with the general principles of evolution that have been laid down. Arising, as it does, when the automatic actions, from increasing complexity and decreasing frequency, become hesitating; and consisting, as it then does, of nothing more than the group of sensations received and the nascent motor changes aroused by them; feeling step by step developes [*sic*] into larger and more varied aggregations of psychical states—sometimes purely impressional, sometimes nascently impres sional or ideal; sometimes purely motor, sometimes nascently motor; but very frequently including in one combination, immediate impressions and the ideas of other impressions, with immediate actions and the ideas of other actions. And this formation of larger and more varied aggregations of psychical states, necessarily results from the accumulating cohesions of psychical states that are connected in experience. Just as we saw that the advance from the simplest to the most complex forms of cognition, was explicable on the principle that the outer relations produce the inner relations; so, we shall see that this same principle supplies an explanation of the advance from the simplest to the most complex feelings.[1]

Prior to Spencer—or, more generally, prior to the theory of evolution —the associationists had been no more successful in explaining emotions than they had been with instincts. This was admitted by J. S. Mill in his review of 'Bain's Psychology': 'It is certain that the attempts of the Association psychologists to resolve the emotions by association, have been on the whole the least successful part of their efforts.'[2] This judgement was repeated by their expositor, Ribot.[3] Bain's psychology —the culmination of pure associationism—did not contain a general analysis of the emotions. Although successive editions of Bain's work included results of the new evolutionary studies of Spencer and Darwin, these are 'added on', and the new thinking did not vitally affect his essentially pre-evolutionary view.[4] Evolutionary associationism could acknowledge the stability of the emotions in a species, which had been the strength and danger of Gall's faculty psychology, while retaining their experiential origins—the strength and weakness of associationism.

That the experience-hypothesis, as ordinarily understood, is inadequate to account for emotional phenomena, will be sufficiently manifest. If possible, it is even more at fault in respect to the emotions than in respect to the cognitions. The doctrine maintained by some philosophers, that all the

[1] Spencer, 1855, pp. 597–8.     [2] Mill, 1867, p. 132.     [3] Ribot, 1873, p. 327.
[4] Cf. Warren, 1921, pp. 115, 118–20.

desires, all the sentiments, are generated by the experiences of the individual, is so glaringly at variance with hosts of facts, that I cannot but wonder how any one should ever have entertained it. Not to dwell on the multiform passions displayed by the infant, before yet there has been such an amount of experience as could by any possibility suffice for the elaboration of them; I will simply point to the most powerful of all passions—the amatory passion—as one which, when it first occurs, is absolutely antecedent to all relative experience whatever.[1]

Attempts at explanation of complex emotions as developments wholly within the life of an individual are absurd. The alternative to explanation of the origin of emotions within the life of the individual is the view that their evolution takes place through countless generations.

By the accumulation of small increments, arising from the constant experiences of successive generations, the tendency of all the component psychical states to make each other nascent, will become gradually stronger. And when ultimately it becomes organic, it will constitute what we call a sentiment, or propensity, or feeling, having this set of circumstances for its object.[2]

Spencer had little more than this to say about emotions in the *Principles of Psychology*. Fortunately, he wrote a critical review of Bain's *The Emotions and the Will*, in which he provides a very incisive comment on the limitations of pre-evolutionary associationism, and spells out the implications of the new context for future investigations. The remarkable thing about the review is how clearly he saw the meaning of evolution for associationism at a time (1860) when evolution was just attaining the centre of intellectual discourse. The first systematic observations in evolutionary psychology were still over twenty years away. One should recall, though, that by 1860 he had been writing on evolutionary psychology for almost ten years.

Spencer clearly understood one of Bain's two principal contributions, as well as his major limitation.

The facts brought to light by anatomists and physiologists during the last fifty years, are at length being used towards the interpretation of this highest class of biological phenomena; and already there is promise of a great advance. The work of Mr. Alexander Bain . . . may be regarded as especially characteristic of the transition.[3]

On the other hand, Spencer betrays no hint that he grasped either Bain's theory of activity or its significance. Given his reading habits

[1] Spencer, 1855, p. 606.     [2] Ibid.     [3] Spencer, 1901, I, 242.

it is even doubtful if he read the relevant parts of Bain's book.[1] His criticism of Bain's concept of volition has as its text a single sentence from the first paragraph of the book.[2] Consequently, Spencer is silent on the aspect of Bain's work which later evolutionary and functional psychologists would use to complement the tendency toward passivity in Spencer's concept of adaptation.

Spencer also recognizes Bain's place in the development of psychology from a speculative and deductive branch of metaphysics to that of a biological science.

Until recently, mental science has been pursued much as physical science was pursued by the ancients; not by drawing conclusions from observations and experiments, but by drawing them from arbitrary *a priori* assumptions. This course, long since abandoned in the one case with immense advantage, is gradually being abandoned in the other; and the treatment of Psychology as a division of natural history, shows that the abandonment will soon be complete.[3]

Bain's work aimed to provide a 'natural history of the mind'.[4] As such 'we believe it to be the best yet produced'.[5] 'Of its kind it is the most scientific in conception, the most catholic in spirit, and the most complete in execution.'[6] However, the natural history method as used by Bain is not enough, and his work is therefore essentially transitional.[7]

Bain's classification of the emotions was derived from the expressions and feelings displayed in the adult.

Thus, then, Mr. Bain's grouping is throughout determined by the most manifest attributes—those objectively displayed in the natural languages of the emotions, and in the social phenomena that result from them, and those subjectively displayed in the aspects the emotions assume in an analytical consciousness. And the question is—Can they be correctly grouped after this method? We think not.[8]

We think that Mr. Bain, in confining himself to an account of the emotions as they exist in the adult civilized man, has neglected those classes of facts out of which the science of the matter must chiefly be built.[9]

The complete natural-history-method involves ultimate analysis, aided by development; and Mr. Bain, in not basing his classification of the emotions on characters reached through these aids, has fallen short of the conception with which he set out.[10]

In brief, he has written a Descriptive Psychology, which does not appeal to Comparative Psychology and Analytical Psychology for its leading ideas.

[1] Spencer, 1908, pp. 417–19.    [2] Spencer, 1901, I, 258–9.    [3] Ibid., I, 243.
[4] Ibid., I, 242.    [5] Ibid., I, 264.    [6] Ibid., I, 243.
[7] Ibid., I, 244.    [8] Ibid., I, 247.    [9] Ibid., I, 257.    [10] Ibid., I, 249.

And in doing this, he has omitted much that should be included in a natural history of the mind; while to that part of the subject with which he has dealt, he has given a necessarily imperfect organization.[1]

Spencer argues that comparative and developmental psychology can supply the studies which Bain's work lacked. Four types of investigation must precede and guide the traditional associationist analysis:

1. 'Study the evolution of the emotions up through the various grades of the animal kingdom . . . and how they are severally related to the conditions of life.'
2. Compare the emotions in lower and higher human races.
3. 'In the third place, we may observe the order in which the emotions unfold during the progress from infancy to maturity.'
4. Comparing the results 'displayed in the ascending grades of the animal kingdom, in the advance of the civilized races, and in individual history', we should seek harmony and general truths.[2]

It is only *after* the above studies have been made that one can attempt the analysis of complex adult human emotions into their elements. Such analysis must be guided by comparative and developmental information.[3]

Spencer's approach to the analysis of the emotions provides a very significant advance on the previous work of the associationist tradition. By insisting that comparative and developmental studies must precede and guide the application of the genetic method to the emotions as experienced subjectively, he challenged a fundamental assumption of those psychologists who believed that philosophical and introspective analyses were adequate methods. The assumption was that the actual development of emotions, indeed of all psychological phenomena, conforms to the categories and sequences according to which we can interpret them introspectively. Spencer insisted that biological studies must precede introspective analysis and thus raised the issue of whether the analytic classification conforms to a natural classification, whether psychologists' accounts of the synthesis of complex psychological phenomena are accurate reflections of their actual synthesis in evolution and in individual experience. The study of psychological phenomena is thereby transferred from plausible verbal analysis of the complex to the simple (like James Mill's), or verbal syntheses of everyday psychological life from simple elements (like Condillac's). Speculative and verbal analyses are replaced by biological observations and (later)

---

[1] Spencer, 1901, I, 257.     [2] Ibid., I, 250–1.     [3] Ibid., I, 251–2.

experiment. Once again, Spencer's arguments echo Gall's objections to the sensationalists while his answers depart from Gall's innately given static faculties and supply an alternative within the associationist tradition by uniting it with evolution.

It must be recognized, that in spite of his biological viewpoint, Spencer did not transcend the classificatory scheme of the association psychology. He offered a more plausible explanation of the genesis of psychological functions than his predecessors, but he retained their classification of those functions. He showed that explanation in terms of faculties was fallacious, and this was an advance on Gall. However, he failed to derive, or even advocate, the set of biological functions which Gall had sought, for which the evolutionary theory provided a sound basis. Evolutionary associationism thus failed to provide an integrated, biological psychology, and its objective descendant, behaviourism, has done no better. Instinct, Reason, Perception, Conception, Memory, Imagination, and so on, remain the topics or chapter headings in contemporary psychological works. One approach —modern ethology—offers hope of finally transcending the categories of medieval psychology and providing a nomenclature that fulfils the promise of evolutionary psychology by means of naturalistic observation followed by controlled experiments.

## The Mechanism of Evolution

Spencer's criticism of accounts by traditional associationists closes with his explanation of how new emotions are evolved. This discussion raises an issue which has been deliberately ignored throughout the present study: Spencer's belief in the inheritance of acquired characteristics. His theory will first be given and then considered in its historical context.

The mechanism which he adopted was avowedly 'Lamarckian'. Acquired habits are passed from generation to generation until they become fixed in the nervous system. 'Every one of the countless connections among the fibres of the cerebral masses, answers to some permanent connection of phenomena in the experiences of the race.'[1] What the individual feels as homogeneous emotions undecomposable into specific experiences, are in fact 'the organized results of certain daily-repeated combinations of mental states' and consist of 'aggregated and consolidated groups of those simpler feelings which habitually occur together in experience'.[2]

[1] Spencer, 1855, p. 581.    [2] Spencer, 1901, I, 254; cf. 256.

Spencer spells out this view in some detail, and since his exposition considers the question which most troubles the modern reader, it will be given in full.

When, in the circumstances of any race, some one kind of action or set of actions, sensation or set of sensations, is usually followed, or accompanied, by various other sets of actions or sensations, and so entails a large mass of pleasurable or painful states of consciousness; these, by frequent repetition, become so connected together that the initial action or sensation brings the ideas of all the rest crowding into consciousness: producing, in some degree, the pleasures or pains that have before been felt in reality. And when this relation, besides being frequently repeated in the individual, occurs in successive generations, all the many nervous actions involved tend to grow organically connected. They become incipiently reflex; and, on the occurrence of the appropriate stimulus, the whole nervous apparatus which in past generations was brought into activity by this stimulus, becomes nascently excited. Even while yet there have been no individual experiences, a vague feeling of pleasure or pain is produced; constituting what we may call the body of the emotion. And when the experiences of past generations come to be repeated in the individual, the emotion gains both strength and definiteness; and is accompanied by the appropriate specific ideas.[1]

In the next paragraph he considers and rejects the mechanism of natural selection. The example he considers is that of birds, on a formerly undiscovered island, whose behaviour evolves from an initial lack of fear of man to innate dread.

Now unless this change be ascribed to the killing-off of the less fearful, and the preservation and multiplication of the more fearful, which, considering the comparatively small number killed by man, is an inadequate cause; it must be ascribed to accumulated experiences; and each experience must be held to have a share in producing it. We must conclude that in each bird which escapes with injuries inflicted by man, or is alarmed by the outcries of other members of the flock (gregarious creatures of any intelligence being necessarily more or less sympathetic), there is established an association of ideas between the human aspect and the pains, direct and indirect, suffered from human agency.[2]

He goes on to infer that the emotion is a memory of these pains. In the course of generations, the nervous system is modified by these experiences, and thus young birds fly away at the sight of man as a result of a partial excitement of the nerves previously excited in their ancestors and the consequent painful consciousness. 'The vague painful consciousness thus arising, constitutes emotion proper.'[3]

[1] Spencer, 1901, I, 254–5.     [2] Ibid., I, 255.     [3] Ibid., I, 256.

Later, Spencer slightly modified his belief that natural selection was an 'inadequate cause'. He added the following note to the 1870 edition of the *Principles of Psychology*:

Had Mr. Darwin's *Origin of Species* been published before I wrote this paragraph, I should, no doubt, have so qualified my words as to recognize 'selection,' or artificial, as a factor. At the time the first edition was written the only factor I recognized was the inheritance of functionally-produced changes; but Mr. Darwin's work made it clear to me that there is another factor of importance in mental evolution as in bodily evolution. While holding that throughout all higher stages of mental development the supreme factor has been the effect of habit, I believe that in producing the lowest instincts natural selection has been the chief, if not the sole, factor.[1]

Spencer defended this position in the face of growing objections in the last quarter of the century, and reiterated it as late as 1899.[2]

Flugel points out that Spencer's belief in the inheritance of acquired characteristics 'contributed not a little to the general decline of interest in his work'.[3] It should be remembered, however, that this judgement did not begin to become operative until well after the period under consideration here (until after Weismann distinguished somatic changes from the stability of the transmitted 'germ-plasm' in 1885), and that Darwin himself laid increasing emphasis on use-inheritance in his writings after 1859. In fact it was Spencer who pointed this out in a careful analysis of Darwin's later writings. 'The Factors of Organic Evolution' (1886).[4] Darwin had no reason to quarrel with Spencer's view and altered the brief but crucial passage on man in the *Origin* to include a highly complimentary reference to Spencer. The first edition says, 'In the distant future I see open fields for far more important researches. Psychology will be based on a new foundation, that

[1] Spencer, 1908, p. 565.

[2] Ibid., p. 547. See also various articles by Spencer on the formula of evolution, mental evolution, inheritance of acquired characteristics, Weismannism, heredity, and so on, written between 1871 and 1898 and listed in his bibliography. (Spencer, 1908, pp. 581–6.) Most of these are reprinted in the second edition of *Principles of Biology* (1898–9), *Various Fragments* (1900), and *Facts and Comments* (1902). For an excellent discussion of the contemporary debate, see Romanes (1892, pp. 253–7; 1916, pp. 64–8, and *passim*). Spencer makes a greater concession to natural selection in his *Autobiography*: 'The *Origin of Species* made it clear to me that I was wrong; and that the larger part of the facts cannot be due to any such cause' [as 'the inheritance of functionally-produced modifications']. (Spencer, 1904, II, 50.)

[3] Flugel, 1951, p. 119.

[4] Spencer, 1901, I, 389–466. Cf. Romanes, 1916, pp. 2–12. Spencer reiterates his Lamarckian psychological views in the Preface to a pamphlet version of this essay (1887, pp. iii–iv) which is omitted from the *Essays*. (See Young, 1967). It was on the basis of their belief in the inheritance of acquired characteristics (even though by means of nervous arrangements) that both Darwin and Spencer were accused of reverting to belief in 'innate ideas'. (Höffding, 1909, p. 451; Meynert, enlisting support from Weismann, 1885, pp. viii, 274).

of the necessary acquirement of each mental power and capacity by gradation. Light will be thrown on the origin of man and his history.'[1] Darwin had not read Spencer's *Principles of Psychology* when he wrote his. In later editions of the *Origin* (6th edition, 1872), Darwin altered these sentences to read, 'Psychology will be securely based on the foundation already well laid by Mr. Herbert Spencer'.[2] Darwin's private opinion of Spencer underwent very wide fluctuations, from extreme admiration of him as perhaps England's greatest philosopher, and feelings of inferiority, to personal dislike and even contempt for his speculative bent.[3]

One further judgement should be given to help obviate the current reaction to Spencer's views on the mechanism of evolution. Speaking of the period 1851–58, T. H. Huxley said,

The only person known to me whose knowledge and capacity compelled respect, and who was, at the same time, a thoroughgoing evolutionist, was Mr. Herbert Spencer, whose acquaintance I made, I think, in 1852, and then entered into the bonds of a friendship which, I am happy to think, has known no interruption. Many and prolonged were the battles we fought on this topic. But even my friend's rare dialectic skill and copiousness of apt illustration could not drive me from my agnostic position.[4]

The point of this discussion of Lamarckianism is that what is now seen as a totally erroneous view of the mechanism of evolution was one of those immensely fruitful errors in the history of science which the historian would be mistaken to criticize. Like phrenology, it must be judged in the light of its heuristic value. There is little point in considering in detail the work generated by the general theory of evolution throughout biology: the whole basis of the science was transformed. This occurred despite the gropings, hesitations, and partial recantations of its early exponents. The same may be said for evolutionary psychology. The concept of psychology as a biological science based on the evolutionary theory was completely reorienting the science in the half-century following the first statements of Spencer and Darwin. When the mechanism of evolution became more clearly understood, it could find its rightful place within the general approach. Use-inheritance gave way to random mutation and natural selection. But the evolutionary basis of concepts which had defeated the associationists such as

[1] Darwin, 1950, pp. 413–14.    [2] Darwin, 1928, pp. 461–2.
[3] See various remarks in Darwin, edited Francis Darwin, 3rd ed., 1887; Darwin, edited Francis Darwin, 1903; Darwin, edited Barlow, 1958; especially Darwin 1958, pp. 108–9.
[4] Darwin, 1887, II, 188.

reflex, instinct, and emotion had been established in the meantime, even though the precise mode of their transmission is still not at all clearly understood. Although Spencer was wrong about the mechanism of evolution, modern views support his main theme: the adaptations of living things to their surroundings are evoked by problems posed by their environments.[1] That they are evoked by natural selection of random genetic mutations was not the main issue in converting psychology to a biological science of adaptation.

Therefore, Spencer's erroneous mechanism for evolution has been deliberately and properly ignored in discussing his work, because it is irrelevant to the historical development of the concepts with which the present discussion is concerned.

## The Influence of Spencer

Two changes have been emphasized as extremely important in the nineteenth-century development of psychology away from its position as a branch of epistemology. The first is its conception as a biological science; the second is its close relations with neurophysiology. It was argued above that Gall played an important role in establishing both approaches at the beginning of the nineteenth century. Spencer and Gall shared these two major premises about psychology, and there is much evidence to suggest that Spencer arrived at them during the period of his early phrenological allegiance. Spencer also shared with Gall the stylistic and personal traits of pomposity, conceit, and long-windedness, as well as the fate of being reviled and ridiculed by the subsequent generations which were most indebted to him. Finally, they both influenced others more through important general principles and approaches than by specific empirical findings. In Gall's case the findings were erroneous and in Spencer's nonexistent. Both advocated studies which they did not successfully conduct themselves.

Spencer's position in the last half of the nineteenth century was that he shared with Darwin the establishment of psychology on a biological, evolutionary foundation and with Bain the close alliance of associationism with sensory-motor psychophysiology.

Darwin pioneered studies in comparative and genetic psychology in the chapter on 'Instinct' in the *Origin* (1859), Chapters III and IV of the *Descent of Man* (1871), *The Expression of the Emotions in Man and Animals* (1872), 'A Biographical Sketch of an Infant' (1877), various

[1] See Wallace and Srb, 1961, pp. 104–5, and *passim*.

shorter papers,[1] and the extensive materials on instinct which he made available to Romanes and which appeared in *Mental Evolution in Animals* (1883). Although an adequate account of Darwin's psychological work remains to be written, there have been a number of studies dealing with aspects of his overwhelming importance in the development of psychology as a branch of evolutionary biology in the three separable areas of comparative psychology, functional psychology, and the study of the nervous system.[2]

While Darwin was primarily responsible for the general climate of evolutionary thinking and provided many detailed observations, he was somewhat naïve in his approach to psychology, and could not provide the language with which to express the implications of his own work. It is in this area between the general climate and the specific findings that Spencer is the major figure. Spencer was applying evolutionary principles to psychological phenomena for years before Darwin published the *Origin*. The attention of Darwin's circle was turned to man's body rather than his mind for twelve more years until the *Descent of Man* appeared.[3] It was Spencer who provided the first, and the most thorough, conception of adaptive, evolutionary psychology. His work was more seminal than directly contributory. He argued for a consistent application of empiricism but was characteristic of the parent tradition of associationism in not actually employing the empirical method. He advocated comparative and developmental studies but conducted none. He conceived psychology as the study of the adaptation of organisms to their environments, but failed to free himself completely from the epistemological bias of associationism, being concerned with the origin of ideas, the forms of thought, and a correspondence theory of truth.

One measure of Spencer's significance, therefore, is through his influence on major figures in three aspects of the new biological psychology: George J. Romanes in animal and comparative psychology, William James in functional psychology, and John Hughlings Jackson in sensory-motor psychophysiology.

G. J. Romanes wrote the first modern animal psychology based on

---

[1] See Darwin, 1887, III, 368–9.
[2] On comparative psychology, see Warden, 1927; Hilgard, 1960; Boring, 1950; Brett, 1953; Murphy, 1949; Young, 1967*a*. On functional psychology, see Baldwin, 1905, 1913; Angell, 1907, 1909; Young, 1966, pp. 26–28. On nervous system, see Magoun, 1960, 1961. The research of Howard Gruber of Rutgers University promises to shed considerable light on Darwin's psychological work.
[3] Huxley, 1863; Lyell, 1863. Cf. Greene, new ed., 1961, ch. 10.

the evolutionary theory and employing the empirical method.[1] He set out to trace the main outlines for mental evolution, as Darwin had done for bodily evolution. In his first volume, *Animal Intelligence* (1882) his purpose is to lay the foundations in comparative psychology for an understanding of mental evolution. He starts from Darwin and Spencer. 'With the exception of Mr Darwin's admirable chapters on the mental powers and moral sense, and Mr Spencer's great work on the Principles of Psychology, there has hitherto been no earnest attempt at tracing the principles which have been probably concerned in the genesis of Mind.'[2] The second volume of Romanes' work is concerned with mental evolution proper and finally takes the position that was still equivocal in Bain and Spencer.

I am in no wise concerned with 'the transition from the object known to the knowing subject', and therefore I am in no wise concerned with any of the philosophical theories which have been propounded upon this matter. . . . I cannot too strongly impress upon the memory of those who from previous reading are able to appreciate the importance of the distinction, that I thus intend everywhere to remain within the borders of psychology, and nowhere to trespass upon the grounds of philosophy.[3]

Darwin provided the main inspiration and many of the data for these volumes and made his extensive notes on instinct available to Romanes. The second major source in *Mental Evolution in Animals* (1883) is Spencer, who provides the starting point of the discussion on instinct as well as the psychological framework of evolutionary associationism which Romanes adopts.

Comparative psychology developed from these beginnings to a more rigorous formulation by C. Lloyd Morgan, who drew heavily on Romanes' work and was his literary executor. Morgan improved on Romanes' rather uncritical anecdotal method and anthropomorphism.[4] The next developments in animal psychology involve support for Morgan's methods by Jacques Loeb, who put forward the existence of 'associative memory' as the point in the scale of beings where animal life becomes conscious.[5] The introduction of the puzzle-box method into comparative psychology by E. L. Thorndike in 1898 was the point at which objective experimental methods were introduced into psychology, and prepared the way for its absorption into behaviourism.[6] Behaviourism and modern learning theory may seem remote from

[1] Boring, 1950, pp. 473–4.       [2] Romanes, 1882, p. vi.       [3] Romanes, 1883, p. 11.
[4] Morgan, 1890–91.               [5] Loeb, 1901.
[6] On these developments see Warden, 1927; Boring, 1950, pp. 472–6, 497–8; Carr, 1927; Young, 1967a, pp. 125–6.

evolutionary associationism to the modern reader. It may be useful to recall that the units of the conditioned reflex are new terms for the basic concepts of sensory-motor psychophysiology. The extreme complexity of current discussions and the sophisticated methods and techniques of work in modern learning theory must not be allowed to obscure its conceptual basis. John Dewey noted as early as 1896, that the use of the reflex concept in psychology was an admission that the sensory-motor view was basic to nerve structure and function, as well as to experience and behaviour.[1] It is clear that, although most studies of conditioning and learning depend on the evolutionary theory for their relevance to human psychology, the evolutionary aspect of the discipline has been largely ignored. However, the continued influence of associationism on this tradition has recently been reviewed with results which bear on one's appreciation of Bain and Spencer.

In a chapter entitled 'Modern Concepts of Association', Murphy begins by echoing Guthrie's belief that association is the only theory of learning that has ever been proposed.[2] He reviews the work of the behaviourists and learning theorists and shows that the central point of their work has been the principle of association placed in the objective context of the reflex paradigm. Stimulus-response psychology and the various schools of conditioning and learning theory have added a great deal to the old domain: the experimental method, various control procedures, quantification, and a behaviourist emphasis on the periphery of the organism. That is, they have made the study of association an objective science whose data are in the external world of objects and behaviour. New concepts such as 'operant' have been elaborated from Thorndike's restatement of Bain's early law of effect. However, the central conception has remained associationist. This unites Pavlov, Watson, Skinner, and a host of lesser figures. Reflecting on the century since Bain brought associationism into relation with physiology and Spencer with evolution, Murphy concludes,

If one had to summarize the main trend as it now exists in the middle of the century, it would almost certainly have to be to the effect that despite huge and continuous protests of strong and active personalities, the conceptions of Spencer and Bain a hundred years ago remain dominant. . . . An enormous amount of sophistication has gone into experimental and quantitative refinement of the theory of association; but the framework set up by the associationists remains.[3]

[1] Dewey, 1896, p. 357.
[2] The theory of innate ideas seems to have dropped from the memory of at least one eminent scientific psychologist by 1937. See above, p. 120.    [3] Murphy, 1949, p. 283.

Spencer's role as a major source of James' founding of functiona
psychology cannot be demonstrated in detail here. Once again, how
ever, Darwin provided the general issue and influence, while Spence
supplied its psychological embodiment, and Bain the specific theory o
activity which was developed in the writings of early pragmatists an
was expressed in William James' *Principles of Psychology* (1890). Amon,
the sources for this work, Spencer played the double role of being it
major one for the adaptive, evolutionary view and—through Hughling
Jackson and Ferrier—for the specific sensory-motor psychophysiolog;
of its early chapters. James grew increasingly critical of Spencer'
vagueness on matters of general evolution, but he had nothing bu
praise for the fact that Spencer stressed its universality.[1] 'To Spencei
is certainly due the immense credit of having been the first to see ir
evolution an absolutely universal principle.'[2] James' biographer report
that 'the writings of Spencer furnished the most important part of hi
early philosophical pablum'.[3] He read the *First Principles* between 186(
and 1862, and its initial influence was very stimulating.[4] James usec
Spencer's *Principles of Psychology* as the text for his first course in physio
logical psychology at Harvard (1876–77), and his first original publication was a commentary on Spencer.[5] His course on the philosophy
of evolution used Spencer's *First Principles* as a text beginning in 188c
and as late as 1897.[6] It should be stressed that James was very critica]
of Spencer's detailed formulations. However, Spencer's aims and the
topics he discussed were just those which most interested James. As his
own thought developed he retained these interests while rejecting many
of Spencer's answers and reacting strongly against his intellectua]
muddiness and pretensions toward explaining everything.[7]

The influence of Spencer's *Principles of Psychology* on James' work
of the same title written thirty-five years later is clear from the
following remarks in James' introductory chapter.

On the whole, few recent formulas have done more real service of a rough
sort in psychology than the Spencerian one that the essence of mental life and
of bodily life are one, namely, 'the adjustment of inner to outer relations'.
Such a formula is vagueness incarnate; but because it takes into account
the fact that minds inhabit environments which act on them and on which
they in turn react; because, in short, it takes mind in the midst of all its
concrete relations, it is immensely more fertile than the old-fashioned

[1] Perry, 1935, I, pp. 474–5.    [2] James, 1924, p. 124.    [3] Perry, 1935, I, 474.
[4] Ibid., I, 474.    [5] Ibid., I, 478.    [6] Ibid., I, 482.
[7] Perry, 1935, I, 484; James, 1924, pp. 128–39.

rational psychology', which treated the soul as a detached existent, sufficient into itself, and assumed to consider only its nature and properties.[1]

James' final evaluation of Spencer was harsh, but he continued to admire his psychological work:

My impression is that, of the systematic treatises, the 'Psychology' will rank as the most original. Spencer broke new ground here in insisting that, since mind in its environment have evolved together, they must be studied together. He gave to the study of mind in isolation a definitive quietus, and that certainly is a great thing to have achieved. To be sure he overdid the matter, as usual, and left no room for any mental structure at all, except that which passively resulted from the storage of impressions received from the outer world in the order of their frequency by fathers and transmitted to their sons. The belief that whatever is acquired by sires is inherited by sons, and the ignoring of purely inner variations, are weak points; but to have brought in the environment as vital was a master stroke.[2]

Functional psychology was born of a union of this formulation and a more active view of adaptation, which James drew from Bain.

The work of Bain and Spencer eliminated the credibility of a simple *tabula rasa* psychology. Bain's careful study of the role of muscular motion in learning undermined the persistent belief in passive sensationalism, while Spencer's evolutionary view revealed the absurdity of a psychology which confines itself to individual experience. Almost exactly a century after Condillac's statue provided the basis of a plausible explanation of learning,[3] psychologists could point to this 'thought experiment' as the opposite of a fruitful hypothesis. Bain and Spencer showed convincingly that organisms feel, know, and act as they do, by virtue of what they have inherited as a result of the vicissitudes of their species, and by virtue of what they have already done.

Bain and Spencer dominate the union of associationism with biology. Bain brought about its integration with sensory-motor physiology. Spencer reinforced this and based the new sensory-motor psycho-physiology on an evolutionary foundation. Magoun has convincingly argued that to their contemporaries and early successors, Spencer's ideas of the evolution of the brain and its functions were fully as

[1] James, 1890, I, 6. Cf. Perry, 1935, I, 476-8, 489-90. For a fuller consideration of the sources of James' *Principles*, see Perry, 1935, II, Chapters LII–LVI, especially LV.

[2] James, 1924, pp. 139-40.

[3] Condillac had tried to prove the sensationalist thesis by adding the senses, one by one, to a marble statue, and argued that the result accounted for all psychological phenomena. See Condillac, 1930; above, p. 15.

14

significant and influential as Darwin's, if not more so, in the development of concepts of evolution of the brain and behaviour.[1] This aspect of Spencer's work will be pursued through its influence on Hughling Jackson, and its union with other evidence for cerebral localization in the writings of Ferrier to provide an experimental sensory-motor psychophysiology based on the assumption of cerebral localization.[2]

[1] Magoun, 1960, p. 204; 1961, p. 16; see also Wiener, 1949.

[2] There are three further aspects of Spencer's influence which should be mentioned (1) Spencer's social theory and its influence on Social Darwinism has been explored by Hofstadter. (2) His role in the foundation of modern sociology along with Auguste Comte who also began his work as a student of phrenology and remained loyal to Gall, deserves a full study. See Greene (1959); Burrow (1966), ch. 6. In addition to his seminal influence in functional psychology, Spencer's influence on Durkheim and others was of fundamental importance in the development of functionalism in sociology and social anthropology (3) His theory of psychophysical parallelism, through Jackson's 'Law of Concomitance' provided the form of Freud's psychoanalytic theory and provided the position which Freud held on the mind-body problem from his first work (*On Aphasia*, 1891) to his last (*Outline of Psychoanalysis*, 1940). This aspect of relations among Spencer, Jackson, and Freud should be pursued as part of a more general study of the central role psychophysical parallelism has played in the history of neurology, psychiatry, and psychoanalysis.

# 6

## SPENCER, JACKSON, CARPENTER, AND THE APPLICATION OF SENSORY-MOTOR LOCALIZATION TO THE CEREBRAL CORTICES

We must remember, too, that many doctrines were stated years ago in principle which were then novel and much disputed, but are now so generally accepted that we are in danger of ceasing to think of the very early propounders of those doctrines.

John Hughlings Jackson, 1881.

### Spencer and Jackson

The aspects of Spencer's evolutionary associationism which had the most direct influence on the history of the study of the brain can be best appreciated in the context of their immediate effects. Magoun points out that there can be no question of 'the predominant influence of Spencer upon Hughlings Jackson and, through him upon the formation of evolutionary concepts of the organization and function of the brain in Western neurological thought'.[1] This influence began early and continued throughout Jackson's career. When he first arrived in London after completing his medical training in 1859 (aged twenty-four), he had already become so thoroughly interested in Spencer's evolutionary psychology that he 'had fully resolved to give up medicine and devote himself to philosophy'.[2] He was dissuaded from this course by Sir Jonathan Hutchinson,[3] but his interest in Spencer's philosophical and psychological views dominated his distinguished career as a pioneer neurologist and theoretician whose writings and example have strongly influenced subsequent clinical work. Jackson was to neurology what Bain was to psychology: a figure who almost single-handedly gave the discipline an identity apart from its parent sciences. His appointment as Assistant Physician to the National Hospital, Queen Square, in 1862 (where he continued to work for forty-five years), was the beginning of an influence exerted by the man and the institution which became predominant in the English-speaking world. His biographer says,

[1] Magoun, 1961, p. 17.  [2] Jackson, 1931, I, ix. Cf. Jasper, 1960, p. 97.
[3] Hutchinson, 1925, pp. 28-9.

There is little doubt that the advent of Jackson infused a new spirit into neurology, and was the beginning of that systematic orderliness which now [1925] characterizes neurology, more perhaps than any other branch of medical science. Although his influence on neurology cannot be over-estimated, it must also be remembered that his contributions to the physiology of the nervous system are no less valuable.[1]

The claim that he was 'the founder of modern neurology'[2] is therefore not a gross exaggeration.[3] Again, like Bain, he was the founder (along with Ferrier and others) of the first English journal devoted exclusively to his field of interest: *Brain* (1877–).[4]

Darwin's work is referred to once in Jackson's *Selected Writings*; the context gives a clear picture of the source of Jackson's views on evolution. 'I need scarcely mention the name of Herbert Spencer, except to express my vast indebtedness to him; the first edition of his *Principles of Psychology* appeared so long ago as 1855, five years before the publication of the *Origin of Species*.'[5]

Spencer is by far the most often-quoted figure in Jackson's writings. There is hardly a single matter of principle or detail for which he does not at some point cite Spencer as source, inspiration, or authority. These citations, which appear at the head of many of his publications, are always made with great diffidence. 'I should say that a very great part of this paper is nothing more than an application of certain of Herbert Spencer's principles, stated in his *Psychology*, were it not that I dare not risk misleading readers by imputing crudities of my own to this distinguished man.'[6] 'I should consider it a great calamity, were

---

[1] Taylor, 1925, p. 12.    [2] Riese, 1959, p. 199.

[3] A parallel influence in France was exerted by Jean-Martin Charcot (1825–93) and the Hospital of Sâlpetrière. See Guillain, translated Bailey, 1959; Charcot, translated Sigerson, 1881, Charcot, translated Hadden, 1883. Cf. Haymaker, 1953, pp. 266–9; Thorwald, translated Winston, 1960, Chapter I.

[4] Jackson's life, his clinical work and his theories will not receive a full treatment here. His work has been most ably expounded by Sir Francis Walshe and Henry Head. (Walshe, 1948, 1953, 1954, 1957, 1958, 1961; Head, 1926, I, 30–53, 134–41). The sources of Jackson's views are (somewhat unevenly) reviewed by Riese, 1949, 1956, 1959; Riese and Hoff, 1950–51. The classical study of the history of the investigation of epilepsy is Temkin's *The Falling Sickness* (1945; see especially pp. 288–324). Jackson's influence on psychiatry, especially on Freud, is very well dealt with by Stengel (1953, 1954, 1963). Biographical information is available in three short essays by his mentor (Hutchinson), a colleague (Mercier), and a pupil (Taylor) in Jackson, 1925, pp. 1–46. Other useful information on his life and work may be found in Jefferson, 1960, pp. 35–44, 122–4; Jasper, 1960; Brain, 1958; Haymaker, 1953, pp. 308–11; Thorwald, 1960, Chapter I; Levin, 1953, 1960. Jackson's papers are scattered through many obscure journals. The works which are relatively easily accessible include the papers on aphasia and the bibliography reprinted by Head in *Brain* 38, 1915, 1–190, the *Neurological Fragments* (1925); and two volumes of *Selected Writings* prepared by Taylor (1931); cf. Greenblatt, 1965, which includes a bibliography of Jackson's early publications.    [5] Jackson, 1931, II, 395.    [6] Ibid., II, 40.

any crudities of mine imputed to a man to whom I feel profoundly indebted.'[1]

The unifying conception of Jackson's work is the application of the theory of evolution to the structure, functions, and diseases of the nervous system. He saw his own investigations in the following context:

Here, for the first time in this article I use the term Dissolution, I most gratefully acknowledge my vast debt to Herbert Spencer. What I have to say of the constitution of the nervous system appears to me to be little more than illustrating his doctrine on nervous evolution by what I may metaphorically speak of as the experiments of disease. I should make more definite acknowledgements were it not that I do not wish to mislead the reader, if, by any misunderstandings of his doctrines on my part, I impute to Mr. Spencer particular opinions he might not endorse. Anyone interested in diseases of the nervous system should carefully study Spencer's *Psychology*.[2]

This is not the place to review Jackson's applications of nervous system evolution in detail. Many of them fall outside of the temporal limitations of the present study and were derived from the more explicitly neurological second edition of the *Principles of Psychology*. Given the all-pervasive influence of Spencer on Jackson, two aspects of his evolutionary neuropsychology are of direct relevance to the issues being considered here. It served as a new basis for the extension of the sensory-motor view from the spinal cord to the hemispheres, and for a belief in the cerebral localization of sensory and motor processes.

Spencer's principles of continuity and evolution provided Jackson with a single, consistent set of variables for specifying the physiological and psychological elements of which experience, thought, and behaviour are composed: sensations (or impressions) and motions. All complex mental phenomena are made up of these simple elements—from the simplest reflex to the most sublime thoughts and emotions.[3] All functions and faculties can be explained in these terms. The application

---

[1] Jackson, 1931, II, 80, 346. This form of acknowledgement is repeated again and again. Cf. Jackson, 1931, I, 238, 375; Jackson, 1931, II, 45, 98, 431–2.

[2] Jackson, 1931, I, 147. Dr Charles Mercier, Jackson's colleague and friend, contributed the following judgement on Jackson's allegiance to Spencer: 'He had also a great admiration for Herbert Spencer, with which he inoculated me, but I always thought—and in this I think Sir Jonathan Hutchinson agrees—that Dr. Jackson gave Spencer far too much credit as the founder and suggester of Dr. Jackson's own doctrines. In this opinion I have been confirmed by reading Spencer's Autobiography, which destroyed not only my respect for man, but also illogically perhaps, my faith in his doctrines. It seems impossible that the opinions of a man who depicts himself as the glorified quintessence of a prig can be worth anything.' (Mercier, 1925, pp. 42–3.) Cf. 'Two', 1906.

[3] Cf. Spencer, 1904, I, 470–1.

to emotions has been noted.[1] Ideas 'are nothing else than weak repetitions of the psychical states caused in us by actual impressions and motions—partial excitements of the same nervous agents'.[2]

The tradition of sensation and association had, in principle, a single hypothesis which explained the origins of all experience. Through Mueller and Bain this explanation was applied to motion and linked closely with the nervous system, including specific sensory modalities. But, until the advent of the evolutionary theory, the consistent application of a sensory-motor psychophysiology was faltering in one respect or another, whether instinct, emotion, or various higher processes. The extension of the principles throughout the brain was held back by the theories of Flourens and the findings of those who worked in his shadow. Spencer eliminated all reason for hesitation, and Jackson grasped this fact. Impressions and motions became the elements of nervous processes in one aspect and of psychological processes in the other. The principles of Haller, Bell, and Magendie drove all other elements from the nervous system as Spencer had from the mind, and the theory of evolution supported both. The applications of these principles will be considered presently.

The same theory of evolution provided a new basis for the conception of cerebral localization which Jackson adopted from Spencer. Writing on this topic in 1867 and 1868, Jackson says, 'I would especially draw attention to the quotations from Spencer's *Psychology*, as the doctrine on localization I here try to illustrate further is, I believe, the one he has put forward'.[3] The passages which Jackson mentions[4] reveal the attitude which Spencer maintained toward phrenology in his later work. (They are rearranged but not changed in later editions of the *Principles*.)

The phrenological views which had played an important part in the early development of adaptive and biological thinking and led Spencer to formulate his evolutionary psychology are now considered in the light of the hereditary transmission of complex emotions. What is left of his early phrenological organ-function view now appears as a corollary of evolutionary associationism.

That an organized tendency towards certain complex aggregations of psychical states, supposes a structural modification of the nervous system— a special set of complex nervous connections whereby the numerous excitations constituting the emotion may be co-ordinated—no one having even a superficial knowledge of Physiology can doubt. As every student of the

[1] Above, pp. 182–3.       [2] Spencer, 1855, p. 568.
[3] Jackson, 1931, II, 216.   [4] Ibid., II, 234.

nervous system knows, the combination of any set of impressions, or motions, or both, implies a ganglion in which the various nerve-fibres concerned are put in connection.[1]

Thus, there must be greater and smaller ganglionic masses which coordinate the more or less complex emotions and which constitute their seats. Spencer recognizes that the controversies engendered by some of 'the unscientific reasonings of the phrenologists' had quite naturally led physiologists to deny or ignore localization of functions in the cerebrum.

But no physiologist who calmly considers the question in connection with the general truths of his science, can long resist the conviction that different parts of the cerebrum subserve different kinds of mental action. Localization of function is the law of all organization whatever: separateness of duty is universally accompanied with separateness of structure: and it would be marvellous were an exception to exist in the cerebral hemispheres. Let it be granted that the cerebral hemispheres are the seat of the higher psychical activities; let it be granted that among these higher psychical activities there are distinctions of kind, which, though not definite, are yet practically recognizable; and it cannot be denied, without going in direct opposition to established physiological principles, that these more or less distinct kinds of psychical activity must be carried on in more or less distinct parts of the cerebral hemispheres.[2]

Everything known about the peripheral nervous system supports this view.

It is proved experimentally, that every bundle of nerve-fibres and every ganglion, has a special duty; and that each part of every such bundle and every such ganglion, has a duty still more special. Can it be, then, that in the great hemispherical ganglia alone, this specialization of duty does not hold?[3]

Everything known about the spinal cord further supports this view, including specialization of function with no perceptible differences in structure.

The specialization of function in the hemispheres is analogous to that in the spinal cord.[4] Thus, the principle of continuity provides an evolutionary basis for extending the Bell–Magendie law to the hemispheres in support of cerebral localization. The functional division of the spinal roots plays a double role in the views which Spencer sharpens

[1] Spencer, 1855, pp. 606–7.    [2] Ibid., p. 607.
[3] Ibid., p. 608.    [4] Ibid.

and passes on to Jackson: the fact of the division supports a general principle of functional specialization of structures, while the nature of the division provides the sensory-motor categories of functional analysis which are applied to all physiological and psychological processes.

Thus, Spencer accepts the 'fundamental proposition'[1] of cerebral localization.

> Indeed, any other hypothesis seems to me, on the face of it, untenable. Either there is some arrangement, some organization in the cerebrum, or there is none. If there is no organization, the cerebrum is a chaotic mass of fibres, incapable of performing any orderly action. If there is some organization, it must consist in the same 'physiological division of labour' in which all organization consists; and there is no division of labour, physiological or other, of which we have any example, or can form any conception, but what involves the concentration of special kinds of activity in special places.[2]

It should be recalled that the association psychologists and most physiologists since Gall had been opposed to cerebral localization. Spencer reintroduced this concept. The development of his thinking on this topic can be seen as a circuitous path by which he started from, left, and finally returned to Gall's first physiological proof of the plurality of the organs of the soul: 'In all organized beings, different phenomena suppose different apparatus; consequently, the various functions of the brain likewise suppose different organs.'[3] It should be clear, though, that the developments from Haller to Bell-Magendie to Spencer involve a very different conception of the functions of the brain from the one Gall put forth.

'But to coincide with the doctrine of the phrenologists in its most abstract shape, is by no means to coincide with their concrete embodiments of it.'[4] He objects to their 'great. . . unwillingness to listen to any criticisms on the detailed scheme rashly promulgated as finally settled' and to the fact that phrenology represents itself as 'a complete system of Psychology'.[5] Most important, he opposes both the attempt to demarcate organs precisely in the brain and to set up rigid concepts of the functions. It was this undogmatic aspect of Spencer's scheme that most appealed to Jackson. 'The only localization which we may presume to exist, and which the necessities of the case imply, is one of a comparatively vague kind—one which does not suppose specific limits, but an insensible shading-off.'[6] The mental plexuses answering to relations

---

[1] Spencer, 1855, p. 611.   [2] Ibid., p. 608.
[3] Gall, 1835, II, 254. Cf. Gall, 1835, VI, 307.
[4] Spencer, 1855, p. 608.   [5] Ibid., p. 609.   [6] Ibid.

n the external world cannot be represented in the nervous system by anything less complex and overlapping than the phenomena to which they correspond.

Nor can the categories of function be any less flexible than the 'phenomena habitually surrounding any race of organisms'.[1] Spencer was quite right to insist on flexible categories corresponding to the progressive adaptations implied by evolution and to reject Gall's static, fixed faculties based on the pre-established adaptations of the chain of being. 'So little specific are the faculties, that no one of them is quite the same in different persons: they severally differ as the several features differ.'[2] Gall's faculties were formulated in anticipation of this objection and were supposed to be rich and subtle enough in their various combinations to account for individual differences. But Spencer is correct on the more basic issue of the changing nature of the functions through evolution. Finally, Spencer attacks the organology itself—the simple view of one faculty to one organ—and insists that the seat of an emotion is merely the '*centre of co-ordination*' of a number of complex aggregates of sensory and motor fibres distributed throughout the cerebrum.[3]

This is all that remains of Spencer's early phrenological allegiance. His conclusion on the discipline itself is that 'At best, Phrenology can be but an appendix to Psychology proper; and one of but comparative unimportance, scientifically considered'.[4] However, it has been argued here that much of his psychology grew out of his phrenological beginnings, and that the transformations his views underwent during his development show the continuity of some of the basic aims and approaches of phrenology with the adaptive and biological aspects of Spencer's psychology. Nevertheless, evolutionary sensory-motor psychophysiology is incompatible with the static chain of being and the faculty psychology of phrenology, and the concept of cerebral localization which carries over from the phrenological period in Spencer's development is a very different concept from that of Gall.[5]

---

[1] Spencer, 1855, p. 610.    [2] Ibid.    [3] Spencer, 1855, pp. 610–11fW    [4] Ibid., p. 609.

[5] It is extremely likely that phrenology remained an occasional topic of conversation with Spencer, since he continued to make periodic week-long visits to Mr and Mrs Charles Bray. Bray was a free-thinking manufacturer who was a close friend of George Combe and an ardent phrenologist. He wrote phrenological works in his abundant leisure and remained a sincere and complete believer throughout his life. His works are *The Education of the Feelings* (1838); *The Philosophy of Necessity* (1841); *Phases of Opinion and Experience During a Long Life* (1885). He and his wife were close friends of George Eliot, and he was responsible for her interest in the subject. He succeeded in getting her to sit for a phrenological 'delineation' and, through her, aroused G. H. Lewes' interest in phrenology. Spencer had become friends with the Brays through George Eliot, and he notes visits with them twice in 1852, in 1856,

## Hughlings Jackson Extends Sensory-Motor Psychophysiology to the Cerebral Cortices

Spencer's rather vague notion of localization is combined by Jackson with a thoroughgoing sensory-motor view of all mental processes, and this is applied to the cerebral cortices. The extension of the sensory-motor paradigm to the cortex had been implicit in earlier analyses which identified higher mental processes with the cortices and treated these in associationist terms, but it had not been made central to any theory of the functional organization of the hemispheres which influenced the major figures under review here. Jackson based his argument on two theories: '[Thomas] Laycock's hypothesis of Reflex Cerebral Action and Spencer's hypothesis of Nervous Evolution'.[1]

Jackson had been associated with Laycock (later professor of medicine at Edinburgh) early in his medical career at the York Dispensary, and it has been presumed that he first stimulated Jackson's interest in the nervous system.[2] In acknowledging his debt, Jackson quotes a version of Laycock's doctrine which was first put forth in 1840. In 1845, Laycock said,

Four years have elapsed since I published my opinion, supported by such arguments as I could then state, that the *brain*, although the organ of consciousness, *is subject to the laws of reflex action, and that, in this respect, it does not differ from the other ganglia of the nervous system.* I was led to this opinion by the general principle that the ganglia within the cranium, being a continuation of the spinal cord, *must necessarily be regulated, as to their reaction on external agencies, by laws identical with those governing the spinal ganglia, and their analogues in the lower animals.*[3]

The reflex aspect of Laycock's view played an important part in Jackson's theories, but it is less important for present purposes than the principle of continuity of functional organization between lower and higher centres in the nervous system. This continuity justified the extension of the Bell-Magendie law to the highest centres in the nervous system. Jackson took it to be 'a necessary implication of the doctrine of nervous evolution as this is stated by Spencer'.[4] In another place

---

1862 and (with Mrs Bray) 1886. (Spencer, 1904, I, 407, 434, 484; Spencer, 1904, II, 84, 411.) See also Cross, n.d. pp. 45, 56–7, 169–70; Jefferson, 1960, pp. 40–42; Haight, 1968, for information on the Brays and George Eliot.

[1] Jackson, 1931, I, 123.  [2] Ibid., I, ix. Cf. Jasper, 1960, p. 97.

[3] Ibid., I, 167. The same quotation heads his paper (1875) claiming that he had attributed motor functions to the cortex prior to Fritsch and Hitzig (Ibid., I, 37). Emphasis added by Jackson. Mr. Roger Smith, King's College, Cambridge, is making a study of the theories of Laycock. Cf. Young, 1966, pp. 25–6.

[4] Ibid., I, 42.

(after he has the supporting evidence of Hitzig and Ferrier), Jackson says,

If the doctrine of evolution be true, all nervous centres must be of sensori-motor constitution. *A priori*, it seems reasonable to suppose that, if the highest centres have the same composition as the lower, being, like the lower, made up of cells and fibres, they have also the same constitution. It would be marvellous if, at a certain level, whether we call it one of evolution or not, there were a sudden change into centres of a different *kind* of constitution. Is it not enough difference that the highest centres of one nervous system are greatly more complicated than the lower?[1]

In a long preface (written in 1875) to a republication of an earlier paper (1873), he reviews his previous writings to support his claim to priority in viewing the convolutions as containing nervous arrangements representing movements.[2] This view had become automatic with him and was not explicitly stated except in a footnote. He nowhere tried to *prove* it, he says, since 'I cannot conceive of what other materials the cerebral hemispheres can be composed than of nervous arrangements representing impressions and movements'.[3] 'In fact, in every paper written during and since 1866, whether on chorea, convulsions, or on the physiology of language, I have *always* written on the assumption that the cerebral hemisphere is made up of processes representing impressions and movements.'[4] The famous footnote, written in 1870 and quoted again and again by Jackson, says,

It is asserted by some that the cerebrum is the organ of mind, and that it is not a *motor* organ. Some think the cerebrum is to be likened to an instrumentalist, and the motor centres to the instrument; one part is for ideas, and the other for movements. It may then be asked, How can discharge of part of a *mental* organ produce *motor* symptoms only? I say motor symptoms only, because, to give sharpness to the argument, I will suppose a case in which there is unilateral spasm without loss of consciousness. But of what 'substance' can the organ of mind be composed, unless of processes representing movements and impressions; and how can the convolutions differ from the inferior centres, except as parts representing *more* intricate co-ordinations of impressions and movements in time and space than they do? Are we to believe that the hemisphere is built on a plan *fundamentally* different from that of the motor tract? What can an 'idea', say of a ball, be, except a process representing certain impressions of surface and particular muscular adjustments? What is recollection, but a revivification of such processes which, in the past, have become part of the organism itself? What is delirium, except the *disorderly* revival of sensori-motor processes received in the past:

[1] Jackson, 1931, II, 63.  [2] Jackson, 1931, I, 37.
[3] Ibid., I, 42.  [4] Ibid.

What is a mistake in a word, but a wrong movement, a chorea? Giddiness can be but the temporary loss or disorder of certain relations in space, chiefly made up of muscular feelings. Surely the conclusion is irresistible, that 'mental' symptoms from disease of the hemisphere are fundamentally like hemiplegia, chorea and convulsions, however specially different. They must all be due to lack, or to disorderly development, of sensori-motor processes.[1]

This quotation has been given in full, since it provides the basic statement of Jackson's whole position. As it stands it is a unified view of neurological symptomatology. It was elaborated by him into a general theory of the functional organization of the nervous system, and constituted the last stage of the integration of the association psychology with sensory-motor physiology. It involved an explicit rejection of the aspects of the clinical and physiological work which had hindered a unified view: the faculty formulation of Broca, and the unwillingness of Flourens, Magendie, Mueller, and others to treat the organ of mind —the highest centres—in consistently physiological terms.

Broca owned both his concept of localization and its formulation in terms of faculties to phrenology. Jackson had been prepared in 1864 to speak in terms of a 'faculty of language' which 'resides' in a given convolution or vascular region. But by 1866 he found it 'incredible that "speech" can "reside" in any limited spot'.[2] The formulation in terms of localization of faculties was rejected. 'I think, then, that the so-called "faculty" of language has no existence.'[3] It was replaced by a motor view which Jackson derived from Bain.[4] The anatomical

---

[1] Jackson, 1931, I, 26. Quoted again, pp. 42, 58; Jackson, 1931, II, 63–4, 67, etc.

[2] Jackson, 1931, II, 233–4.

[3] Ibid., II, 123. Jackson and Broca are reputed to have clashed publicly over their respective views of aphasia at a meeting of the British Association in 1868. Broca is said to have carried the day. (Haymaker, 1953, pp. 260–1.) Broca opened the discussion on the physiology of speech and was followed by Jackson. There is no record of their discussion in the *Proceedings of the British Association*. Broca's paper was published and contains no reference to Jackson's views. He defends the existence of a faculty of articulate language which is independent of other functions, and considers the issue of whether or not it has a localized seat in the brain, still open. The greater part of the paper is concerned with the nomenclature of speech disorders and the differential diagnosis among four classes: 'alogia' (due to loss of the ideas for words), 'verbal amnesia' (due to loss of the memory of words), 'aphemia' (loss of the ability to repeat words, although their meaning is understood), and 'mechanical alalia' (impairment of the agencies for articulation). The term 'aphasia' is reserved for cases where one of the above diagnoses is not yet established. (Broca, 1869. Cf. Head, 1926, I, 26–7.) A synopsis of Jackson's argument appeared, but it conveys little sense of the conflict between their views. He says that disease separates healthy language into intellectual and emotional aspects, and that the impairment in aphasia is one of intellectual expression by movements; those most special (those of speech) suffering most, simpler ones (such as gestures) suffering least. (Head, 1926, I, 34–5.)

[4] See above, p. 110.

ubstrata of words are *motor* processes, and the defect in aphasia is one of articulatory movements.[1] Jackson calls this view 'but a particular expansion of views which Bain has long taught, and which, indeed, he has applied to speech'.

When we recall,' he says, 'the impression of a word or a sentence, if we do not speak it out, we feel the twitter of the organs just about to come to that point. The articulating parts,—the larynx, the tongue, the lips,—are all sensibly excited; a *suppressed articulation* is, in fact, the material of our recollection, the intellectual manifestation, the *idea* of speech'.[2]

Similarly, in 1864, he was prepared to speak of the *corpus striatum* ('the highest part of the motor tract') as 'the point of emission of the orders of the "will" to the muscles'.[3] This was the traditional formulation used by Magendie, Mueller, Todd and Bowman, Carpenter, Bain, and others and was implicit in the separation of sensory-motor analysis of lower centres from vague reference to the functions of will, intelligence, sensation, and so on, in the hemispheres. It left a hiatus in the analysis which Jackson sets out to eliminate, again as an extension of Spencer's psychophysiology. He cites his own previous confusion of mental and physiological states and terms, as 'an additional reason why I should point out the evil results of the confusion'.[4] His criticism is aimed at those who 'speak as if at some place in the higher parts of the nervous system we abruptly cease to have to do with impressions and movements, and begin all at once to have to do with mental states'.[5]

There are motor centres, and above these are centres for ideas, for memory, volition, etc., which 'play on' the motor centres. . . . There are in use such expressions as that an '*idea* produces a movement'. It would be a marvellous thing if there were any such sudden and total change in function. Supposing that we do *begin* in the cerebrum to have to do with mental states, does it follow that we cease to have to do with impressions and movements? For have we not to do with the nature of the *material basis* of the mental states?[6]

Those who speak of 'centres for memory of words', or of 'centres for ideas' of any kind, as arbitrarily acting on and governing motor centres, are, as regards their method, essentially like those who speak of the soul producing movements, etc. The difference is that the former practically talk as if the soul were a solid one, made up of fibres and cells. This physiologico-materialistic method practically ignores anatomy and physiology. It leads to verbal explanations, such as that an aphasic does not speak '*because* he has lost the memory for words'; that 'chorea is a disorder of volition'; that

---

[1] Jackson, 1931, I, 39.    [2] Ibid., I, 50–1. Cf. the theories of J. B. Watson.
[3] Jackson, 1931, II, 233. Cf. 121, 122, 127.
[4] Jackson, 1931, I, 48.    [5] Ibid.    [6] Ibid.

'ideas are formed in the cortical grey matter of the brain, and produce
movements by acting on lower centres'; 'that we combine two retina
impressions by a mental act'; it leads to the free use of such phrases as
'volitional impulses', 'by an act of memory', etc.[1]

Jackson is opposed to this mixture of morphological and physiological
terms. His objections are based on the philosophical assumption of
psychophysical parallelism and involve a rigid conception of the
proper domain of physiology.

It is sometimes objected that we cannot 'understand' 'how energising of
nervous processes, representing *movements*, can give or share in giving us
*ideas*'. This is a very naïve objection. We cannot understand how any
conceivable arrangement of any sort of matter can give us mental states of
any kind. Is it more difficult to understand why we remember a word during
energising of cells and fibres because we believe those cells and fibres represent
articulatory *movements*? I do not concern myself with mental states at all,
except indirectly in seeking their anatomical substrata. I do not trouble
myself about the mode of connection between mind and matter. It is enough
to assume a parallelism. That along with excitations or discharges of nervous
arrangements in the cerebrum, mental states occur, I, of course, admit; but
how this is I do not inquire; indeed, so far as clinical medicine is concerned,
I do not care.[2]

His position is that mental states arise *during*, not from, physiological
processes.

'Sensations', in the sense of 'mental states', arise, I submit, during energising
of motor as well as of 'sensory' nerve processes—with the 'out-going' as well
as with the 'in-going' current. I say 'arise during'; I have used no expressions
which imply, even remotely, that in the penetralia of the highest centres,
physical vibrations, however fine they may become, fine away into mental
states—such as for example that molecular changes in optic nerves and
centres turn into sensations of colour.[3]

The result for his analysis is that 'faculties' and their corresponding
processes, such as volition, ideation, reasoning, and emotion, are
'artificially distinguished' aspects of consciousness. During the activity
of the highest centres these are simultaneously displayed. These centres
represent, not the faculties, but movements of all parts of the body.
In health they function normally; in disease they are disordered.
However, there is no incongruity between obvious disorders of motion
such as epilepsy and less obvious ones like insanity: both are diseases
of sensory-motor processes.[4]

[1] Jackson, 1931, I, 51–2.      [2] Jackson, 1931, I, 52. Cf. Freud, 1891, pp. 52–7, 56n, 61.
[3] Ibid., I, 55.               [4] Jackson, 1931, II, 66.

The result for physiology is that it is concerned with the 'degrees and conditions of excitation or discharge of nervous centres. . . . Physiology deals with the *functions* of nervous arrangements'.[1] He does not deny that the functions of the hemispheres include

'ideation,' 'consciousness,' etc. Sensori-*motor* processes are the physical side of, or, as I prefer to say, form the anatomical substrata of, mental states. It is with these substrata only that we, in our character as physicians and physiologists, are directly concerned.[2]

Neural physiology is concerned only with the varying conditions of the anatomical arrangements of nerve cells and fibres—with the physics of the nervous system.[3]

The proper activity of the physiologist involves resolving all the functions of the various structures of the brain into sensory-motor processes. Jackson's scheme of localization was concerned only with these.

Jackson's analysis marked the end of the long movement away from the attempt to define physiology in terms of correlation of faculties with organs: the attempt to localize mental functions. The mental aspect was reduced to the conscious parallel of sensory-motor substrata. This formal hypothesis about the relations of mental with physiological phenomena was coupled with a genetic hypothesis which analysed all complex mental contents and processes into simple sensory and motor elements. This does not mean that movements or cerebral arrangements serve in mentation as a subjective activity. Words serve in mentation, but these, in turn, are defined as the concomitants of discharge of cerebral arrangements representing articulatory movements. The foregoing analysis has attempted to demonstrate this for Bain and Spencer. Jackson shared the view,[4] and Ferrier followed him. In about fifty years, cerebral localization had moved from a conception of physiology dominated by psychological faculties with no precise designation of the related material processes, to a physiology of sensory-motor processes which dominated the psychological functions by placing them in a sensory-motor framework. For Gall the functions of the brain were the faculties; physiology was defined as the study of these. For Jackson and Ferrier the only functions proper to physiology were sensory-motor phenomena. There was no place left for Gall's faculties except as artificial abstractions. The concomitants of sensory-motor phenomena were ideas of sensation and movements, and associated

---

[1] Jackson, 1931, I, 56.  [2] Ibid., I, 49.
[3] Ibid., I, 52.  [4] Cf. Jackson, 1931, I, 81–2.

complexes built up from these elements. With Jackson's analysis, the development of the concept of function was completed in the form it would retain until the end of the nineteenth century. The concept of localization, however, underwent further development, and the whole approach still lacked experimental demonstration. It should be noticed that Spencer, Jackson, and Ferrier had no interest in the biological issue of *what are* the functions of the brain.

### *William Carpenter and the Climate of Opinion in 1870*

Jefferson has provided an excellent picture of the coexistence of irreconcilable views, and the hesitancy on the part of everyone concerned to juxtapose their findings in such a way as to include the cortex in the motor system. Two dogmas coexisted with their contraries. First, the cortex had been found inexcitable on mechanical and electrical stimulation. Second, the corpus striatum was the highest motor ganglion. However, clinical findings and theoretical considerations indicated that the convolutions were involved in convulsions and paralyses, and that they contained nervous arrangements and processes 'representing movements and impressions'.[1] Jefferson's summary of the state of affairs is excellent.

From Haller (1755) and Lorry (1760) to Legallois, onwards to the best observer of them all, Flourens, and on again to Magendie and everyone else, all were agreed upon this—the brain was unresponsive except at the lower and lowest levels. The hemispheres were the seat of the 'will'; they excited movement by playing on these motor mechanisms. But how they did so no one knew and no nice man would ask![2]

Longet (1842), in confirming once again that the cortex was inexcitable, granted that in cerebral disease affections of the brain were able to produce epileptiform phenomena. He could reconcile these phenomena only by saying that 'in men disease can stir in the bosom of the brain irritations such as artificial and immediate stimulation cannot provoke'.[3] R. B. Todd had produced epileptic movements by mid-brain stimulation in 1849, but no one seems to have taken any notice, and the artificial stimulation of epileptiform movements was discovered anew by Fritsch and Hitzig, and Ferrier twenty years later. Todd stressed that the prevailing spinal and medullary theories of epilepsy could not explain the many fits in which loss of consciousness was the only symptom (now known as *petit mal* seizures).[4] In their

[1] Jackson, 1931, I, 26, 37.          [2] Jefferson, 1960, p. 116.
[3] Quoted in Jefferson, 1960, p. 118.     [4] Jefferson, 1960, pp. 118–9.

authoritative *Physiology*, Todd and Bowman had extended the Bell-Magendie law only as far as the thalami for sensation and the corpora striata for motion.[1]

The corpora striata seem to have held the loyalties of all as the major motor organs. When, in 1865, Luys assigned discrete motor functions to cortical cells on histological grounds, he still held that the corpora striata were the effective motor organs.[2] Carpenter's standard text on *Physiology* held in 1869 that the corpus striatum was the motor ganglion and the thalamus the sensory.[3]

William Carpenter's writings provide a clear picture of the orthodox view, and an opportunity to contrast this with the new approach of Spencer and Jackson. He is a convenient figure for this purpose in that he exemplifies Palmer's dictum that 'The tendencies of an age appear more distinctly in its writers of inferior rank than in those of commanding genius'.[4] Carpenter was explicit on topics where more subtle thinkers were troubled, uncertain, and ambiguous. He was a leading expositor of experimental physiology, and his *Principles of Human Physiology* was, according to T. H. Huxley, the standard English work between 1842 and the early 1870s.[5] It went through five English and several American editions under his hand by 1855, and four more (edited by others) appeared by 1881. This work, along with his *General and Comparative Physiology*, played a large part in establishing physiology as an autonomous discipline in Britain.[6] His impressive bibliography shows that he was at the centre of biological and physiological debate until his death in 1885.[7] Early in Carpenter's career, J. S. Mill wrote to Comte that he considered him 'the most philosophical of all those in England who study the laws of the living body, who has written the best treatise on general and human physiology which we possess in our language'. At that time (1843) Mill lamented that Carpenter had, as yet, found no financial support for his research.[8] This situation soon changed, and Carpenter's official positions included Lectureships at the Royal Institution and the British Museum, and the Professorship of Physiology and Forensic Medicine at University College and Hospital, London.

---

[1] See above, pp. 111–2.  [2] Jefferson, 1960, pp. 121–2.  [3] Ibid., p. 114.
[4] Quoted in Lovejoy, 1936, p. 20. Mr Roger Smith of King's College, Cambridge is involved in a detailed study of Carpenter's views on the functions of the nervous system which is likely to alter considerably the account which I have given of him as a representative figure. I am indebted to him for his criticisms but do not wish to anticipate publication of his own interpretation. See below p. 212n.
[5] Quoted in Carpenter, 1888, p. 66.
[6] Carpenter, 1888, p. 64. Cf. pp. 64–9 for the views of Sir James Paget, Huxley, etc.
[7] Ibid., pp. 467–83.  [8] Mineka, 1963, p. 567.

15

He was also a Fellow of the Royal Society, President of the British Association (1872), Editor of the *Medico-Chirurgical Review*, and Registrar of London University for twenty-three years until his retirement in 1879. At the end of his career a colleague summarized Carpenter's contribution:

The great work of his life was, after all, that he gathered up the new knowledge, digested it and put it before the world in a coherent and logical form. Stated in this way, the task accomplished may not seem much. In effect it was of the deepest importance. In my judgment he laid the foundations of that breadth and comprehensiveness of the English biological school, which will, I hope, be its lasting heritage.[1]

At least as early as 1846, Carpenter had stated the limits of the principle of continuity with respect to the sensory-motor view of the nervous system.[2]

[1] Thiselton-Dyer, quoted in Carpenter, 1888, p. 142. In the following discussion Carpenter's views will be presented as representative of the prevailing climate of opinion before 1870. It should be stressed, however, that the original aspects of his work are not being discussed and are not representative. His theories of 'unconscious cerebration' and the common centre of sensation are not relevant to the present discussion. See Walshe, 1957, where Carpenter's theories are outlined and used as a stick with which to beat Penfield and discredit his concept of a 'centrencephalic integrating system'.

Carpenter's psychological writings were closely integrated with his physiological treatises, and T. H. Huxley called him a leading figure in 'the foundation of a rational, that is, to say, a physiological psychology'. (Quoted in Carpenter, 1888, p. 67.) Carpenter may be said to have played the same role from the physiological side that Bain did from the psychological in integrating the two disciplines. He added sections on Psychology to the fourth and fifth editions of his *Principles*. The growth of new physiological discoveries pushed this matter out of subsequent editions, but it was expanded and issued separately in 1874 as *Mental Physiology* (a title which was very significant of developments in the period). The psychological matter in this work is not discussed in the text, since it is drawn directly from the association psychology (except for the original matters mentioned above). His biographer reports that 'He had been trained by his father in the principles of Hartley; his psychological text-book had been James Mill's *Analysis of the Human Mind*; and his acquaintance with John Stuart Mill, and the perusal of his treatise on Logic, had not tended to weaken the general notions thus impressed upon him'. (Carpenter, 1888, p. 38.) To complete the picture, it is noteworthy that he was drawing heavily from Bain even before the publication of Bain's major work. He acknowledges his debt in Carpenter, 1855, p. 580. Conversely, Bain was very impressed by Carpenter's physiological writings and drew on them in his treatment of the nervous system (Bain, 1904, pp. 132–3, 164).

[2] These passages come from Carpenter's analysis of a work on phrenology (1846, see above, pp. 164–5). I have not read the first edition of Carpenter's *Principles* and do not know when he first held these views. Carpenter's analysis of phrenology is not being discussed in the text, but it should be noted that it adds further weight to the argument that the assumptions of later brain research developed partly on the basis of and partly in reaction to the issues posed by the phrenologists. In this article Carpenter acknowledged the debts of both neuro-physiology and psychology (especially comparative) to Gall, while lamenting the excesses and poor standards of evidence of the cranioscopists and opposing their view of the cere-bellum (Carpenter, 1846, pp. 520–5, 529–43). He adds that important advances in the understanding of reflex actions and related phenomena had occurred since Gall's time (p. 520). The care which Carpenter took in examining Noble's phrenological work is noteworthy in itself.

Knowing, as we do, that the sensory ganglia not only receive the sensory nerves, but are connected, by their implantation on the fibrous tracts of the medulla oblongata, with the motor system, we can at once understand the channel through which sensations should thus produce movements, without involving any higher act of the mind, or any exertion of the will. In the case of common or tactile sensation, there seems good reason for regarding the corpora striata as the motor portion of the ganglionic mass, of which the thalami optici constitute the sensory; the relation between them being, as well pointed out by Messrs. Todd and Bowman, the same as that which subsists between the anterior and posterior peaks of vesicular matter in the spinal cord.[1]

He makes an explicit separation of the thalami and corpora striata on the one hand from the cerebrum on the other. He refers to the cerebral hemispheres as 'distinguished from other ganglionic masses by their *superadded* character, having no direct connexion with any of the nerves, but being implanted, as it were, upon the summit of the strands which pass upwards from the nervous centres of the trunk'.[2] In a later passage he repeats (and italicizes) this point and adds that as the cerebrum 'receives sensations through the medium of the various ganglia, in which the sensory nerves terminate, so it executes the mandates of the will through the motor fibres which originate from those same ganglia, or from others in immediate connexion with them'. He emphasizes the independence of the cerebrum from the thalami and corpora striata.[3] Although the cerebrum *receives* sensations, Carpenter denies that this means that sensations are localized in the cortices. He was much more explicit on this point than many of his predecessors. He points out that Flourens, who had originally said that cortical ablation destroys all sensibility, 'substituted, in the second edition of his *Experimental Researches*, the term *perception* for *sensation*, whenever he speaks of the function which is destroyed by the removal of the cerebrum'.[4]

Having argued that the corpora striata and thalami are the highest motor and sensory ganglia, Carpenter attributes to the cerebrum the functions which are not accounted for by lower centres. It 'has no concern in the purely excito-motor actions'.[5] Nor is it the seat of pleasures and pains. Rather, it is the seat of ideas respecting the objects of sensation: perception, memory, and conception (or storing and recalling ideas).[6] The cerebrum is 'restricted to *intellectual* operations;

[1] Carpenter, 1846, p. 505.   [2] Ibid., p. 500.
[3] Ibid., p. 510. Cf. p. 517.   [4] Ibid., p. 508; see above, p. 69.
[5] Ibid., p. 512.   [6] Ibid., pp. 510–12.

understanding, by that term, the operations which are concerned in the formation of a voluntary determination'.[1]

In the fourth edition of his *Principles*, Carpenter reviews the evidence for his position.

All the results of experiments concur to establish the fact, that no irritation, either of the vesicular or of the fibrous substance, produces either sensation or motion. These results are borne-out by pathological observations in Man; for it has been frequently remarked, when it has been necessary to separate protruded portions of the Brain from the remainder, that this has given-rise to no sensation, even in cases in which the mind has been perfectly clear at the time, nor has any convulsive action been produced.[2]

This last phrase points to the issue which will be seen to trouble Jackson most. Carpenter repeats the argument given in the earlier paper,[3] and stresses the separation of the lower, automatic sensory-motor centres from the superadded cerebrum, whose functions are those of mind: perception, intelligence, and will. The sensory-motor centres are the instruments of consciousness and will.[4]

Finally, Carpenter reiterates the identical views in his *Mental Physiology*, written just before the appearance of Ferrier's work.[5] This book is a very useful document. Its text is pre-Ferrier, and an appendix was added to take account of Ferrier's first findings. The text of the appendix is almost identical with a paper which Carpenter delivered at the Annual Conversazione at the West Riding Lunatic Asylum in November of 1873.[6] That Carpenter was induced (by Crichton-Browne) to travel to Wakefield and deliver the address at the site of Ferrier's experiments indicates the significance which was immediately attached to his findings. That Carpenter shared this evaluation is further indicated by his adding it to his book after it was in page proofs. He says in his introduction that he ranks Ferrier's findings among 'the greatest advances in the Physiology of the Nervous System which have been made during the last fifty years'.[7] That Carpenter and Ferrier belonged to very different generations in physiological thought is indicated by the fact that Carpenter's review of Ferrier's results interprets the evidence as being in favour of the corpora striata as the primary motor

---

[1] Carpenter, 1846, p. 515. Cf. p. 517.    [2] Carpenter, 1855, p. 534.
[3] See Ibid., pp. 534–5, 489–90, 497–511.    [4] Ibid., pp. 508–11.
[5] Carpenter, 1874a, pp. 99–100.
[6] Carpenter, 1874, p. 1. It appears that he did not take cognizance of the findings of Fritsch and Hitzig until after he delivered the address. See Carpenter, 1874, p. 10.
[7] Ibid., p. 2.

centres and the optic thalami as the sensory.[1] He remained convinced that 'the Cerebrum does not act immediately on the motor nerves, but that it plays downwards on the motor centres contained within the Axial Cord; from which, and not from the Cerebral convolutions, the motor nerves take their real departure'.[2] The point must not be missed that Carpenter is here reiterating the old view of the separation of the cortex from the sensory-motor centres in his comments on the very work which would finally overthrow this discontinuity. He still saw the cerebrum as a separate, superadded organ, although he did mention the fibres connecting it with the striata and thalami, an acknowledgement which is at variance with his earlier claim that the cerebrum had no direct connection with any of the lower centres.[3] Even so, he recalls Flourens' experiments to support the belief that the cerebrum is independent of the thalami and striata.[4] The juxtaposition of the old and the new is dramatized by the fact that Carpenter somehow manages to reiterate his former views *and* to praise Ferrier's findings. For example, he points out that one of the strongest arguments in favour of the validity of Ferrier's work is 'that Dr. Ferrier can *predict* with almost positive certainty the movements he will call forth by the localized stimulation of certain parts of the Cerebral convolutions; and that very dissimilar movements follow the application of the stimulus to points nearly adjacent'.[5] In so far as he questions Ferrier's findings, he suggests that they may be secondary phenomena produced by hyper-aemia.[6] However, in his conclusion he grants that there are motor centres 'which are now proved to be definitely localized in the Cerebral convolutions' and which call forth coordinated movements when electrically stimulated.[7] Nevertheless, Carpenter somehow fails to grasp that Ferrier's findings contradict his own doctrine of the separation of the cortex from the lower centres and draws the implausible consequence that 'the office of the Cerebrum is not immediately to evoke, but to co-ordinate and direct, the muscular contractions' excited through lower centres.[8]

[1] Carpenter, 1874a, p. 715.    [2] Ibid., p. 719.    [3] Carpenter, 1874, pp. 7–8.
[4] Ibid.    [5] Ibid., p. 2.    [6] Ibid., pp. 10–12.    [7] Ibid., pp. 18–19.
[8] Ibid., p. 20. There may be a simple explanation for this, given by Carpenter in the introduction to the printed version of his address at the West Riding Lunatic Asylum: while he grasped that Ferrier's findings were very significant, he did not look closely enough into the experimental findings to see their detailed implications. He said, 'the time I can spare from Official duty has been so completely engrossed for several years past by other studies, that I could not presume to enter into such a critical examination of these results as would be required to satisfy Physiologists who have paid special attention to this department of inquiry.' He delivered the address with no thought of its eventual publication. (Ibid., pp. 1–2.)

Carpenter's ability to ignore the implications of new facts and to make them fit old doctrines in the period after 1870 is complemented by Jackson's difficulty (in the period just before 1870) in seeing that new facts, seen in the light of new doctrines, should transcend the orthodox belief in the corpora striata as the highest motor centres. Before turning to Jackson's difficulties, however, it is important to appreciate just how far physiological doctrine was at variance with anatomical fact. What anatomical basis was there for making a separation between the corpora striata and thalami on the one hand and the cortices on the other? The experimental evidence for this has been reviewed. Similarly, it is clear that at least since Flourens, this evidence conveniently supported philosophical prejudices which separated the mind and its organs from the sensory-motor view of the rest of the nervous system. How does this position relate to modern conceptions of the anatomy, relations, and functions of the structures involved?

It is perfectly understandable that the investigators of the brain in the nineteenth century related the sensory tracts to the optic thalamus and the motor tracts to the corpus striatum. Todd and Bowman were quite right in tracing the posterior columns of the spinal cord to the thalami and the anterior columns to the corpora striata. But why did they stop there? It appears that their preconceptions allowed them to see this far and no farther. Neither the thalami nor the corpora striata are the termini of the tracts which are seen to pass into them.

The situation with respect to the thalami is easier to understand and to reconcile with modern knowledge than that concerning the corpora striata. The spino-thalamic tract passes into the nuclei of the thalamus, carrying sensory impulses from the periphery. However, these nuclei serve only as relay stations. The spinothalamic tract synapses with the fibres of the thalamo-cortical tract which relays sensory impulses (partly by way of the anterior limb of the internal capsule) to the primary sensory projection areas of the cerebral cortices. Thus, the thalami do have sensory functions. The error of the nineteenth-century physiologists was therefore not anatomical. It was also recognized that the thalami passed information on to the cortices, though the fibres involved were sometimes conveniently ignored. However, until the sensory functions of the cerebral cortices were discovered in the mid-1870's, a physiological distinction was made between the functions of the thalami and those of the cortices. It was believed that the thalami were the highest sensory centres and served to connect the sensations coming from the external world with the organ of mind, where physical sensations became mental perceptions and served as the elements of ideas and the matter for intellectual operations. Since the association psychology had always been sensationalist, there was little resistance to extending the sensory tract to the cerebral cortices, and the literature does not mark the change of emphasis and the relative downgrading of the thalami as an important problem. The thalami were soon seen in proper perspective as relay stations for sensory impulses on their way to the cortices, the problem of the relations between sensations and perceptions ceased to have a convenient anatomical analogue, and the issue reverted to its proper philosophical context.

The situation with respect to the corpora striata is at once less clear and more interesting. Modern neuroanatomy and physiology provide almost no basis for the view which was so tenaciously held by most physiologists before (and by many after) 1870. In order to separate the corpora striata from the cerebral cortices, it was necessary to create a discontinuity where none exists. How did this happen? In order to appreciate the enormous influence of preconception, it may help to present the modern view and then try to reconcile it with the findings of earlier workers. First, the term 'corpus striatum' refers to no simple anatomical structure. It is a collective term sometimes used to refer to a number of closely related nuclei: the caudate and lenticular nuclei. 'Lenticular nucleus,' in turn is a collective term for the putamen and globus pallidus. Each of these structures was named for its shape. Their functions are very imperfectly understood today, and the most that can be said is that they are part of an 'extrapyramidal motor system', injury to which produces characteristic motor dysfunction, e.g., the tremor of Parkinsonism. Their functions in normal life are not understood at all. What is clear is that they *do not* play an important part in the direct control of muscular movements, the function which was assigned to them by all major investigators by 1870. How, then, did this enormous blunder occur?

The name 'corpus striatum' refers to the characteristic striated appearance of the collection of structures discussed above when they are sectioned and examined grossly. The striate appearance is produced by connecting bands of grey matter passing between the caudate and lenticular nuclei through the white matter of the internal capsule. It is the internal capsule which explains the findings of the nineteenth-century investigators. This structure is made up of fibres passing to and from the cortices. En route they pass *between* the caudate and lenticular nuclei. The cortico-spinal or pyramidal tract which carries motor impulses from the cortex to the spinal nerves (which, in turn, control muscular contractions), passes through part of the internal capsule on its way to the pyramids. Thus, the primary motor pathway occupies the posterior third of the anterior limb, the genu, and the anterior two thirds of the posterior limb of the internal capsule.[1]

The point of this anatomical description is to show how the nineteenth-century investigators came to associate the corpus striatum with muscular motion. Their descriptions and illustrations show that they meant the same thing by the term corpus striatum that we do today. What they failed to appreciate is that the motor tract is merely passing through on its way from the cortex (to which they denied primary motor functions) to the spinal cord. They did not deny that the corpora striata were related to the organ of will in the hemispheres, since the will was supposed to give orders which were executed by the putative motor centres in the corpora striata. Nor would a modern investigator deny that stimulation of the corpora striata produces muscular motions. Stimulation of the cortico-spinal tract at any point produces movement of the relevant muscles. Thus, the physiological findings are valid. Similarly, until 1870, cortical stimulation consistently failed to produce muscular contractions. The consequence seemed clear. However, no one noticed the continuity between the white matter of the corpora striata and the hemispheres. In fact, Carpenter (supported by Todd and Bowman on physiological grounds, and Kölliker on histological evidence) claimed that the radiating fibres of the hemispheres 'take a fresh departure' from the thalami and corpora striata.[2] As has been shown, the former claim is valid, while the latter has no anatomical basis.

The only conclusion that can fairly be reached on the fundamental role ascribed to the (in this context fundamentally unimportant) corpora striata is that the incidental passing through of the fibres of the motor tract which, when stimulated, gave violent muscular contractions and convulsions, combined with the failure to evoke contractions from cortical stimulation, proved too convenient a set of findings for those who wanted to separate the organ of the will from mundane muscular movements. This coalescence of physiological findings (positive and

---

[1] The anatomical and physiological matter of the foregoing discussion has been drawn from Peele, 1954; Brain, 5th ed., 1955; Dorland, 23rd ed., 1957; and consultation with professional neuroanatomists and neurologists. I should like to thank Sir Francis Walshe for referring me to the works of Carpenter.

[2] Carpenter, 1855, p. 490. Cf. Jefferson, 1960, p. 115, for an earlier (1827) illustration which shows the pyramids ending in the corpus striatum.

negative) with psychological convictions and philosophical assumptions led them to see just what they wanted in a way that is reminiscent of the anatomists who dissected bodies only to confirm what Galen had written centuries before. Their assumptions prepared (or permitted) them to see only so much. For important philosophical reasons the cortex was considered separate in function from the sensory-motor system. What they saw was what they expected: discontinuity. It had been a great step to admit that the brain was the organ of the mind. To reduce mind to crude sensory-motor terms was asking too much of most investigators of the pre-Spencerian school.

The belief in the pre-eminence of the corpora striata did not disappear with the findings of Fritsch and Hitzig, and Ferrier, and Carpenter's response has already been noted. Similarly, the Report to the British Association which called Ferrier's findings 'the most important work which has been accomplished in physiology for a very considerable time past'[1] and explicitly argued that the convolutions of the cerebrum were shown by Ferrier to be concerned with muscular movements and not entirely with purely intellectual operations,[2] contained the following passage on the same page: 'that the corpus striatum is concerned in motion, while the optic thalamus is concerned in sensation, and that intellectual operations are manifested specially through the cerebral hemispheres, are conclusions which were indicated by the study of diseased conditions',[3] and Ferrier's experiments are said to confirm this doctrine.[4] The origin of the pyramidal tract was shown by Betz to be in the cortex, where, he said, the great pyramidal cells were found in just those parts of the cortex which Fritsch and Hitzig had found excitable.[5] This was in 1874. In 1876, William Broadbent was referring to the corpus striatum as 'the motor ganglion for the entire opposite half of the body. It translates volitions into actions, or puts in execution the commands of the Intellect'.[6] This passage was quoted by Bastian in 1880, as the best expression of a view which he supported.[7] He goes on to discuss Ferrier's findings in detail, but he retains an important motor role for the corpora striata.[8] As late as 1886, Jackson indicated that most physicians thought epilepsy to be a dysfunction of sub-cortical and medullary centres.[9] It is not until 1890 that one finds, in Foster's standard *Text Book of Physiology*, the modern view which sees the fibres of the cortico-spinal tract merely passing through the corpora striata,

---

[1] Rutherford, 1874, p. 122.     [2] Ibid., p. 121.     [3] Ibid.
[4] Ibid., p. 122.     [5] Jefferson, 1960, p. 121.     [6] Quoted in Bastian, 1880, p. 567.
[7] Ibid., pp. 564-7.     [8] Ibid., pp. 569-88.     [9] Jefferson, 1960, p. 116.

structures whose functions are unknown.[1] It is with this subsequent history in mind that one must return to the 1860's and examine Jackson's tentative attempts to implicate the cerebral cortices in muscular motions.

## Jackson's Ambiguous Position

Jackson's case is instructive and is worth considering in detail, not for the sake of priority (no claim is feasible that Jackson predicted Fritsch and Hitzig's findings), but because it emphasizes the slowness with which the elements of a thoroughgoing sensory-motor view, which included the cortex and its functions, were finally brought together. All the necessary conceptions had existed in the literature at least since Mueller, and they had been developed into a thoroughgoing sensory-motor psychophysiology by Bain and Spencer, but Jackson's work shows that there was an extreme reluctance to apply them unequivocally to the cortex, even though there were data in abundance to justify the application, and even though it was required by Spencer and Jackson's evolutionary view of the continuity of functional organization of the nervous system.

If Jackson's statements on the convolutions and the corpus striatum up to 1870 are brought together and compared, the simple truth is that they defy integration into a consistent, unified view. Two positions remain constant: (1) The corpus striatum was considered the highest part of the motor tract,[2] and the movement of limbs and of speech were represented there.[3] (2) The convolutions, usually referred to as 'convolutions near the corpus striatum', represented impressions and movements.[4] As early as 1866, he began making statements which sometimes juxtaposed these views and sometimes ignored one while advocating the other with regard to disease. Thus, in one article he names the corpus striatum 'the highest part of the motor tract', through which 'we are able to direct our *limbs* voluntarily'.[5] But two years later

---

[1] Foster, 5th ed., 1890, pp. 970–8. The present study is confined to the period which begins with empirical localizations, and I have not looked into the earlier history of views on the functions of the corpus striatum. Meyer (1960, p. 789) attributed the origin of the view to Thomas Willis. I have not read Willis' works and can only report that other secondary sources do not support this attribution. Willis' role in the founding of comparative neurology and the shift of emphasis from the ventricles to the solid parts of the brain deserves a much more careful treatment at the hands of historians than it appears to have had until now.

[2] Jackson, 1931, II, 127, 122–3.

[3] Ibid., II, 216, 244; Jackson, 1931, I, pp. 26–7.

[4] Jackson, 1931, I, 27, 38; Jackson, 1931, II, 123.

[5] Jackson, 1931, II, 122–3. Jackson's emphasis is irrelevant to my point.

he was using a looser formulation for movements of the limbs: they are 'represented in *each* part near the corpus striatum'.[1] He next refers to 'convolutions near the corpus striatum for superintending those delicate movements of the hands which are under the immediate control of the mind'. These convolutions are spoken of as 'higher centres of movement', and disease of them can cause chorea.[2] However, he is occasionally less explicit, naming only 'the locality of the corpus striatum'.[3]

Jackson's style is always vague, but it appears that his lack of explicitness here is the result of hesitancy and/or muddle rather than his usual style. He regards the corpus striatum as the seat of the lesion in hemiplegia[4] and in convulsions beginning unilaterally.[5] But where aphasia is concerned, he is less explicit. The arrangements of fibres and cells representing the movements of speech lie 'close upon the corpus striatum' in one reference and are located in *convolutions* near the corpus striatum in another on the same page.[6] The confusion about the highest motor centres is made explicit in the last reference where, having localized the movements of speech and the lesion of aphasia in the convolutions, he says that these cause symptoms by affecting the corpus striatum, which alone is the place where the will can move muscles: 'disease near the corpus striatum produces defect of expression (by words, writing, signs, etc.), to a great extent, because this is the way out from the hemisphere to organs which the will can set in motion'.[7] This was written in 1866. Two years later he reported a case of 'Corpus Striatum Epilepsy' which involved a post-mortem finding of blood, the bulk of which 'lay in one spot over the frontal convolutions, and was so placed as, I imagined, to squeeze the corpus striatum'.[8] The discussion refers all symptoms to the corpus striatum and does not mention the convolutions. In this case Jackson was clearly wedded to the corpus striatum in spite of a striking finding which pointed to the convolutions.

By 1870 he was to implicate the convolutions in *severe* convulsions: 'As the convolutions are rich in grey matter I suppose them to be to blame, in *severe* convulsions at all events'. However, he immediately reverts to the corpus striatum in the rest of the sentence: 'but as the corpus striatum also contains much grey matter I cannot deny that it may be sometimes the part to blame in slighter convulsions. Indeed, if the discharge does begin in convolutions, no doubt the grey matter

---

[1] Jackson, 1931, II, p. 241. Jackson's emphasis is irrelevant to my point.
[2] Ibid., II, 240–1, 122–3.     [3] Ibid., II, 239.     [4] Ibid., II, 239, 246.
[5] Jackson, 1931, I, 38.     [6] Jackson, 1931, II, 123.     [7] Ibid.     [8] Ibid., II, 218.

of lower motor centres, even if these centres be healthy, will be discharged secondarily by the violent impulse received from the primary discharge'.[1]

After the findings of Fritsch and Hitzig and Ferrier, Jackson's hesitancy and/or confusion disappeared, and he attempted to rehabilitate his former views with the wisdom of hindsight, claiming that his only real error was in assigning the lesion of unilateral epilepsy to the corpus striatum, rather than to the convolutions near to it.[2] He also held, as part of his hierarchical view of the nervous system, a conception of these convolutions as representing 'over again, but in new and more complex combinations, the very same movements which are represented in the corpus striatum. They are, I believe, the corpus striatum "raised to a higher power"'.[3]

The accusation of vagueness against many of Jackson's statements should be mitigated in the light of the fact that he was dealing with clinical phenomena at a time when the underlying neurophysiological processes were not known and could not provide a precise set of correlates for his gross observations of symptoms and lesions. For example, his failure to make a clear demarcation between the convolutions and the corpus striatum in cases of epilepsy is partially explained by his seeing them both as parts supplied by the middle cerebral artery.[4]

The purpose of the foregoing analysis will have been served if it communicates some of the confusion about the convolutions among physiologists and clinicians up to 1870. Clinical views based on the associationist sensory-motor psychophysiology were directly implicating the cortex with more or less hesitancy, but the strictly experimental data from physiology gave an unequivocal answer: the cortex was inexcitable to artificial stimulation, whether mechanical, chemical, or electrical.

Although the subject matter of the last several chapters, beginning with the association psychology, has all been properly included within the experimental tradition, it should be noted that no new experiments fundamentally affecting the aspects of brain physiology which are being considered here were conducted between 1822 and 1870. The intervening years were occupied with the progressive extension of the sensory-motor view to the brain in the (non-experimental) writings of association psychologists in the light of clinical and clinico-pathological findings. In a sense, then, no strictly experimental work was

[1] Jackson, 1931, I, 9.        [2] Ibid., I, 38.
[3] Ibid., I, 68. Cf. 114–15.     [4] Ibid., I, 9.

going on between 1822 and 1870. Experimental neurophysiology was dominated by three firmly-based findings: the Bell-Magendie law, the regulatory function of the cerebellum, and the inexcitability of the cortex. A fourth aspect of the climate of ideas was in an equivocal position: cerebral equipotentiality had been challenged by the clinical findings of Bouillaud and Broca in France, and cerebral localization was being considered (though less heatedly and in very different functional and anatomical terms) by Spencer and Jackson. Three of these four reigning ideas were primarily the results of Flourens' findings and preconceptions. Consequently, Fritsch and Hitzig address their experimental findings back through fifty years to Flourens.

# FRITSCH AND HITZIG AND THE LOCALIZED ELECTRICAL EXCITABILITY OF THE CEREBRAL HEMISPHERES

All this has never yet been seen—But Scientists who ought to know Assure us that it Must Be So: O, Let us never, never doubt What nobody is Sure About!

H. Belloc

IN 1870, Gustav Fritsch and Eduard Hitzig published a paper entitled 'On the Electrical Excitability of the Cerebrum',[1] which demonstrated by experiment that

A part of the convexity of the hemisphere of the brain of the dog is motor . . . another part is not motor. The motor part, in general, is more in front, the non-motor part more behind. By electrical stimulation of the motor part, one obtains combined muscular contractions of the opposite side of the body.[2]

This finding must be set apart from the foregoing analysis for two reasons. It stands apart, first, because of its significance. The work of Fritsch and Hitzig was a truly epoch-making classical experiment in the sense that all subsequent work in cerebral physiology was done with reference to this single publication. It dethroned a doctrine that had reigned for fifty years, and its appearance introduced order into the confused picture indicated above. The second reason is less obvious. It has to do with the context of the experiment and the psychological theory with which it is allied. Fritsch and Hitzig's psychological views neither arose from nor were they compatible with the sensory-motor associationist tradition which has been traced from Locke to Bain, Spencer, and Jackson. Their *finding* was one of the two direct stimuli for Ferrier's experiments, but their psychophysiology was part of the tradition which Jackson explicitly rejected. Consequently, the finding of Fritsch and Hitzig must be considered separately from its interpretation by them. This separation is relatively easy, since their comments

---

[1] The original publication was 'Über die elektrische Erregbarkeit des Grosshirns', and it appeared in *Arch. f. Anat., Physiol. und wissenschaftl. Mediz.*, Leipzig, **37**, 1870, 300–32. All quotations are taken from the translation in von Bonin, 1960, and page references refer to it.

[2] Fritsch and Hitzig, 1870, p. 81.

on psychophysiology are incidental to their main thesis about the 'central places of muscular movement'.

Gustav Fritsch and Eduard Hitzig were two young German physicians. Their experiments were conducted on a dressing table in a small Berlin house, because the University had no space for such studies.[1] Hitzig became a renowned psychiatrist with a reputation for 'incorrigible conceit and vanity complicated by Prussianism'.[2] He continued to play a major role in the experimental work on localization in the ensuing decades and gave the 'Hughlings Jackson Lecture' in 1900. Fritsch was a man of independent means who spent much of his life travelling. His 1870 paper with Hitzig was his only important contribution to medicine.[3]

Their report begins with a statement of the anomalous positions of the hemispheres with respect to the law of specific energies of the rest of the nervous system. 'Physiology ascribes to all nerves as a necessary condition the property of excitability, that is to say, the ability to answer by its specific energy all influences by which its properties are changed with a certain speed.'[4] While the artificial excitability of the brain stem and spinal cord had been hotly disputed, 'since the beginning of the century we were quite generally convinced that the hemispheres were completely inexcitable for all modes of excitation generally used in physiology'.[5] They review the negative findings of Longet (1842), Magendie (1839), Matteucci (1843), and others, setting Flourens aside for fuller treatment. Their quotations from Weber and Schiff are instructive. Weber shows the confidence with which the dogma was held.

If one can conclude from the present standpoint of science that there are no motor fibers in a nervous part in which after excitation no contractions occur, one can say with the greatest certainty there is not one fiber in the hemisphere of the brain which goes to voluntary muscles. Not a single observer saw movements of such muscles after stimulation of the central parts.[6]

Schiff is equally certain and extends the inexcitability from somatic muscular motion to the intestines, which also remain quiescent after excitation of the lobes of the brain.[7] One can vicariously experience the

---

[1] Haymaker, 1953, pp. 138–42.    [2] von Bonin, 1960, p. xii.
[3] Ibid. Cf. Grundfest, 1963.
[4] Fritsch and Hitzig, 1870, p. 73. Helmholtz had measured the velocity of a nerve impulse in a motor nerve in 1850. See Boring, 1950, pp. 41–3, 47–9. Helmholtz's original report is translated and reprinted in Dennis, 1948, pp. 197–8. On specific energies of nerves, see Boring 1950, pp. 80–95. This topic deserves further study.
[5] Fritsch and Hitzig, 1870. p. 73.    [6] Ibid., p. 75.    [7] Ibid.

inconosclastic excitement with which Fritsch and Hitzig conclude their review. 'Even in other fields than in physiology, there can hardly be a question about an opinion which seems so completely settled as that of the excitability of the cerebral hemisphere. It would be easy to give more citations in the same vein if there would be any point to it.'[1]

Flourens' findings were discussed in greater detail. There must be no question about the respect in which Fritsch and Hitzig held him. At the beginning of their review they say. 'This gifted and lucky observer by using as clean a method as possible came to results which deserve to be considered as a basis for all later experiments in this field.'[2] Flourens' ablations on birds and mammals had shown the 'signs of will and consciousness of sensations disappear, while nevertheless, by stimuli coming from the outside, quiet engine-like movements could be produced in all parts of the body'.[3] He had quite naturally concluded that 'the cerebral hemispheres were not the seat of the immediate principle of muscular movements but only the seat of volition and sensation'.[4]

Given Flourens' methods, Fritsch and Hitzig grant that these conclusions seemed satisfying. However, Flourens' further findings and the concepts associated with them were 'difficult to harmonize . . . with experience gained in other ways'.[5] These further results had led Flourens to believe in cortical equipotentiality. If he ablated a hemisphere, the resulting blindness and occasional weakness on the opposite side were transient. Ablation of the grey matter of both cortices (apparently in a pigeon) was also followed by complete recovery. Progressive slicing away of the hemispheres led to 'a uniform gradual decrease of sensory perceptions and volition', which was regained within a few days, provided a sufficient amount of tissue was left intact. If the extirpations exceeded a certain limit all faculties disappeared and were not recovered. 'Flourens concluded that the cerebral lobes with their whole mass subserved their functions, and that there is no special seat either for the different faculties or for the different sensations.' Also, an intact remaining part of the hemispheres 'could relearn the complete use of all functions'.[6]

The resulting view of 'the central places of muscular movement' was that there were muscular mechanisms in most parts of the brain stem and cord which could be excited reflexly from the periphery or centrally 'by way of volition or of the impulse of the soul'. The soul was believed

---

[1] Fritsch and Hitzig, 1870, p. 75.  [2] Ibid., p. 76.  [3] Ibid.
[4] Ibid.  [5] Ibid.  [6] Ibid., pp. 76–7.

to have its seat in the grey matter of the hemispheres, 'without however, the parts of the psychic center being localizable on to parts of the organic center'. Unfortunately, the investigation of the probable seat or 'nearest tools' of the soul was closed, 'since the substrate will not answer with an overt reaction to any normal stimulus'.[1]

Fritsch and Hitzig thus raised three closely related issues: the excitability of the hemispheres, localization of functions, and the relation of the hemispheres to the immediate principle of muscular movements. Prior to their own experiments there had been equivocal results which bore on the traditional views on each of these points. In 1756, Haller and Zinn had seen convulsive movements after lesions of the white matter of the brain, but the limitation of the stimuli they used was not precise, and their findings were explained away as the likely result of pushing their instruments into the medulla oblongata.[2] In 1867, Eckhard mentioned an unspecified source which noted movements of the anterior extremities on ablation of the anterior lobes.[3] Neither of these results had any effect on the prevailing doctrines. Clinical findings had been discounted because of the notorious difficulties involved in interpreting post-mortem examinations. In any case, many congenital and acquired defects of parts of the brain involved no interference with cerebral functions. Nevertheless, it was such clinical findings which contributed to the gradual modification of the prevailing view. Bouillaud and Broca found aphasia 'caused by destruction of a small eccentric part of the brain', and cases had been reported in the literature of monoplegias of an arm or leg associated with post-mortem findings of 'small defects of the cerebral hemispheres'.[4] As early as 1834, Andral had expressed the frustration which these results engendered: in the present state of the science it is impossible to assign a distinct cerebral seat for limb movements, although the findings of monoplegias leave no doubt that such a seat exists.[5]

Other clinical results came from cases involving the corpus striatum and thalamus. As long as there was no question of a role for the cortex in movements, these had been taken into account by physiologists. However, once Fritsch and Hitzig began to take seriously the possibility of involvement of the cortex, they became wary of reasoning on the basis of such cases, since the corpus striatum and thalamus contained conduction pathways from the hemispheres and therefore could not

---

[1] Fritsch and Hitzig, 1870, pp. 77-8.    [2] Ibid., pp. 73-4.
[3] Ibid., p. 75.    [4] Ibid., p. 78.
[5] Ibid.

16 (20 pp)

give certain evidence regarding 'the first locus where the lost movement began'.[1]

Clinical findings in favour of both localization and cortical representation of movements were supported by morphological investigations, notably those of Meynert. He considered the cerebral cortex to be a 'focus of perceptions' and argued that it could be 'subdivided into many, more or less circumscribed parts, the importance of which for the various perceptions is due to the nerve fibers of its so-called projection system'.[2] Fritsch and Hitzig refer to Meynert as one of the few neurologists prior to their report who had 'talked in favour of a strict localization of psychological faculties, although differently from Gall'.[3] This is the only mention of Gall in their paper. However, it may help to see the significance of his concepts for their work if it is recalled that what Flourens, Bouillaud, and Broca said about localization is directly related to Gall, and that these figures provided the issues which Fritsch and Hitzig are addressing. Their conclusion is that 'Such facts show that the origin of at least some function of the soul is bound up with circumscribed parts of the brain'.[4] It is against this background that they began their own work.[5] 'In the meantime, by the results of our own investigations, the premises for many conclusions about the basic properties of the brain are changed not a little.'[6]

In a previous experiment Hitzig had elicited eye movements by conducting galvanic currents through the 'posterior part' and temporal region of the head of a man. He claimed that these were 'the first movements of voluntary muscles elicited by direct stimulation of the central organ in man'.[7] The question arose whether the temporal stimulations involved spread of current to subcortical centres 'or whether

---

[1] Fritsch and Hitzig, 1870, p. 78.     [2] Ibid., p. 79.

[3] Ibid., p. 92.     [4] Ibid., p. 78.

[5] Jackson's name is conspicuously absent from Fritsch and Hitzigs's otherwise thorough review of work leading up to their discovery. It is true that in his Hughlings Jackson Lecture in 1900, Hitzig claimed that he was the first to confirm by experiment and to define more closely what Jackson had concluded from clinical facts. However, I have seen no evidence that Jackson's ideas played any role in leading Fritsch and Hitzig to conduct their experiments. The relationship seems to be that they arrived at their views on the basis of the work listed in their paper. Their findings, along with Jackson's theories, inspired Ferrier to conduct his experiments. The discoveries of Fritsch and Hitzig, and of Ferrier, were, in turn, taken up by Jackson as confirming his earlier views and as a sure basis for extending them. A false impression could be gained from the way Sir Francis Walshe quotes Hitzig's remark about confirming Jackson. (Walshe, 1961, p. 119.)

[6] Fritsch and Hitzig, 1870, p. 79.

[7] Fritsch and Hitzig, 1870, p. 79. Walker reports that Fritsch is said to have 'observed, while dressing a head wound some years earlier, that mechanical irritation of the brain caused twitching of the contralateral limbs'. He gives no reference, and no mention is made of this in the 1870 article. (Walker, 1957, p. 106.)

the cerebral hemispheres in contrast to the general assumption were after all electrically excitable'.[1] A preliminary experiment on a rabbit by Hitzig gave a positive result, and he and Fritsch undertook a large number of further experiments on dogs which gave 'results . . . uniform even to the smallest details'.

Their findings overthrew three theories that had stood since Flourens: they established cortical excitability, a role for the cortex in the mechanism of movements, and cerebral localization. 'The possibility to stimulate narrowly delimited groups of muscles is restricted to very small foci which we shall call centers.'[2] Five centres were specified in constant loci (see Fig. 1): for the muscles of the neck, the extensors

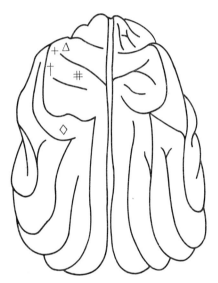

Fig. 1. Dorsal view of dog's brain. Cortical centres for muscles of neck, Δ; for extensors and adductors of anterior leg +; for flexion and rotation of same leg †; for posterior leg #; and for facial nerve ◇.

and adductors of the anterior leg, flexion and rotation of the same leg, the posterior leg, and the facial nerve. Using minimal intensity of stimulation, the areas between these centres were not excitable, though a greater intensity or separation of the electrodes led to generalized movements on both sides of the body, and tetanic stimulation led to after-movements which, in two cases, developed into generalized epileptic attacks.

[1] Fritsch and Hitzig, 18070, p. 79.   [2] Ibid., p. 81.

16A

Two points should be made about their presentation. First, their meticulous attention to operative techniques (especially the necessity to control bleeding) and stimulation parameters, is a new and important feature of their paper as compared with earlier work. The technology of neurophysiological research becomes more and more a matter of central concern in subsequent work. A second matter of increasing importance was a standard nomenclature of cerebral areas. This was provided for Fritsch and Hitzig by Richard Owen's *On the Anatomy of the Vertebrates* (1868).[1]

Much of their discussion is concerned with issues that took a decade to settle. Were they really stimulating the cortex, or were current loops spreading to lower centres? They conducted experiments which convinced them that it was the convexity itself which was producing the contractions. Were the fibres alone, or the cells as well, excitable? This was a confusing question in 1870, which they felt unable to decide. One reason for their indecision is reflected in its statement as a dichotomy: fibres *or* fibres and cells. It should be remembered that the explicit statement of the neurone theory was almost twenty years away. Fritsch and Hitzig tentatively attempt to eliminate the dichotomous issue with an early statement of the theory. 'Since no other reason can be found why the fibers should come closer to the ganglion cells just here than to meet their fate to enter into them, one can assume that these ganglionic masses are predestined to produce organic stimuli just for these nerve fibers.'[2] They are quite properly not over-concerned with this last issue in their first publication, nor are they particularly worried about other questions they left open, such as the relation between the poles of their stimulating instrument or the character of the muscular twitches obtained. 'The new facts which were shown by these investigations are so manifold, and their consequences go into so many directions, that it would be of little advantage to try to follow all these trails at once.'[3]

They insist on only two firm conclusions. The first, 'that central

[1] Standard cerebral anatomy has become the cornerstone of method in cerebral physiology. In 1908, Victor Horsley and A. H. Clarke designed a stereotaxic instrument which made it possible to use a standard atlas and standard three-dimensional co-ordinates for specifying any point on the surface and, more importantly, in the deeper portions of the brain. Subsequent developments of this technique have led to very impressive localized stimulation, ablation, electrical recording, and implantation of pharmacologic substances. 0·5 mm is the current acceptable standard of error for a good instrument and atlas. The original instrument was described in Horsley and Clarke, 1908. Several articles describing current stereotaxic technology appear in Sheer, 1961. The enormous bibliography to that work is a rich mine of sources.

[2] Fritsch and Hitzig, 1870, p. 93.     [3] Ibid., p. 84.

nervous structures answer our stimuli with overt reactions',[1] eliminates the anomaly with which they opened their paper. The hemispheres, like all other nervous structures, have the property of excitability that had formerly been denied to them alone. The second certain conclusion is that 'a large part of the nervous masses composing the hemispheres, about half of it, stands in immediate connection with muscular move ments, while another part has evidently directly nothing to do with it'.[2]

Fritsch and Hitzig reveal the two most important principles of the new era in cerebral physiology which this paper begins as they attempt to answer the very pertinent question of 'how it came about that so many earlier investigators, among them the most illustrious names came to opposite results. To this we have only one answer, "Methods give the results"'.[3] This statement is double-edged. It recalls Flourens' identical statement as he advocated the experimental method rather than Gall's anecdotal and correlative approach. Since it is being used by Fritsch and Hitzig as they overthrow Flourens' findings, the state ment also shows that new methods give new results. From 1870 to the present day, this technology has provided increasingly more refined and fruitful techniques, which have largely determined the progress of experimental work: new surgical and aseptic techniques, stimulation sources, electrodes and methods of placing them accurately (and, later, of implanting them permanently). Beginning in the second quarter of the present century, the above methods were aided by the addition of very elaborate methods of recording the electrical activity of the brain as a whole, and very tiny regions of it down to a single neurone. Some appreciation of these advances can be gathered by comparing a modern stimulating and recording console with their measure of stimulus intensity—that which 'produced just a sensation on the tongue when it was touched by the heads'.[4]

Their answer to previous failures was not only concerned with methods. In fact, they acknowledge that *assumptions* had, in large measure, determined the results.

It is impossible that our predecessors have laid bare the whole convexity, for otherwise they must have obtained contractions. The posterior lateral wall of the cranial vault of the dog, under which there are no motor parts, recommends itself by its configuration for the first trephine opening. Here one most likely began the operation and then did not go forward, assuming erroneously, that the various parts of the surface were equivalent. One based

---

[1] Fritsch and Hitzig, 1870, p. 91.    [2] Ibid., p. 92.
[3] Ibid., p. 90.    [4] Ibid., p. 81.

oneself on the supposition still widely disseminated and mentioned in the beginning, that all psychological functions are present in all parts of the cortex. Had one only thought of the localization of psychological functions, one would have considered the seemingly inexcitability of certain parts as something quite obvious and would have examined every part separately.[1]

Their paper closes with a reiteration of this rejection of cerebral equipotentiality and its replacement by cerebral localization.

This shows clearly, that in the former colossal destructions of the brain, either other parts have been chosen or that the final mechanisms of movements were not particularly noticed. It further appears, from the sum of all our experiments that the soul is not, as Flourens and others after him had thought, a function of the whole of the hemispheres, the expression of which one might destroy by mechanical means in the whole, but not in its various parts but that on the contrary, certainly some psychological functions and perhaps all of them, in order to enter matter or orginate from it need certain circumscribed centers of the cortex.[2]

The assumption of cerebral localization which was given its first firm experimental support in this publication by Fritsch and Hitzig was to dominate cerebral research (with dissent that took its meaning by contrast) until the 1930's, and is again the ruling assumption in clinical and experimental work.[3]

## Ontological Dualism and Interaction in Fritsch and Hitzig

The phrasing of the closing sentence in their paper raises the issue of the philosophic assumptions underlying Fritsch and Hitzig's experiments and their incompatibility with the assumptions of the associationist tradition to which Jackson and Ferrier belonged. Put simply, Fritsch and Hitzig were ontological dualists and believed in separate substances of mind and its mechanisms. The brain is the material instrument of the immaterial soul, and the grey matter of the cortices constituted the 'first tools of the soul'.[4] The soul can execute its orders by its property or faculty of will, and this provides an impulse which excites the motor mechanisms by interaction. Excitation by a mental act is an alternative means of exciting the motor mechanisms; reflex excitation from the periphery by purely physiological means being the other. They differed from Flourens, who held a similar interactionist view, in that they were prepared to localize at least some of the functions of the soul and to place some of its instruments for muscular

---

[1] Fritsch and Hitzig, 1870, p. 90.  [2] Ibid., p. 96.
[3] See Zangwill, 1961; Krech, 1962.  [4] Fritsch and Hitzig, 1870, p. 77.

motion in the hemispheres. Flourens had reserved the hemispheres for sensation and volition, holistic functions served by an equipotential and inexcitable cerebral mass.

Fritsch and Hitzig were not prepared to say that they had found the centres of volition or even that their centres were the first mechanical link in the execution of volitions. The methods they used could not tell them if their stimuli led to the same movements as normal mental and physiological mechanisms. The last sections of their paper are concerned with a tentatively-held view that their centres served an intermediate function between 'that part of the brain which harbors the origin of the volition of the movement' and lower muscular mechanisms which were less well-coordinated.[1] They conducted ablation experiments which, they believed, left room for 'purely psychological possibilities' 'more central' than their motor centres. These were presented very briefly and interpreted very tentatively. The result of ablating the centre for the right anterior extremity was not complete paralysis but only impairment of the ability to move the limb. They saw this finding as supportive of the existence of 'still other centers and pathways to originate and to run to the muscles of that leg'.[2] The further interpretation of the partial nature of the impairment is reserved, but the whole discussion is in the service of an interactionist conception.

There is nothing to be gained for present purposes from a detailed examination of their interactionism and the complex problems it involves. (For example, like Flourens, they were involved in a double interaction: between will and its material substrate in the first instance, and then between the mental act of will and the muscular mechanisms it activates.) The point to be made is that the psychophysical parallelism of the Spencer–Jackson–Ferrier view eliminates all these complex issues by precluding interaction and even the discussion of psychological faculties in a physiological context. The support for his concepts which Jackson derived from Fritsch and Hitzig is confined to the involvement of the hemispheres in movement. The stimulus they gave to Ferrier is confined to their demonstration of the localized electrical excitability of the cerebral hemispheres. The philosophical assumptions of the Germans' view were anathema to the Englishmen, whose parallelism allowed them the luxury of ontological agnosticism while they got on with their work.

[1] Fritsch and Hitzig, 1870, p. 92.    [2] Ibid. p. 96.

# 8

## DAVID FERRIER: LOCALIZATION OF SENSORY-MOTOR PSYCHOPHYSIOLOGY

On the whole, then, it seems impossible to allow that Dr. Ferrier has done more than take a first step towards discovering the relation of different parts in the brain; nor is it possible to say thus far that much psychological insight is likely to be gained upon the new line of inquiry. Certainly, although he gives us in chapter xi a view of 'the hemispheres considered psychologically' which is much above the level of common physiological opinion, it does not appear to depend specially upon his own investigations. And that we are now put in the way to obtain a truly scientific phrenology, embodying what was true in the old phrenological doctrine (the notion of definite organ for definite function) but based, as that was not, upon exact anatomical and physiological inquiry in relation to exact psychological analysis—this, which is becoming a fond conviction with many, is, to say the least, a very premature hope. In some respects, the old phrenology was itself more scientific than that which would now be substituted for it.

George C. Robertson, 1877.

Unless our laboratory results are to give us artificialities, mere scientific curiosities, they must be subjected to interpretation by gradual reapproximation to conditions of life.

John Dewey, 1900.

### Ferrier's Localizations

It took time to persuade the critics of the validity of Fritsch and Hitzig's findings. Tests were conducted throughout the 1870's, and commissions consisting of noted physiologists reported favourably from New York, Boston, and Italy.[1] New objections by Burden-Sanderson in England were overcome by a French exponent of the new physiology, François-Franck.[2] The literature on cerebral localization after 1873 became so extensive that contemporary reviewers listed hundreds of references and made no pretence of providing exhaustive reports.[3] Once the principle of cerebral localization was established, it provided a paradigm within which searching for centres became, and to a large extent has remained, a part of normal science.[4] Unlike

---

[1] Jefferson, 1960, p. 127.    [2] Ibid., pp. 127–8.
[3] Dodds, 1878; Bastian, 1880; Mills 1890; Ferrier, 1890; Bateman, 1890; and Foster, 1890 (Part III), provide extremely useful contemporary reviews. Cf. Jefferson, 1960.
[4] Cf. Kuhn, 1962.

many important discoveries in science, the appreciation and exploitation of Fritsch and Hitzig's findings, were in no way delayed. Almost without exception the articles and texts which appeared in the 1870's, 80's, and 90's convey the atmosphere of 'electric excitement' engendered by their discovery.

A great deal of classical work on the cerebral hemispheres followed in the next few years, and centres for various functions were mapped by workers in Germany, France, Italy, and especially England. The principal figures supporting localization in this period were Hitzig, Munk, François-Frank, Luciani, Beevor, Schafer, Horsley, and David Ferrier. New and more precise techniques of stimulation and ablation developed apace and were used to extend the initial findings on motor functions, and to discover cerebral areas related to sensation. Johannes Mueller's doctrine of specific nerve energies (which related to specific senses in the peripheral nervous system) was extended to the brain, and centres for vision, hearing, touch, olfaction, and taste, were more or less established over the next two decades, although the centres for taste and smell remained uncertain, and there was considerable debate over particular sensory centres between the two principal contributors to these developments—Ferrier and Munk. Ferrier had mentioned the possibility of localizing sensory centres in his first papers,[1] and the first edition of his book had a thirty page section on the topic. Ten years later the second edition had a section almost three times as long.[2]

The work of these investigators was informed by the growing appreciation of the implications of the theory of evolution. Thus, one finds them taking comparative anatomy quite as seriously as Gall did (and as Flourens did not), and the concept of continuity of nervous structures and functions became a basic assumption. Their writings contain specific findings with reference to the increase in cortical control (encephalization of functions) as the evolutionary scale is ascended toward higher primates and man.

The work of David Ferrier was at the centre of these developments and prototypical of the new physiology. Ferrier's experiments (first published in 1873) were the first to confirm Fritsch and Hitzig's. Where they had found five localized centres for various movements in the dog, he soon found in the monkey fifteen different areas where movement could be elicited by electrical stimulation. His ablation work contributed to the localization of each of the sensory functions

[1] Ferrier, 1873, pp. 50, 55–6; 1874a, pp. 2, 80, 97, 127, 134–5.
[2] Ferrier, 1876, pp. 163–98; 1886, pp. 268–345.

mentioned above. The significance of Ferrier's work for neurophysiology can be glimpsed from the fact that Sir Charles Sherrington dedicated his classical lectures on *The Integrative Action of the Nervous System* (1906) to Ferrier: 'In token recognition of his many services to the experimental physiology of the nervous system.' In fact, Sherrington's first publication was an examination of the brains which Ferrier and Goltz had presented in 1881 on the issue of cerebral localization. The work of Ferrier was thus one of the bases of Sherrington's whole new emphasis in the study of neurophysiology, involving the use of the concepts of integration, evolution, and reflex as guiding principles. In his obituary notice on Ferrier for the Royal Society, Sherrington points out that Ferrier had been the main figure in proving the concept of cerebral localization, placing it at the centre of neurological interest,[1] and providing the basis for a 'scientific phrenology'.[2]

In spite of the ambiguities in his writings before 1870, there can be no doubt that Jackson's conceptions were the principal inspiration of Ferrier's research. In his first paper Ferrier describes the object of his experiments as the testing of Jackson's theory that localized and unilateral epilepsies are caused by irritation or discharging lesions of the cortex. He sets out to confirm these deductions by 'artificial reproduction of the clinical experiments performed by disease'.[3] He concludes that his results confirm Jackson's theories,[4] and says later that he considers Jackson the source of the revival of interest in cerebral localization. 'The doctrine of cerebral localization has in recent years assumed quite a new aspect, and differs so much from older speculations in the kind of evidence on which its rests, as to be essentially a new growth. Hughlings-Jackson made the first decided steps in this direction.'[5] He acknowledges that Jackson's views were based on the 'rude experiments of disease', a circumstance which precluded exact localizations. 'But to Hughlings-Jackson belongs the credit of having first indicated the motor functions of certain regions of the cortex, and given a rational explanation of the phenomena of unilateral cerebral convulsions.'[6] Ferrier's lavish acknowledgement of his debts to Jackson is reminiscent of Jackson's statements about Spencer. In his first paper to the Royal Society, Ferrier prefaces a reference to a paper by Jackson on aphasia with the following remark: 'Without being sure of agreeing

---

[1] Sherrington, 1928, p. x.    [2] Ibid., p. xiii. Cf. Sherrington, 1937, p. 303.

[3] Ferrier, 1873, pp. 30, 85. Cf. Ferrier, 1874a, pp. 1, 14; Ferrier, 1886, p. 223; Ferrier, 1874b, p. 49.

[4] Ferrier, 1873, pp. 85–7. Cf. Ferrier, 1874b, p. 44.    [5] Ferrier, 1878, p. 14.

[6] Ibid.

with this distinguished writer in all his views on this subject, I must express my sense of the great obligations I am under to the philosophical doctrines he has long taught, both as regards the initiation of this research and the interpretation of its lessons.'[1] It was therefore natural that when Ferrier published his classical monograph, he said 'to Dr Hughlings Jackson who from a clinical and pathological standpoint anticipated many of the more important results of recent experimental investigation into the functions of the cerebral hemispheres this work is dedicated as a mark of the author's esteem and admiration'.[2]

Ferrier is less enthusiastic in acknowledging his debts to Fritsch and Hitzig. He gives as his second reason for undertaking his experiments the intention of following up their discovery of the electrical excitability of the hemispheres,[3] and cites his findings as confirming and extending theirs.[4] In his report to the Royal Society, he acknowledges that his method was suggested by their experiments.[5] However, the referees (Michael Foster and George Rolleston) felt that he had made insufficient reference to their work, and T. H. Huxley was called in as a third referee 'for the purpose of ascertaining my opinion whether Dr Ferrier has or has not done sufficient justice to the labours of his predecessors in the same field of investigation'.[6] Huxley concluded that he had not, and Ferrier added a more explicit acknowledgement of their priority in both method and findings.[7] Neither Foster nor Huxley was satisfied, Hitzig complained bitterly, and the referees feared for the reputation of the Royal Society and even of English science.[8] Ferrier preferred to omit the experiments on dogs rather than to make the requested changes,[9] and consequently only his experiments on monkeys were published.[10] After this unfortunate episode, Ferrier's references to Fritsch and Hitzig were more generous,[11] and by 1890 he was prepared to say that 'The whole aspect of cerebral physiology and pathology was revolutionized by the discovery, first made by Fritsch and Hitzig in 1870, that certain

---

[1] Ferrier, 1874a, p. 129 (back).  [2] Ferrier, 1876, p. v.
[3] Ferrier, 1873, p. 30.  [4] Ibid., pp. 31–2, 39, 49, 77.
[5] Ferrier, 1874a, p. 2.  [6] Rolleston et al., 1874, RR. 7. 302.
[7] Ibid.; Ferrier, 1874a, pp. 2, 53 (red ink additions).
[8] Rolleston et al., 1874, RR. 7. 302; RR. 7. 301. Huxley closed his report with the following: 'In conclusion I particularly desire that these remarks may not be supposed to diminish the value of the original results obtained by Dr Ferrier—which appear to me to be very great—especially in respect of the experiments on monkeys.' (Ibid., RR. 7. 301.)
[9] Ibid., RR. 7. 305.
[10] Ferrier, 1875a, 1875b. The two other sets of referees' reports on papers by Ferrier in the Royal Society also complain that he failed to make adequate acknowledgement of the work of his predecessors. (Rolleston, et al., 1874, RR. 12. 103.)
[11] See Ferrier, 1874b, p. 45; Ferrier, 1875b, p. 433; Ferrier, 1876, pp. xv, 146–8; Ferrier, 1878, p. 15.

definite movements could be excited by the direct application of electrical stimulation to definite regions of the cortex cerebri in dogs.'[1]

Ferrier's work was central to the classical period of cerebral localization in the last three decades of the nineteenth century. In his classical monograph on *The Functions of the Brain* he makes explicit the method and the assumption which guided his work. He reviews the difficulties involved in making inferences concerning man from animal studies and from the clinic, but he continues:

Notwithstanding these difficulties and discrepancies, many of which will be found, on careful examination, to be more apparent than real, experiments on animals, under conditions selected and varied at the will of the experimenter, are alone capable of furnishing precise data for sound inductions as to the functions of the brain and its various parts; the experiments performed for us by nature, in the form of diseased conditions, being rarely limited, or free from such complications as render analysis and the discovery of cause and effect extremely difficult, and in many cases practically impossible. The discovery of new methods of investigation opens up new fields of inquiry, and leads to the discovery of new truths. The discovery of the electric excitability of the brain by Fritsch and Hitzig has given a fresh impetus to researches on the functions of the brain, and thrown a new light on many obscure points in cerebral physiology and pathology.[2]

And the assumption: every movement and every sense in a higher animal is produced by a specific part of the brain, in a manner which must still be the subject of extensive research.[3]

Ferrier conducted his original experiments at the West Riding Lunatic Asylum and published his results in the *Report* of that institution for 1873.[4] He was able to produce convulsions experimentally, thus confirming Jackson's speculations by the artificial reproduction of the phenomenon of epilepsy.[5] He also produced precise movements of individual muscles and groups of muscles by the electrical stimulation of localized cortical centres in dogs, rabbits, cats, and guinea pigs. Thus, he confirmed the motor significance of the grey matter of the

[1] Ferrier, 1890, p. 17.   [2] Ferrier, 1876, pp. xiv–xv.   [3] Thorwald, 1960, pp. 39–40.
[4] The West Riding Lunatic Asylum is interesting in its own right, since it was an early example of the combination of clinical and experimental work. See Viets, 1938. Its director, James Crichton-Browne, apparently invited Ferrier there to do his research, and Ferrier acknowledges his debt (Ferrier, 1874a, p. 136). Hollander claims that Crichton-Browne was an adherent to phrenology and that he invited Ferrier to conduct his experiments in order to test phrenology. (Hollander, n.d., I, 405–6.) I have seen no support for this claim in Ferrier's writings or in the many volumes of reminiscences which Crichton-Browne wrote. However, Crichton-Browne does mention phrenology often, and Hollander (Ibid.) quoted some flattering references to Gall and Spurzheim. Crichton-Browne later joined with Ferrier and Jackson to found the neurological journal *Brain*.
[5] Ferrier, 1873, p. 85.

cerebral cortex.[1] In addition to the implications of his findings for physiology and clinical neurology, Ferrier planned to use his techniques to 'attempt to artificially excite conditions similar to normal psychic or volitional stimuli'.[2] The hope held out  by these findings was that 'we may ultimately be enabled to translate into their psychological signification and localize phrenologically the organic centres of various mental endowments'.[3]

His initial publications caused an immediate sensation. The work was conducted in the spring and reported to the British Association in September by his former teacher, Professor Rutherford:

These researches mark the commencement of a new era in our knowledge of brain function. Of all the studies in comparative physiology there will be none more interesting, and few so important, as those in which the various centres will be mapped out in the brains throughout the vertebrate series. A new, but this time a true, system of phrenology will probably be founded upon them: by this, however, I do not mean that it will be possible to tell a man's faculties by the configuration of his skull; but merely this, that the various mental faculties will be assigned to definite territories of the brain, as Gall and Spurzheim long ago maintained, although their geography of the brain was erroneous . . . these investigations constitute the most important work which has been accomplished in phsyiology for a very considerable time past.[4]

Ferrier's findings were noted by the retiring President of the Royal Society in December: 'In Anatomy, the most striking subject appears to be Professor Ferrier's experimental discussion of the actions of different parts of the brain, explained at the late Meeting of the British Association.'[5] His findings were communicated to the Royal Society the following March. He was nominated as a candidate for election the same year and elected in 1876. The Royal Society also granted him money to extend his researches to the brains of monkeys. He gave the Croonian Lectures in 1874 and again the following year. When his monograph appeared in 1876, George Croom Robertson (in his review in *Mind*), referred to it as 'this eagerly looked for work'[6] and noted that it was classical.

His physiological results have been obtained with great skill, and, whatever may be said against his interpretations, they are at once clearly conceived and forcibly argued. It is little to say of both that they must henceforth be

[1] Ferrier, 1873, p. 90.      [2] Ibid., p. 72. Cf. Ferrier, 1874a, p. 1.
[3] Ibid., p. 76. Ferrier's findings are considered in greater detail in Young, 1968.
[4] Rutherford, 1874, p. 122.      [5] Airy, 1873, p. 9.      [6] Robertson, 1877, p. 92.

reckoned with, by psychologists as well as physiologists, for any doctrine of the brain in relation to mind.[1]

By 1881, the lines were clearly drawn between Ferrier's views supporting localization and those of Goltz, who advocated cortical equipotentiality. The result of the confrontation between them, at the Seventh International Medical Congress in London, was that Ferrier carried the day with his more precise methods and dramatic findings.[2] Ferrier's success in demonstrating the experimental reproduction of localized motor dysfunctions by cerebral lesions is epitomized by the remark Charcot is reported to have made on seeing one of Ferrier's monkeys limping about the room with unilateral paralysis of the arm and leg: 'It is a patient!'[3] Ferrier's work was equally significant in establishing centres for the sensory modalities on the basis of ablation experiments.[4]

The developments which culminated in Ferrier's work had led from Broca's clinico-pathological localization of the speech centre (1860) to Fritsch and Hitzig's demonstration of cerebral excitability and localized motor functions (1870), and the experimental localization of sensory functions by the mid 1880's. By the close of the century the main cortical centres for motor functions and the various sensory modalities in mammals were established to the general satisfaction of workers in the field. By 1901, the most complete compendium of knowledge in philosophy and psychology defined cerebral localization as 'the doctrine that various parts of the brain have relatively distinct functions'.[5] The theory that certain psychical and physiological functions are limited to definite areas of cortex is, 'in its broadest form . . . thoroughly substantiated by anatomical, pathological, and experimental data'.[6] In 1902, the *Encyclopedia Britannica* reflected the orthodoxy of the 'new phrenology' and recalled its beginnings: 'the principles of cerebral localization are, after all, only a scientific statement of matters that are of general belief. We are all more or less phrenologists'.[7]

## Ferrier's Conception of the Functions of the Brain

Ferrier's conception of the function of the brain is a corollary of the theories of Bain, Spencer, and Jackson, for which he provided the experimental evidence.

[1] Robertson, 1877, p. 92.

[2] MacCormac, 1881, I, 218–242d. Cf. the wholly accurate dramatization of this confrontation in Thorwald, 1960, Chapter I.

[3] Thorwald, 1960, pp. 37–9. Cf. Viets, 1938.

[4] Ferrier, 1876, pp. 163–98; Ferrier, 1886, pp. 268–345; Ferrier, 1890, pp. 38–126.

[5] Baldwin, 1901, II, 15.          [6] Ibid. See above p. 11.          [7] Anon, 1902, p. 710.

It must follow from the experimental data that mental operations in the last analysis must be merely the subjective side of sensory and motor substrata. This view has been repeatedly and clearly enunciated by Hughlings-Jackson, with whose physiological and psychological deductions from clinical and pathological data I frequently find myself in complete accordance.[1]

In the second edition, he adds, 'For the cerebral hemispheres consist only of centres related respectively to the sensory and motor tracts, which connect them with the periphery and with each other'.[2] Ideas are revived associations of sensations and movements,[3] thought is internal speech,[4] and intellectual attention is ideal vision.[5] In short, all conceptions of function are reducible to sensation, motion, and association. Ferrier's work represents the final extension of the Bell–Magendie paradigm to the most rostral part of the neuraxis—the cerebral cortex—and its use as an all-embracing explanatory conception in both physiology and psychology.

In order to make these sweeping claims for his findings, Ferrier had to attribute psychological significance to the simple phenomena which he observed on stimulation and ablation. In his experiments on motor functions, this involved two stages: the muscular contractions elicited on stimulation were interpreted as coordinated, purposive actions; these, in turn, were interpreted as the overt manifestations of complex psychological functions.

Many of the movements such as those of the hands, the legs, the facial muscles and the mouth have the aspect of purpose or volition and are of the same nature as those which the animal makes in its ordinary intelligent action.[6]

Thus in monkeys capable of highly complex and differentiated movements of the hands and feet, we find in the brain a comparatively large region presiding over these movements. For it is found on irritation, that combined muscular actions, which, in their individuality and totality, are such as the animals make in carrying out their desires and purposes, are capable of being excited at will, by stimulation of various localised centres in this region.[7]

He reports the same findings in lower organisms, although their less-specialized movements have less differentiated centres.[8] He considers

---

[1] Ferrier, 1876, pp. 256–7.     [2] Ferrier, 1886, p. 426.     [3] Ibid., p. 437.
[4] Ibid., p. 462.     [5] Ibid., pp. 463–4.     [6] Ferrier, 1874a, p. 95.
[7] Ibid., pp. 117–18. Cf. Ferrier, 1874b, pp. 47–9, where Ferrier elaborates his conception of a voluntary motor centre (and provides a diagram which shows the corpus striatum as a centre for coordination of voluntary movements).
[8] Ferrier, 1874a, pp. 117–18.

these regions the 'centres for voluntary initiation of the same movements as result from faradization'.[1]

These centres, however, have another signification in so far as they form the motor substrata of mind. Besides being centres for the accomplishment of acts of volition, they form the organic centres for the memory of accomplished acts. The centres for articulation besides their function of setting in action the complex and delicate movements involved in articulate speech, have the power of permanently recording the results of their functional activity.[2]

By similar, though indirect, reasoning, he concludes that the sensory centres are the 'seat of the sensory memory or organic basis of ideation'.[3] The frontal regions gave no response to stimulation, but on ablation the animals behaved in a way which Ferrier felt resembled dementia.[4] He concluded that the frontal lobes were the probable 'substrata of those psychical processes which lie at the foundation of the higher intellectual operations'.[5]

It should be stressed that Ferrier's localizations were neither the fulfilment of Gall's hopes nor those of Flourens. His relations with Gall's views will be considered presently. Though he agrees with Flourens in a superficial way, his alternative scheme eliminated the hiatus which Flourens and his followers had been at pains to preserve.

> Intelligence and will have no local habitation distinct from the sensory and motor substrata of the cortex generally. There are centres for special forms of sensation and ideation, and centres for special motor activities and acquisitions, in response to and in association with the activity of sensory centres; and these in their respective cohesions, actions, and interactions form the substrata of mental operations in all their aspects and all their range.[6]

The above was written in 1886. In his first report to the Royal Society (1874), Ferrier was cautious but hopeful about the possibility of drawing sweeping inferences from simple motions.

One would not be justified in fixing on the centres of the zygomatic muscles as the seat of a hypothetical faculty of mirth or such like. The complexity of even the simplest mental conception renders the localization of faculties in the phrenological sense a mere chimera. We must not however shut out the

---

[1] Ferrier, 1874a, pp. 95–7.    [2] Ferrier, 1874b, pp. 55–6.
[3] Ibid., p. 57. Cf. Ferrier, 1874a, p. 97.
[4] Ferrier, 1874a, pp. 101, 103, 123. Cf. Ferrier, 1878, p. 6.
[5] Ferrier, 1886, p. 467.    [6] Ibid.; cf. p. 436.

possibility that the comparative development of special regions may be taken as an index of a capacity for certain acquirements—as an instance, it may be said that a considerable development of the region of Broca's convolution may be, ceteris paribus, taken as an index of a capacity for the acquisition of languages. Whether this is so or not is a subject which will require careful scientific investigation. The line of research is one which is likely to lead to valuable results, and may form the basis of a scientific phrenology.[1]

However, it is clear from his later writings (and the example given above) that he progressively drew on the theories of Bain, Spencer, and Jackson and interpreted alterations in simple sensory and motor phenomena as the basis for a comprehensive psychophysiology or, in the jargon of the times, a 'New Phrenology'.[2]

## Some Practical and Conceptual Implications of Classical Localization

Whereas the only immediate practical fruit of Gall's work was the pseudo-science of phrenology (with its dubious character delineations), the concepts and findings of Broca, Fritsch and Hitzig, Ferrier, and Jackson led directly to the development of modern neurosurgery. The significance of their work has been dramatized by an historian of medicine, Jürgen Thorwald, and his description vividly conveys the issue through the eyes of those involved:

As we saw it, the problem of cerebral surgery was not so much the opening of the cranium and exposure of the brain; neither was it the removal of a tumour, but the localizing of the tumour before operation. The trouble spot was concealed beneath the cranium. None of the diagnostic methods of the time could establish its position so clearly that the skull could be directly entered at the right spot. Pain was distributed over whole sections of the brainpan and could not serve as an indicator of the site of a tumour. Here was the gulf that had to be bridged.

In the light of this problem it is clear why the experiments and arguments of Fritsch, Hitzig, and Ferrier meant so much. . . . If it were true that some small part of the brain were the fixed controlling organ of every muscle and every sense, and if it were also true that this functional centre

---

[1] Ferrier, 1874a, pp. 133–4. Cf. the remarkable 'phrenological' conclusion of his monograph (1886, pp. 467–8).

[2] This was the phrase used by Bastian and Wundt, among many others, and became the usual way of referring to the localizers in the period up until about 1910. The last of the old' phrenologists, of course, attempted to use Ferrier's own reasoning as a means of appropriating his findings to their theories. (See Williams, 1894, pp. 176–92, and the writings of Hollander. It has been noted—above p. 44—that A. R. Wallace accepted this interpretation. Wallace, 1901, Chapter 16.)

occupied a particular and unvarying place in the brain, then it should be possible to deduce from the paralysis or other affliction of the body the site of the abnormality in the brain, the location of, say, a tumour. It should then be possible to attack the disease by surgery aimed at the precise spot where excision was required.[1]

Ferrier had pointed out in his first paper on cerebral localization that his findings could be instructive for diagnosis and exact localization of the seats of lesions.[2] As soon as he had reported his initial findings, he began investigating their clinical implications by interpreting some cases from the West Riding Lunatic Asylum.[3] Although he was considerably handicapped by the poor specification of the sites of lesions,[4] his paper provided the model which future clinical localizers would use. He also suggested the application of these principles to intracranial surgery.

It was this reasoning that led Professor William Macewen, at Glasgow, to undertake some of the earliest operations inside the cranium in modern times.[5] In 1879 he removed a swelling from one of the coverings of the brain which had been producing convulsions. He performed this and several other operations successfully, basing his localizations on Ferrier's reasoning. The first deliberate operation for cerebral tumour occurred in 1884, after Ferrier had forcefully reiterated his views in 1883.[6] The patient, a man named Henderson, had been progressively paralysed on the left side and suffered severe headaches. Using Ferrier's localization patterns, it was decided that the tumour was in the region of the hand and finger centres and not more than two inches in diameter. The operation was performed by Dr Rickman Godlee, a nephew of Lister, who was practised in the relatively new techniques of asepsis. Dr Hughes Bennett had conceived the operation and directed it, but he was not a surgeon. In fact, at that time there were no surgeons at the new National Hospital, Queen Square, where the operation was performed. Ferrier was present at the operation, in which the surgeon cut into the cerebral substance and removed the tumour. It had been feared that the patient would die when the knife entered the cerebral substance. He improved and could move his left leg, although his arm was worse. Unfortunately, although the operation was a success the patient died of surgical infection, which has been attributed to ineffective methods of treating his headaches before the operation. The

[1] Thorwald, 1960, pp. 12–13.      [2] Ferrier, 1873, pp. 30, 87–8, 95.
[3] Ferrier, 1874b.      [4] Ibid., pp. 30–1.
[5] Jefferson, 1960, pp. 132–49.      [6] Sherrington 1937, pp. 302–4.

operation eliminated his headaches and demonstrated the practicability of neurosurgery based on local diagnosis.[1]

The modern science of localizing neurosurgery was thus a lineal descendant of Gall's principle of cerebral localization. From the enormous study of cerebral localization, physicians have derived a body of observations which allow them to diagnose and localize brain lesions with a degree of refinement that has not been equalled in the study of any other organ. It has become possible to predict with accuracy the local involvement of a few square millimeters of the most intricate cerebral or spinal tissue.[2]

Having indicated these dramatic practical fruits of cerebral localization, I am bound to mention that the history I have traced has been decidedly biased. In fact, the localization of lesions is the only major tenet of the concept of cerebral localization that has not been challenged on experimental, logical, or conceptual grounds by some of the most eminent investigators of the functions of the nervous system. It has recently been argued that 'Instead of speaking of cerebral localization, we should be satisfied with the less prejudiced, less involved, and more cautious concept of vulnerability of a given function or behaviour to regional lesions'.[3]

I have shown the demise of Flourens' objections. But, even in the classical period which I have reviewed, the work of F. L. Goltz stood as a constant challenge to the work of Fritsch and Hitzig, Munk, and Ferrier. Hughlings Jackson became progressively opposed to the rigidity of the prevailing view, and the flowering of his concepts in Sherrington's investigations lent plasticity, variability, and complexity to the relatively simple concepts that prevailed before. The same complexities arose in the clinical aphasia tradition. Henry Head calls the period from 1906 onward—following the preeminence of the diagram-makers and the iconoclastic work of Pierre Marie—simply 'chaos'.[4] The concept faculty of articulate language had fallen long before. In fact, the very article quoted above as the high water mark of acceptance of the theory of cerebral localization stresses its diagnostic and surgical applications and adds, 'but it has much less significance for the proper construction of mental processes than has sometimes been supposed'.[5]

[1] See Ballance, 1921; Thorwald, 1960; Ferrier, 1878.
[2] Riese and Hoff, 1950–51.
[3] Riese, 1959, p. 148. Cf. Walshe, 1957.
[4] Head, 1926, I, Chapter VI.
[5] Baldwin, 1901, II, 16.

*Gall and Ferrier*

In contrasting Ferrier's *The Functions of the Brain* with Gall's work of the same title, written fifty years earlier, one finds the balance between physiological and psychological statements reversed. Gall's work is almost wholly concerned with the description and analysis of the faculties (functions) and the attempt to arrive at methods and criteria for discovering the fundamental variables in experience and behaviour. Ferrier devotes only ten per cent. of his text to what he calls 'the subjective aspect [of] the functions of the brain'.[1] Most of his monograph is devoted to the 'physiological aspects', and he concluded that these consist of 'a system of sensory and motor centres. In their subjective aspect the functions of the brain are synonymous with mental operations, the consideration of which belongs to the science of psychology'.[2] All Ferrier felt that was needed to convert his physiological findings into psychologically significant statements was the assumption of psychophysical parallelism (which he adopted from Bain, Spencer, and Jackson) and the phrase 'subjective aspect'.

If Gall was naïve in believing that the organization and physiology of the brain correspond with his faculties in a simple one-to-one fashion, Ferrier was equally so in suggesting that the primary sensory and motor areas could explain psychological functions in a simple manner. He had localized sensory and motor areas, but he had not provided a psychophysiology which accounts for the adaptations of organisms to their environments. As Zangwill says, 'Whatever its role in the production of muscular activity, the motor cortex cannot be regarded as the seat of any function recognisable to the student of behaviour'.[3]

The experimental sensory-motor psychophysiology which had been founded on the concepts of Bain and Spencer was on a very firm physiological basis. It had been built up by a progressive extension of the Bell-Magendie law—a certain fact about the nervous system—and then united with the concept of cerebral localization. However, cerebral localization had become scientific only by abandoning the goal which Gall had laid down in the beginning of his work: to relate the significant variables in the character and behaviour of men and animals to the functioning of the brain. The sensory-motor school was undoubtedly correct in rejecting Gall's faculty psychology as an inadequate explanation of psychological phenomena. But, in grounding itself on a secure physiological basis, the sensory-motor tradition cut itself off from the

[1] Ferrier, 1886, p. 424.    [2] Ibid.    [3] Zangwill, 1963, p. 337.

approach to psychology which was the most important aspect of Gall's work and which had been extended in Spencer's conception of psychology as a biological science. In rejecting Gall's answers, it lost sight of the significance of his questions and of the possibilities inherent in the biological, adaptive view shared by Gall and Spencer. Insufficient attention was paid to what the sensory-motor elements should be required to explain. In default of significant questions, the only answers that were forthcoming were about sensory modalities and muscular movements. The sensory-motor analysis was therefore psychologically insignificant and led only to a partial understanding of the primary projection areas of the somatic cortex. The role of many of these for normal behaviour has yet to be determined. Questions about adaptive, biologically significant functions had to be asked anew by other branches of biology which developed independently from the ideas of Bain, Spencer, and Darwin. The problem that Ferrier's work left for the twentieth century was that of retaining scientific rigour, while regaining contact with biologically significant functions.

Gall and Ferrier can be seen as extremes on a continuum of possible approaches in brain and behaviour research. Gall stresses functions as adaptive and as related to character, personality, mastery of the environment, social intercourse, and intellectual, artistic, and mechanical achievement. He lets his adaptively conceived and naturalistically derived functions dictate to the brain. His conception of its functioning involves no direct physiological knowledge. Ferrier, on the other hand, sacrifices the significance of functions to physiological accuracy. His view reduces all the functions which Gall determined by observing behaviour, to the two categories of sensation and motion. His data are derived solely from direct experimentation on the brain and observation of the phenomena produced. Further progress in the field would have to mediate between these extremes. If the functions were to be conceived adaptively, the underlying physiology would have to be worked out. If the physiology was to be investigated as carefully as Ferrier did, it would have to be related to the independent findings of psychologists and ethologists. Future hope lay in bringing these extremes of function and physiology into closer communication. Gall sacrificed one for the sake of the other; Ferrier is the complementary case. Neither will do alone. Though Gall was unable to follow his own advice, the modern investigator is in a much better position to do so.

Whoever would not remain in complete ignorance of the resources which cause him to act; whoever would seize, at a single philosophical glance, the nature of man and animals, and their relations to external objects; whoever would establish, on the intellectual and moral functions, a solid doctrine of mental diseases, of the general and governing influence of the brain in the states of health and disease, should know, that it is indispensable, that the study of the organization of the brain should march side by side with that of its functions.[1]

[1] Gall, 1835, II, 45–6.

# 9

## CONCLUSION

Understanding can be advanced only through our modification of present concepts. These in turn are subject to change only through resourceful experimental and theoretical pursuits. There is a continuing need for careful examination of our fundamental assumptions. The assumptions which we accept with least reflection are those common to our intellectual community; they may not even be recognized as assumptions.

Robert B. Livingston, 1962.

Today we study the day before yesterday, in order that yesterday may not paralyze today and today may not paralyze tomorrow.

F. W. Maitland.

THIS book has been concerned with two separable issues, and one of the main conclusions implicit in my argument is that the issues should not be separated. On the one hand, I have emphasized the need for a set of functions which are biologically significant. On the other, I have stressed the need for a set of analytic terms which can be experimentally investigated throughout the nervous system. The history of empirical cerebral localization from Gall to Ferrier involved the advance of the latter thesis at the expense of the former, even though the theoretical basis for the latter provides the strongest argument for the former. That is, the theory of evolution which justified the extension of the sensory-motor paradigm throughout the nervous system also demanded that the concepts of function should directly reflect the important variables in the adaptation of organisms to their environments. Gall argued that the faculties used by his predecessors were irrelevant to the lives of organisms, but he failed to analyse his own functions into more basic units. Ferrier adopted a set of useful units and provided an experimental basis for their application to all parts of the brain, but he failed to transcend the categories of function which his intellectual mentors had perpetuated. The obvious need for the future was a combination of analysis with a biologically significant set of functions. This desideratum has yet to appear. Advances since Ferrier have been more technological than conceptual. The paradigm established by Bain, Spencer, Jackson, and Ferrier still dominates the assumptions of research in physiological psychology.

The most difficult historical issue with which I have been concerned is the role of phrenology in both the history of the concept of cerebral localization and in the development of psychology as a biological science. As I was making notes for this conclusion a passage came to my attention which perfectly expresses the difficulty. In a discussion of 'The Influence of Evolutionary Theory upon American Psychological Thought',[1] Boring considers the roots of functional thinking, and concludes,

> We must not, however, exaggerate the importance of evolutionary theory. It was not Darwin who discovered that the body's organs are useful to it, nor was Darwin the originator of the thought that the mind is an organ. Functional psychology has back of it, besides evolutionary theory, all of faculty psychology and also all of the specific analysis of mind into functions, faculties, capacities and propensities by the phrenologists early in the nineteenth century.[2]

Dallenbach has supported this view by attempting to show that the term 'function' as applied to psychological phenomena entered English psychology by way of phrenology.[3] The importance of phrenology in the development of adaptive and functional thinking in psychology has been one of the major themes of the present work, and supporting evidence has been cited in the text and notes. I do not consider the thesis proven, but I do feel that the adduction of evidence for its probability has been one of the most interesting and significant results of my research. Additional evidence will be required to separate direct influences from interesting parallels, but at present I am in agreement with the assessment of one of the major figures in the development of evolutionary psychology, G. H. Lewes, who said,

> Gall rescued the problem of mental functions from Metaphysics, and made it one of Biology.[4]
> In his vision of Psychology as a branch of Biology, subject therefore to all biological laws, and to be pursued on biological methods, he may be said to have given the science its basis.[5]

I have attempted to enlarge our appreciation of the direct debts of the founders of modern psychology to Gall. Bain drew his conception of the importance of uniting the study of physiology with psychology from his early education and interest in phrenology. Spencer developed his concept of adaptation. its neurological context, and his concept of cerebral localization from his early phrenological conceptions. However, the theories of Bain and Spencer were held in a wider context—that of the analytical units and categories which the association psychology

---

[1] In: Boring 1963, pp. 159–84.　　[2] Ibid., p. 167.
[3] Dallenbach, 1915.　　[4] Lewes, 1871, p. 425.　　[5] Ibid., p. 423.

had inherited from medieval and philosophical psychology, and which associationism perpetuated. Modern psychology has not transcended these, and Gall's most important insight has not yet been applied to the relations among mind, brain, and life: the functional role of mind in life as a guide to the formulation of categories of biological analysis according to which psychological investigation should interpret experience and behaviour.

The approach in psychology which benefited most from evolutionary associationism was the functional psychology of William James and John Dewey. As the following passages show, Dewey grasped some of the implications of biological psychology. In 1925, he said,

Reflection is an indirect response to the environment, and the element of indirection can itself become great and very complicated. But it has its origin in biological adaptive behaviour and the ultimate function of its cognitive aspect is a prospective control of the conditions of the environment. The function of intelligence is therefore not that of copying the objects of the environment, but rather of taking account of the way in which more effective and more profitable relations with these objects may be established in the future.[1]

On the basis of the theory of organic evolution it is maintained that the analysis of intelligence and of its operations should be compatible with the order of known biological facts, concerning the intermediate position occupied by the central nervous system in making possible responses to the environment adequate to the needs of the living organism.[2]

It should be noted that Dewey is here indicating the approach of a biological psychologist but has no concepts of function which are commensurate with his aims. Fifteen years later, Sherrington expressed the problem which this situation poses for modern brain research.

Facts rebut the over-simplified conceptions such as ascribe to separate small pieces of the roof-brain, wedged together like a jigsaw puzzle, separate items of highly integrated behaviour. A special place for comprehension of names, a special place for arithmetical calculation, a special place for musical appreciation, and so on. Such savour of old 'phrenology'. To suppose the roof-brain consists of point to point 'centres' identified each with a particular item of intelligent concrete behaviour is a scheme 'over-simplified, and to be abandoned'. Rather, we may think, the contributions which the roof-brain in collaboration with the rest of the brain and spinal cord, makes toward integrated behaviour will, when they are ultimately analysed, resolve into components for which at present we have no names. To state the organization of the mind in terms of roof-brain activities is a desideratum not in sight.[1]

[1] Dewey, new ed., 1963, p. 30.      [2] Ibid., p. 27.
[3] Sherrington, new ed., 1955, pp. 190–1. (The internal quotation is by Lashley.)

Modern brain and behaviour research is, if anything, further away than Gall was in asking and answering the question, What are the functions of the brain? One suspects that all the sophisticated experimental technology and methodology which has developed since Gall will be to no avail until organisms are observed much more closely with this question in mind. In conclusion, I submit that in the first instance this study will owe more to naturalistic observations than to experiments. It was Gall who made the point that we must first know the functions before we can ask intelligent questions about the organization and physiology of the brain. A century and a half later one finds a modern reviewer of the concept of cerebral localization turning to Gall in support of the thesis that 'in exploring the functions of the brain, I am convinced that we must limit ourselves to the study of biologically significant behaviour patterns, no matter how complex their underlying physiology may be'.[1] I hope that the argument of this book will contribute to the continuing appreciation of this fundamental point.

In conclusion, I would like to suggest that modern studies of the functions of the brain—and therefore of man's place in nature—are less free from the constraints of philosophic assumptions than their positivistic advocates have tended to assume.[2] In investigating nineteenth-century theories of mind and brain I hope that it has been possible to gain sufficient perspective to show that Descartes and Locke cast longer shadows than twentieth-century scientists often suppose. The conceptions of modern brain and behaviour research, learning theory, and even psychoanalysis are largely based on the theories which have been examined in this book. These, in turn, are based on an attempt to explain mind and brain in terms of categories derived by analogy from the mechanical, corpuscular paradigm of seventeenth-century science. Hartley and the associationists and sensory-motor psycho-physiologists of the nineteenth-century provide the link between the earlier period and the present. I hope that I have shown the price which psychology paid by failing to transcend Cartesian dualism, the sensationalist and epistemological biases of associationism, and the categories of function of philosophical psychology. I suspect that the reinterpretation of human biology in more meaningful terms will require changes in the ontology of modern science.[3] Whether or not I am right in this, I believe that historical, philosophical and conceptual studies in the interpretation of man's place in nature have a more important part to play than has hitherto been assumed.

[1] Zangwill, 1963, p. 338.    [2] See below p. 273.    [3] Ibid. Cf. Young, 1967a, 1967b.

# BIBLIOGRAPHY

In the brain, which we term the seat of reason, there is not anything of
moment more than I can discover in the crany of a beast: and this is no
inconsiderable argument of the inorganity of the soul, at least in the sense
we generally so receive it. Thus we are men, and we know not how.

Sir Thomas Browne, c. 1635.

It remains sadly true that most of our present understanding would remain
as valid and useful if, for all we knew, the cranium were stuffed with cotton
wadding.

Gerard, 1949.

It would be tedious and pointless to list all the works which have been
examined or consulted in the course of this study, even though a comprehensive bibliography on nineteenth-century psychology and neurology is
an important desideratum today. The bibliography of Benjamin Rand
(Baldwin, 1901, III) is the most convenient single source which has appeared,
while *Current Work in the History of Medicine*, *Psychological Abstracts*, and the
*Journal of the History of the Behavioral Sciences* provide valuable guides to
current literature. I have listed only those works which are cited in the text
or notes, or which have contributed directly to the writing of this book.
On the other hand, I have refrained from mentioning numerous works which
are either useless or actively misleading. It seems to me that the first duty
of a hospital is not to spread disease.

AARON, RICHARD I., *John Locke*, 2nd edn. (Clarendon Press, Oxford, 1955).
ACKERKNECHT, ERWIN, H., 'P.M.A. Dumoutier et la collection phrénologique
   du Musée de l'Homme', *Bull.Soc.Anthrop.* X$^e$ série, **7** (1956), 289–308.
—  'Contributions of Gall and the phrenologists to knowledge of brain
   function,' in: Poynter, F.N.L. (ed.), *The Brain and its Functions*, 149–53
   (Blackwell, Oxford, 1958).
—  *A Short History of Psychiatry* (Hafner, N.Y., 1959).
—  and VALLOIS, HENRI V., *Franz Joseph Gall, Inventor of Phrenology and
   His Collection.*, trans. Claire St. Léon., (Wisconsin Medical School,
   Madison, 1956).
AIRY, GEORGE B., President's address, *Proc. R. Soc.*, **22** (1873–4), 2–12.
ALBEE, ERNEST, *A History of English Utilitarianism* (1901) (reprint, Collier,
   N.Y., 1962).
ALLPORT, GORDON W., *Personality. A Psychological Interpretation* (Holt, N.Y.,
   1937).
ANGELL, JAMES R., 'The relations of structural and functional psychology to
   philosophy', *Philos. Rev.*, **12** (1903), 243–71.

ANGELL, JAMES R., 'The province of functional psychology', *Psychol. Rev.*, **14** (1907), 61–91. (Reprinted in Dennis, W., 1948, pp. 439–56.)
— 'The influence of Darwin on psychology', *Psychol. Rev.*, **16** (1909), 152–69.
ANON., 'Researches of Malcarne and Reil—present state of cerebral anatomy', *Edinburgh Med. and Surg. J.*, **21** (1824), 98–141.
— 'Recent discoveries on the physiology of the nervous system', *Edinburgh Med. and Surg. J.*, **21** (1824), 141–59.
— 'Phrenology', in: *The New Volumes of the Encyclopedia Britannica, constituting . . . the Tenth Edition*, Vol. XXXI, 709–10 (Black, Edinburgh, 1902) [by C. S. Sherrington?].
BACON, FRANCIS, *The New Organon and Related Writings* (Liberal Arts, N.Y., 1960).
BAIN, ALEXANDER, *The Senses and the Intellect* (Parker, London, 1855; 3rd edn., 1868; 4th edn., Longmans, London, 1894).
— *The Emotions and the Will* (Parker, London, 1859; 3rd edn., Longmans, London, 1875).
— *On the Study of Character, Including an Estimate of Phrenology* (Parker, London, 1861).
— *Mental and Moral Science* (1868; Longmans, London, 1875).
— 'Mr. James Ward's "Psychology",' *Mind*, **11** (1886), 457–77.
— 'Association of ideas', in: *Chambers's Encyclopedia*, Vol. I, 511–13 (Chambers, London, 1901).
— *Dissertations on Leading Philosophical Topics* (Longmans, London, 1903).
— *Autobiography* (Longmans, London, 1904).
— *Mind and Body*, 11th edn. (Kegan Paul, London, 1910).
BALDWIN, JAMES M. (ed.), *Dictionary of Philosophy and Psychology*, 3 vols. in 4 (Macmillan, N.Y., 1901).
— 'Sketch of the history of psychology', *Psychol. Rev.*, **12** (1905), 144–65.
— *History of Psychology: A sketch and an Interpretation*, 2 vols. (Watts, London, 1913).
BALLANCE, SIR CHARLES A., *A Glimpse into the History of the Surgery of the Brain* (Macmillan, London, 1921).
BALZ, ALBERT G. A., *Cartesian Studies* (Columbia, N.Y., 1951).
BASTIAN, H. CHARLTON, *The Brain as an Organ of Mind* (Kegan Paul, London, 1880).
— 'The "muscular sense"; its nature and cortical localisation', *Brain*, **10** (1888), 1–89.
BATEMAN, FREDERIC, *On Aphasia, or Loss of Speech, and the Localisation of the Faculty of Articulate Language*, 2nd edn. (Churchill, London, 1890).
BAWDEN, H. HEATH, 'Functional view of the relation between the psychical and the physical', *Philos. Rev.*, **11** (1902), 474–84.
BENTLEY, MADISON, 'The psychological antecedents of phrenology', *Psychol. Monogr.* **21**, 4, No. 92 (1916), 102–15.
BENTON, ARTHUR and JOYNT, ROBERT J., 'Early descriptions of aphasia', *Archs Neurol.*, **3** (1960), 205–22.
BERGMANN, GUSTAV, 'The contribution of John B. Watson', *Psychol. Rev.*, **63** (1956), 265–76.

BICHAT, XAVIER, *Recherches Physiologiques sur la Vie et la Mort* (1800) (Alliance Culturelle du Livre, Paris, 1962).
— *Physiological Researches on Life and Death*, trans. F. Gold (Longmans, London, no date).
BOAS, GEORGE, *French Philosophies of the Romantic Period* (1925; Russell and Russell, N.Y., 1964).
BORING, EDWIN G., *A History of Experimental Psychology*, 2nd edn. (Appleton, N.Y., 1950).
— *History of Psychology, and Science: Selected Papers*, Ed. by Robert I. Watson and D. T. Campbell (Wiley, N.Y., 1963).
BRAIN, W. RUSSELL, *Diseases of the Nervous System*, 5th edn. (Oxford University Press, London, 1955).
— 'Hughlings Jackson's ideas of consciousness in the light of today', in: Poynter, F. N. L. (ed.), *The Brain and its Functions*, 83–91 (Blackwell, Oxford, 1958).
— 'Henry Head: the man and his ideas', *Brain*, **84** (1961), 561–69.
BRAZIER, MARY A. B., 'Rise of neurophysiology in the 19th century', *J. Neurophysiol.*, **20** (1957), 212–26.
— (ed.), *The Central Nervous System and Behavior* (1958; Macy, N.Y., 1959).
— 'The historical development of neurophysiology', in: Field, J. (ed.), *Handbook of Physiology. Neurophysiology*, Vol. I, 1–58 (Am. Physiol. Soc., Washington, 1959).
BRETT, GEORGE S., *Brett's History of Psychology*, ed. and abridged by R. S. Peters (Allen and Unwin, London, 1953).
— 'Associationism and "act" psychology: a historical retrospect', in: Murchison, Carl (ed.), *Psychologies of 1930*, 39–55 (Clark University Press, Worcester, 1930).
BROADBENT, D. E., *Behaviour* (Eyre and Spottiswoode, London, 1961).
BROCA, PIERRE P., 'Remarks on the seat of the faculty of articulate language, followed by an observation of aphemia', (1861), trans. G. von Bonin, in: *Some Papers on the Cerebral Cortex*, 49–72 (Thomas, Springfield, 1960).
— 'Sur le siège de le faculté du langage articulé,' *La Tribune Médicale*, **74** (1869), 254–6; **75** (1869), 265–9.
BROWN, THOMAS, *Lectures on the Philosophy of the Human Mind* (1820; 20th edn., Tegg, London, 1860).
BURROW, JOHN W., *Evolution and Society. A Study in Victorian Social Theory* (Cambridge University Press 1966).
BURTT, EDWIN A., *The Metaphysical Foundations of Modern Physical Science*, 2nd edn. (Routledge and Kegan Paul, London, 1932).
CABANIS, PIERRE J. G., *Rapports du Physique et du Moral de l'Homme*, 2nd edn., 2 vols. (Crapart, Paris, 1805).
CAPEN, NAHUM, *Reminiscences of Dr. Spurzheim and George Combe* (Fowler and Wells, N.Y., 1881).
CARLSON, ERIC T., 'The influence of phrenology on early American psychiatric thought', *Am. J. Psychiat.*, **115** (1958), 535–8.
CARMICHAEL, LEONARD, 'Sir Charles Bell: a contribution to the history of physiological psychology', *Psychol. Rev.*, **33** (1926), 188–217.

CARPENTER, WILLIAM B., 'Noble on the brain and its physiology', *Brit. and For. Med. Rev.*, **22** (1846), 488–544.

—    *Principles of Human Physiology*, 5th edn. (Blanchard and Lea, Phila., 1855).

—    'On the physiological import of Dr. Ferrier's experimental investigations into the functions of the brain', *West Riding Lunatic Asylum Medical Reports*, **4** (1874), 1–23.

—    *Principles of Mental Physiology* (King, London, 1874a).

—    *Nature and Man—Essays Scientific and Philosophical—with an Introductory Memoir by J. Estlin Carpenter* (Kegan Paul, London, 1888).

CARR, HARVEY, 'The interpretation of animal mind', *Psychol. Rev.* **34** (1927), 87–106.

—    'Functionalism', in: Murchison, Carl (ed.), *Psychologies of* 1930, 59–78 (Clark University Press, Worcester, 1930).

CASSIRER, ERNST, *The Philosophy of the Enlightenment* (Beacon, Boston, 1955). *The Philosophy of Symbolic Forms, Vol III. The Phenomenology of Knowledge*, trans. Ralph Manheim (Yale, New Haven, 1957).

CASTIGLIONI, ARTURO, *A History of Medicine*, 2nd edn., trans. E. B. Krumbhaar (Knopf, N.Y., 1947).

CHALMERS, THOMAS, *On the Power Wisdom and Goodness of God as manifested in the Adaptation of External Nature to the Moral and Intellectual Constitution of Man*, 2 vols. (Pickering, London, 1833).

CHAMBERS, ROBERT, *Vestiges, of the Natural History of Creation* (1844; 12th edn. (Chambers, Edinburgh, 1884).

CHARCOT, JEAN M., *Lectures on the Diseases of the Nervous System*, trans. George Sigerson (New Sydenham Society, London, 1881; Reprint, Hafner, N.Y., 1962).

—    *Lectures on the Localisation of Cerebral and Spinal Diseases*, trans. W. B. Hadden (New Sydenham Society, London, 1883).

CHEVENIX, RICHARD, 'Gall and Spurzheim—Phrenology', *For. Quart. Rev.*, **2** (1828), 1–59.

CLARKE, EDWIN, 'The early history of the cerebral ventricles', *Trans. and Stud. of the College of Physicians of Philadelphia* 4 ser, **30** (1962), 85–9.

CLODD, EDWARD, *Pioneers of Evolution from Thales to Huxley*, 2nd edn. (Cassell, London, 1907).

COMBE, GEORGE, *Elements of Phrenology*, 2nd edn. (Anderson, Edinburgh, 1825).

—    *Essay on the Constitution of Man and its Relations to External Objects* (Neill, Edinburgh, 1827).

—    *A System of Phrenology*, 2 vols., 4th edn. (Maclachlan, Stewart and Anderson, Edinburgh, 1836).

CONDILLAC, ÉTIENNE BONNET DE, *Condillac's Treatise on the Sensations* (1754), trans. G. Carr (Favil, London, 1930).

CORNER, G. W., 'Anatomists in search of the soul', *Ann. med. Hist.*, **21** (1919), 1–7.

CRICHTON-BROWNE, SIR JAMES, *The Doctor Remembers* (Duckworth, London, 1938).

CRITCHLEY, MACDONALD, 'The study of language-disorders: past, present and future', in: *The Centennial Lectures Commemorating the One Hundredth Anniversary of E. R. Squibb and Sons*, 268–92 (Putnam's, N.Y., 1959).
— 'Head's contribution to aphasia', *Brain*, **84** (1961a), 551–60.
— 'Broca's contribution to aphasia reviewed a century later', in: Garland, Hugh (ed.) *Scientific Aspects of Neurology*, 131–41 (Livingstone, Edinburgh, 1961b).
CROSS, J. W., *George Eliot's Life as Related in Her Letters and Journals*, new edn. (Blackwood, London, n.d., 1885?).
DALLENBACH, KARL M., 'The history and derivation of the word "function" as a systematic term in psychology', *Am. J.Psychol.*, **26** (1915), 473–84.
— 'Phrenology versus psychoanalysis', *Am. J. Psychol.*, **68** (1955), 511–25.
DARWIN, CHARLES, *On the Origin of Species* (1859; Reprint, Watts, London, 1950).
— *On the Origin of Species*, 6th edn. (1872; Dent, London, 1928).
— *The Descent of Man and Selection in Relation to Sex*, 2nd edn. (Murray, London, 1874).
— *Autobiography*, ed. Nora Barlow (Collins, London, 1958).
DARWIN, ERASMUS, *Zoonomia; or The Laws of, Organic Life*, 2 vols. (Johnson, London, 1794–6).
DARWIN, FRANCIS (ed.), *The Life and Letters of Charles Darwin*, 3 vols., 3rd edn. (Murray, London, 1887).
— *More Letters of Darwin*, 2 vols. (Murray, London, 1903).
DAVIDSON, WILLIAM L., 'Professor Bain', *Mind*, **13** (1904), 151–5.
— 'Prof. Bain's philosophy', *Mind*, **13** (1904), 161–79.
DAVIES, ARTHUR E., 'The influence of biology on the development of modern psychology in America', *Psychol. Rev.*, **30** (1923), 164–75.
DAVIES, JOHN D., *Phrenology, Fad and Science* (Yale, New Haven, 1955).
DENNIS, WAYNE, *Readings in the History of Psychology* (Appleton, N.Y., 1948).
DENTON, GEORGE B., 'Early psychological theories of Herbert Spencer', *Am. J. Psychol.*, **32** (1921), 5–15.
DESSOIR, MAX, *Outlines of the History of Psychology*, trans. Donald Fisher (Macmillan, N.Y., 1912).
DEWEY, JANE M., 'Biography of John Dewey', in: Schilpp, Paul A. (ed.), *The Philosophy of John Dewey*, 3–45 (1939; 2nd edn., Tudor, N.Y., 1951).
DEWEY, JOHN, 'The reflex arc concept in psychology', *Psychol. Rev.*, **3** (1896), 357–70.
— 'Psychology and social practice', *Psychol. Rev.*, **7** (1900), 105–24.
— *The Influence of Darwin on Philosophy* (Holt, New York, 1910).
— 'From absolutism to experimentalism', in: George P. Adams and Wm. P. Montague (eds.), *Contemporary American Philosophy*, **II**, 13–27 (Macmillan, N.Y., 1930).
— 'George Herbert Mead', *J. Philos.*, **28** (1931), 309–14.
— *Philosophy and Civilization* (1931; Capricorn, N.Y., 1963).
DODDS, W. J., 'On the localisation of the functions of the brain: being an historical and critical analysis of the question,' *J. Anat. Physiol. Lond.*, **12** (1878), 340–63, 454–94, 636–60.

*Dorland's Illustrated Medical Dictionary*, 23rd edn. (Saunders, Philadelphia, 1957).

Dow, ROBERT S., 'Thomas Willis (1621–75) as a comparative neurologist', *Ann. med. Hist.* (3s.), **2** (1940), 181–94.

— and MORUZZI, GUISEPPE, *The Physiology and Pathology of the Cerebellum* (Minnesota, Minneapolis, 1958).

DYKHUIZEN, GEORGE, 'John Dewey and the University of Michigan', *J. Hist. Ideas*, **23** (1962), 513–44.

EBSTEIN, ERICH, 'Frans Joseph Gall in Kampf um seine Lehre auf, grund unbekannter Briefe an Bertuch usw. mit zwei Bildern Galls, in: Chas. Singer and H. E. Sigerist (eds.), *Essays on the History of Medicine*, 269–322 (Oxford University Press, London, 1924).

FEARING, FRANKLIN, *Reflex Action. A Study in the History of Physiological Psychology* (Ballière, London, 1930).

FERRIER, DAVID, 'Experimental researches in cerebral physiology and pathology', *West Riding Lunatic Asylum Medical Reports*, **3** (1873), 30–96.

— 'The localization of function in the brain,' (MS), communicated by J. B. Sanderson 5 March 1874; Archives of the Royal Society, AP.56.2; abstract in *Proc. R. Soc.*, **22** (1874a), 229–32.

— 'Pathological illustrations of brain function', *West Riding Lunatic Asylum Medical Reports*, **4** (1874b), 30–62.

— 'Experiments on the brain of monkeys—No. 1', *Proc. R. Soc.*, **23** (1875a), 409–30.

— 'The Croonian Lecture: Experiments on the brain of monkeys (Second series)', *Phil. Trans. R. Soc.*, **165** (1875b), 433–88; abstract in *Proc. Roy. Soc.*, **23** (1875b), 431–2.

— *The Functions of the Brain* (1876; 2nd edn., Smith, Elder, London, 1886).

— *The Localisation of Cerebral Disease* (Smith, Elder, London, 1878).

— *The Croonian Lectures on Cerebral Localisation* (Smith, Elder, London, 1890).

FLOURENS, PIERRE, *Researches Expérimentales sur les Propriétés et les Fonctions du Système Nerveux dans les Animaux Vertébrés*, (1824; 2nd edn., Ballière, Paris, 1842).

— *Phrenology Examined*, trans. Charles De Lucena Meigs (Hogan and Thompson, Philadelphia, 1846).

FLUGEL, J. C., *A Hundred Years of Psychology. 1833–1933: and with additional part on developments 1933–1947*, 2nd edn. (Duckworth, London, 1951).

FOSTER, MICHAEL, 'Physiology. Part I—general view', in: *The Encyclopedia Britannica*, 9th edn., XIX, 8–23 (Black, Edinburgh, 1885).

— *A Text Book of Physiology*, 5th edn., Part III, The Central Nervous System (Macmillan, London, 1890).

— *Claude Bernard* (Unwin, London, 1899).

— *Lectures on the History of Physiology During the Sixteenth, Seventeenth and Eighteenth Centuries* (1901; Cambridge University Press, 1924.)

FOWLER, JESSIE A., *Life of Dr. François Joseph Gall*, 3rd edn. (Fowler, London, 1896).

FRANZ, S. I., 'Conceptions of cerebral functions', *Psychol. Rev.*, **30** (1923), 438–46.

FREUD, SIGMUND, *On Aphasia. A Critical Study* (1891), trans. E. Stengel (International Universities, N.Y., 1953).

— *An Outline of Psychoanalysis* (1940), trans. J. Strachey (Norton, N.Y., 1949).

FRITSCH, GUSTAV, and HITZIG EDUARD, 'On the electrical excitability of the cerebrum' (1870), trans. G. von Bonin, in: *Some Papers on the Cerebral Cortex*, 73–96 (Thomas, Springfield, 1960).

FULTON, JOHN F., *Physiology of the Nervous System*, 3rd edn. (Oxford University Press, N.Y., 1949).

GALL, FRANÇOIS JOSEPH, and SPURZHEIM, J. C., *Anatomie et physiologie du système nerveux en général, et du cerveau en particulier, avec des observations sur la possibilité de reconnaître plusieurs dispositions intellectuelles et morales de l'homme et des animaux, par la configuration de leurs têtes*, 4 vols. with atlas of 100 engraved plates (Schoell, Paris, 1810–19). (Gall is sole author of vols. 3 and 4).

— *Sur les fonctions du cerveau et sur celles de chacune de ses parties*, 6 vols. Baillière, Paris, 1822–25).

— *On the functions of the Brain and of Each of Its Parts: with Observations on the Possibility of Determining the Instincts, Propensities, and Talents, or the Moral and Intellectual Dispositions of Men and Animals, by the Configuration of the Brain and Head*, 6 vols., trans. Winslow Lewis, Jr. (Marsh, Capen and Lyon, Boston, 1835).

— et al., *On the Functions of the Cerebellum by Drs Gall, Vimont and Broussais*, trans. George Combe (Maclachlan and Stewart, Edinburgh, 1838).

GARDNER, MARTIN, *Fads and Fallacies in the Name of Science* (Dover, N.Y., 1957).

GAY, REV. JOHN, 'Preliminary dissertation concerning the fundamental principle of virtue or morality', in: King, Wm., *An Essay on the Origin of Evil*, trans. Edmund Law, and *A Dissertation Concerning the Principle and Criterion of Virtue and the Origin of the Passions*, 2 vols., 2nd edn., I, xxviii–lvii (Thurlbourn, Cambridge, 1732).

GEORGE, WILMA, *Biologist Philosopher. A Study of the Life and Writings of Alfred Russel Wallace* (Abelard-Schuman, London, 1964).

GIBBON, CHARLES, *The Life of George Combe*, 2 vols. (Macmillan, London, 1878).

GILLISPIE, CHARLES C., *Genesis and Geology* (1951; Harper Torchbooks, N.Y., 1959).

GLASS, BENTLEY, et al. (eds.), *Forerunners of Darwin: 1745–1859* (Hopkins, Baltimore, 1959).

GORDON-TAYLOR, SIR GORDON, and WALLS, E. W., *Sir Charles Bell: His Life and Times* (Livingstone, London, 1958).

GREENBLATT, SAMUEL H., 'The major influences on the early life and work of John Hughlings Jackson', *Bull. Hist. Med.*, **39** (1965), 346–76.

GREENE, JOHN C., 'Biology and social theory in the nineteenth century: Auguste Comte and Herbert Spencer; in: Clagett, Marshall (ed.), *Critical Problems in the History of Science*, 419–46 (Wisconsin, Madison, 1959).

GREENE, JOHN C., *The Death of Adam. Evolution and Its Impact on Western Thought* (1959; Mentor, N.Y., 1961).

GRUNDFEST, H., 'The different careers of Gustav Fritsch (1838–1927)', *J. Hist. Med.*, **18** (1963), 125–29.

GUILLAIN, GEORGES., *J.-M. Charcot, 1825–1893. His Life—His Work*, trans. P. Bailey (Pitman, London, 1959).

HAIGHT, GORDON S., *George Eliot. A Biography* (Oxford University Press, London, 1968).

HALDANE, ELIZABETH S., 'Alexander Bain (1818–1903)', in: *Dictionary of National Biography*, 2nd Suppl., I, 79–81 (Smith, Elder, London, 1912).

HALÉVY, ELIE., *The Growth of Philosophic Radicalism*, trans. Mary Morris (Faber, London, 1952).

HAMLYN, D. W., *Sensation and Perception. A History of the Philosophy of Perception* (Routledge, London, 1961).

HARTLEY, DAVID, *Observations on Man, His Frame, His Duty, and His Expectations*, 2 vols. (Leake and Frederick, London, 1749).

HAYMAKER, WEBB (ed.), *The Founders of Neurology. One Hundred and Thirty-Three Biographical Sketches* (Thomas, Springfield, 1953).

HEAD HENRY, 'Aphasia: an historical review', *Brain*, **43** (1920a), 390–411.

—  'Aphasia and kindred disorders of speech', *Brain*, **43** (1920b), 87–165.

—  'Discussion on aphasia', *Brain*, **43** (1920c), 412–50.

—  'Speech and cerebral localization', *Brain*, **46** (1923), 355–528.

—  *Aphasia and Kindred Disorders of Speech*, 2 vols. (Cambridge University Press, 1926).

HEARNSHAW, L. S., *A Short History of British Psychology* (1840–1940) (Methuen, London, 1964).

HEBB, DONALD O., 'A neuropsychological theory', in: Koch, Sigmund (ed), *Psychology: A Study of a Science. Study I*, vol. I, 622–43 (McGraw-Hill, N.Y., 1959).

—  'Intelligence, brain function and the theory of mind', *Brain*, **82** (1959a), 260–75.

HEIDBREDER, EDNA, *Seven Psychologies* (Appleton, N.Y., 1933).

HERRICK, C. JUDSON, 'Localization of function in the nervous system', *Proc. natn. Acad. Sci., U.S.A.* **16** (1930), 643–50.

—  and HERRICK C. L., 'Localization', in: Baldwin J. M. (ed.), *Dictionary of Philosophy and Psychology*, 2nd edn., II, 15–19 (Macmillan, N.Y., 1925).

HILGARD, ERNEST R., *Theories of Learning*, 2nd edn. (Methuen, London, 1958).

—  'Psychology after Darwin', in: Tax, Sol (ed.), *Evolution After Darwin*, II, 269–87 (Chicago, Chicago, 1960).

—  and MARQUIS, D. G., *Conditioning and Learning* (Appleton-Century-Crofts, N.Y., 1940) 2nd edn., revised by Gregory A. Kimble (Methuen, London, 1961).

HIPPOCRATES, *Ancient Medicine and Other Treatises*, trans. Francis Adams (Regnery, Chicago, 1949).

HITZIG, EDUARD, 'Hughlings Jackson and the cortical motor centres in the light of physiological research', *Brain*, **23** (1900), 545–81.

HÖFFDING, H., 'The influence of the conception of evolution on modern philosophy', in: Seward, A. C. (ed), *Darwin and Modern Science*, 446–64 (Cambridge University Press, 1909).

HOFSTADTER, RICHARD, *Social Darwinism in American Thought*, revised edn. (Beacon, Boston, 1955).

HOLLANDER, BERNARD, *The Mental Functions of the Brain: an Investigation into their Localization and their Manifestation in Health and Disease* (Putnam's, N.Y., 1901).

— *The Unknown Life and Works of Dr. Francis Joseph Gall* (Siegle, Hill, London, 1909).

— *In Search of the Soul*, 2 vols. (Kegan Paul, London, n.d., 1920?).

'In commemoration of Francis Joseph Gall (1758–1828)', *Ethnological Journal*, **13** (1928), 51–64.

— *Brain, Mind and the External Signs of Intelligence* (Allen and Unwin, London, 1931).

HORSLEY, VICTOR, and CLARKE, R. H., 'The structure and functions of the cerebellum examined by a new method', *Brain*, **31** (1908), 45–124.

HOWARD, D. T., 'The influence of evolutionary doctrine on psychology', *Psychol. Rev.*, **34** (1927), 305–12.

HUARD, PIERRE, 'Paul Broca (1824–1880)', *Rev. Hist. Sci.*, **14** (1961), 47–60.

HUME, DAVID, *A Treatise on Human Nature* (1738), 2 vols. (Dent, London, 1911).

HUNT, JAMES, 'On the localisation of the functions of the brain, with special reference to the faculty of language', *Anthropol. Rev.*, **6** (1868), 329–45; **7** (1869), 100–16, 201–14.

HUNTER, RICHARD, and MACALPINE, IDA, *Three Hundred Years of Psychiatry*, 1535–1860 (Oxford University Press, London, 1963).

HUTCHINSON, JONATHAN, 'Recollections of a lifelong friendship,' in: Jackson, J. H., *Neurological Fragments*, 27–39 (Oxford University Press, 1925).

HUXLEY, LEONARD, *Life and Letters of Thomas Henry Huxley*, 2 vols. (Macmillan, London, 1900).

HUXLEY, THOMAS H., *Evidence as to Man's Place in Nature* (London, 1863; reprint, Michigan, Ann Arbor, 1959).

JACKSON, J. HUGHLINGS, 'Observations on the localisation of movements in the cerebral hemispheres, as revealed by cases of convulsion, chorea and "aphasia",' *West Riding Lunatic Asylum Medical Reports*, **3** (1873), 175–95.

— 'On the anatomical, physiological, and pathological investigation of epilepsies', *West Riding Lunatic Asylum Medical Reports*, **3** (1873a), 315–39.

— *Neurological Fragments* (Oxford University Press, London, 1925).

— *Selected Writings of John Hughlings Jackson*, 2 vols., Ed. James Taylor (Hodder and Stoughton, London, 1931, reprint, Basic Books, N.Y., 1958).

JAMES, WILLIAM, *The Principles of Psychology*, 2 vols. (Holt, N.Y., 1890).

— *Psychology. Briefer Course* (Macmillan, London, 1892).

— *Memories and Studies* (Longmans, N.Y., 1924).

JASPER, H. H., 'Evolution of conceptions of cerebral localization since Hughlings Jackson', *World Neurol.*, **1** (1960), 97–109.

JEFFERSON, SIR GEOFFREY, *Selected Papers* (Pitman, London, 1960).
JONES, ERNEST, *The Life and Work of Sigmund Freud*, 3 vols. (Basic, N.Y., 1953, 1955, 1957).
JOYNT, ROBERT J., 'Centenary of patient "Tan",' *Archs Intern. Med.*, **108** (1961) 953–6.
KING-HELE, DESMOND, *Erasmus Darwin* (Macmillan, London, 1963).
KIRBY, WILLIAM, *On the Power Wisdom and Goodness of God as Manifested in the Creation of Animals and in their History Habits and Instincts*, 2 vols. (Pickering, London, 1835).
KONORSKI, JERZY, 'Trends in the development of physiology of the brain,' *J. ment. Sci.*, **104**, (1958), 1100–110.
KRAUSE, ERNST, *Erasmus Darwin*, trans. W. S. Dallas (Murray, London, 1879).
KRECH, DAVID, 'Cortical Localization of Function,' in: Postman, Leo (ed.), *Psychology in the Making. Histories of Selected Research Problems*, 31–72 (Knopf, N.Y., 1962).
KUHLENBECK, HARTWIG, *Brain and Consciousness: Some Prolegomena to an Approach of the Problem* (Karger, Basel. 1957).
KUHN, THOMAS S., *The Structure of Scientific Revolutions* (Chicago, Chicago, 1962).
LADD, GEORGE T., *Elements of Physiological Psychology* (Scribner's, N.Y., 1887).
LANGE, FREDERICK A., *The History of Materialism and Criticism of its Present Importance*, 3rd edn., 3 vols. in 1 (1875), trans. E. C. Thomas (Routledge, London, 1925).
LASHLEY, KARL S., *The Neuropsychology of Lashley: Selected Papers of K. S. Lashley*, Beach, F. A., *et al.* (eds.) (McGraw-Hill, N.Y., 1960).
LAVATER, JOHN C., *Essays on Physiognomy* (1775–78), 2nd edn., 3 vols. in 4, trans. Th. Holcroft (Symonds, London, 1804).
LAYCOCK, THOMAS, *A Journal* (Microfilm of typescript), Edinburgh University Library, Mic.M.82.
— 'Phrenology', in: *The Encyclopedia Britanica*, 8th edn., XVII, 556–67 (Black, Edinburgh, 1859).
— *Mind and Brain: or the Correlations of Consciousness and Organisation*, 2 vols. (Sutherland and Knox, Edinburgh, 1860; 2nd edn., Simpkin, Marshall, London, 1869).
LEVIN, MAX, 'Reflex action in the highest cerebral centers: a tribute to Hughlings Jackson', *J. nerv. ment. Dis.*, **118** (1953), 481–93.
— 'The mind-brain problem and Hughlings Jackson's doctrine of concomitance', *Am. J. Psychiat.*, **116** (1960), 718–22.
LEWES, GEORGE H. *A Biographical History of Philosophy*, 4 vols. (Knight, London, 1845–6; 2nd edn., 1 vol., Parker, London, 1857).
— *Comte's Philosophy of the Sciences* (Bohn, London, 1853).
— 'Phrenology in France', *Blackwood's Edinburgh Mag.*, **82** (1857a), 665–74.
— *The Physiology of Common Life*, 2 vols. (Blackwood, Edinburgh, 1859–60).
— *The History of Philosophy from Thales to Comte*, 3rd edn., 2 vols. (Longmans, London, 1867, 1871).
— *Problems of Life and Mind*, 5 vols. (Trübner, London, 1874–79).

LEWIS, AUBREY, 'J. C. Reil's concepts of brain function', in: Poynter, F.N.L., (ed.), *The Brain and its Functions*, 154–66 (Blackwell, Oxford, 1958).

LIDDELL, E. G. T., *The Discovery of Reflexes* (Clarendon Press, Oxford, 1960).

LIVINGSTON, ROBERT B., 'How man looks at his own brain: an adventure shared by psychology and neurophysiology', in: Koch, Sigmund (ed)., *Psychology: A Study of a Science*, IV, 51–99 (McGraw-Hill, N.Y., 1962).

LOCKE, JOHN, *An Essay Concerning Human Understanding*, (1690) 5th edn. (1706; 2 vols., Dent, London, 1961).

LOEB, JACQUES, *Comparative Physiology of the Brain and Comparative Psychology* (Murray, London, 1901).

LOVEJOY, ARTHUR O., *The Great Chain of Being. A Study of the History of an Idea* (1936; Harper Torchbooks, N.Y., 1960).

LYELL, CHARLES, *The Geological Evidences of the Antiquity of Man* (Murray, London, 1863).

MACALISTER, A., 'Phrenology', in: *The Encyclopedia Britannica*, 9th edn., XVIII, 842–9 (Black, Edinburgh, 1885).

— 'Physiognomy', in: *The Encyclopedia Britannica*, 9th edn., XIX, 3–5 (Black, Edinburgh, 1885).

MACCORMAC, SIR WILLIAM (ed.), *Transactions of the International Medical Congress, Seventh Session*, 4 vols. (Kolckmann, London, 1881).

MACKINTOSH, SIR JAMES, 'Dissertation Second: Exhibiting a General View of the Progress of Ethical Philosophy Chiefly During the Seventeenth and Eighteenth Centuries', in: *The Encyclopedia Britannica*, 8th edn., I, 309–445 (Black, Edinburgh, 1860).

MACLEOD, ROBERT B., 'Person perception: a commentary', in: David, H. P. *et al.* (eds.), *Perspectives in Personality Research*, 226–44 (Lockwood, London, 1960).

MAGENDIE, FRANÇOIS, *An Elementary Treatise on Human Physiology*, 5th edn., (1838), trans. John Revere (Harper, N.Y., 1843).

MAGOUN, HORACE W., 'Early development of ideas relating the mind with the brain', in: Wolstenholme, G. E. W., and O'Connor, C. M. (eds.), *The Neurological Basis of Behaviour*, 4–22 (Churchill, London, 1958).

— 'Development of ideas relating the mind with the brain, in: Brooks, Chandler McC., and Cranefield, Paul F. (eds.), *The Historical Development of Physiological Thought*, 81–108 (Hafner, N.Y., 1959).

— 'Evolutionary concepts of brain function following Darwin and Spencer', in: Sol Tax (ed.), *Evolution After Darwin*, II, 187–209 (Chicago University Press, 1960).

— 'Darwin and concepts of brain function', in: Delafresnaye, J. F. (ed.), *Brain Mechanisms and Learning*, 1–20 (Blackwell, Oxford, 1961).

MARX, MELVIN H., and HILLIX, WM. A., *Systems and Theories in Psychology* (McGraw-Hill, N.Y., 1963).

McDOUGALL, WILLIAM, *An Introduction to Social Psychology* (1908) 28th edn. (Methuen, London, 1946).

McFIE, JOHN, 'Recent advances in phrenology', *Lancet*, II (1961), 360–3.

MERCIER, CHARLES, 'Recollections', in: Jackson, J. H., *Neurological Fragments*, 40–6 (Oxford University Press, 1925).

MERZ, JOHN T., *A History of European Thought in the Nineteenth Century*, 4 vols. (Blackwood, Edinburgh, 1896–1912).

MEYER, ALFRED, 'Emergent patterns of the pathology of mental disease', *J. ment. Sci.*, **106** (1960), 785–802.

MEYNERT, THEODOR, *Psychiatry—A Clinical Treatise on Diseases of the Fore-Brain, based upon A Study of its Structure, Functions, and Nutrition* (1884), Part I. *The Anatomy, Physiology and Chemistry of the Brain*, trans. B. Sachs (Putnam's, N.Y., 1885).

— 'On the collaboration of parts of the brain' (1891), trans. G. von Bonin, in: *Some Papers on the Cerebral Cortex*, 159–80 (Thomas, Springfield, Ill., 1960).

MILL, JAMES, *Analysis of the Phenomena of the Human Mind*, 2 vols. (Baldwin and Cradock, London, 1829; 2nd edn., Longmans, London, 1869).

MILL, JOHN S., 'Bain's psychology', (1859), in: *Dissertations and Discussions*, III, 97–152 (Longmans, London, 1867).

— *A System of Logic Ratiocinative and Inductive* (1843), 8th edn. (Parker, London, 1872; reprinted, Longmans, London, 1959).

— *Auguste Comte and Positivism* (London, 1865; reprinted, Michigan, Ann Arbor, 1961).

— *The Letters of John Stuart Mill*, 2 vols., Elliot, Hugh S. R. (ed.) (Longmans, London, 1910).

MILLHAUSER, MILTON, *Just Before Darwin. Robert Chambers and Vestiges* Wesleyan, Middletown, Conn., 1959).

MILLS, CHARLES K., 'Cerebral localisation in its practical relations', *Brain*, **12** (1890), 233–88, 358–406.

MINEKA, FRANCIS E. (ed.), *The Earlier Letters of John Stuart Mill 1812–1848*, 2 vols. (Routledge and Kegan Paul, London, 1963).

MORGAN, C. LLOYD, *Animal Life and Intelligence* (Arnold, London, 1890–91).

MOUTIER, FRANÇOIS, *L'Aphasie de Broca* (Steinheil, Paris, 1908).

MUELLER, JOHANNES, *Elements of Physiology*, 2 vols. (1833–40), trans. Wm. Baly (Taylor and Walton, London, 1838, 1842).

MURPHY, GARDNER, *Historical Introduction to Modern Psychology*, revised edn. (Harcourt, N.Y., 1949).

NORDENSKIÖLD, ERIK, *The History of Biology—A Survey* (1920–24), trans. L. B. Eyre (Knopf, N.Y., 1928).

OCKENDEN, R. E., 'George Henry Lewes (1817–1878)', *Isis.*, **32** (1940), 70–86.

OLDFIELD, R. C., and OLDFIELD, K. 'Hartley's "Observations on Man",' *Annals of Science*, **7** (1951), 371–81.

O'LEARY, J. L., and BISHOP, G. H., 'C. J. Herrick and the founding of comparative neurology', *Archs. Neurol.*, **3** (1960), 725–31.

OLMSTED, J. M. D., *François Magendie—Pioneer in Experimental Physiology and Scientific Medicine in XIX Century France* (Schuman's, N.Y., 1944).

— and OLMSTED, E. H., *Claude Bernard and the Experimental Method in Medicine* (1952; Collier, N.Y., 1961).

— 'Pierre Flourens', in: Underwood E. A. (ed.), *Science Medicine and History*, II, 290–302 (Oxford University Press, London, 1953).

OMBREDANE, ANDRÉ, *L'Aphasie et l'Elaboration de la Pensée Explicite* (Presses Universitaires de France, Paris, 1951).

Packe, Michael St. John, *The Life of John Stuart Mill* (Secker and Warburg, London, 1954).

Pagel, Walter, 'Medieval and renaissance contributions to knowledge of the brain and its functions', in: Poynter, F. N. L. (ed.), *The Brain and its Functions*, 95–114 (Blackwell, Oxford, 1958).

Pasamanick, Benjamin, 'An obscure item in the bibliography of Isaac Ray', *Am. J. Psychiat.*, **111** (1954), 164–71.

Pavlov, Ivan P., *Conditioned Reflexes* (1927), trans. G. V. Anrep (Dover, N.Y., 1960).

— *Selected Works*, trans. S. Belsky (Foreign Languages Publishing House, Moscow, 1955).

Peele, Talmage L., *The Neuroanatomical Basis for Clinical Neurology* (McGraw-Hill, N.Y., 1954).

Penfield, Wilder, 'The interpretive cortex', *Science*, **129** (1959), 1719–25.

— and Roberts, Lamar, *Speech and Brain-Mechanisms* (Princeton University Press, 1959).

Perry, Ralph B., *The Thought and Character of William James*, 2 vols. (Little, Brown, Boston, 1935).

Pillsbury, W. B., *The History of Psychology* (Norton, N.Y., 1929).

Pinel, Philippe, *A Treatise on Insanity*, trans. D. D. Davis (Cadell and Davies, London, 1806).

Pozzi, Samuel, 'Bibliographie de Paul Broca', *Rev. Hist. Sci.*, **14** (1961), 60–86.

Pratt, Carroll C., 'Faculty psychology', *Psychol. Rev.*, **36** (1929), 141–71.

Pribram, Karl H., 'On the neurology of thinking', *Behavl Sci.*, **4** (1959), 265–87.

— 'A review of theory in physiological psychology', *A. Rev. Psychol.*, **11** (1960), 1–40.

— 'Interrelations of psychology and the neurological disciplines', in: Koch, Sigmund (ed.), *Psychology: A Study of a Science*, IV, 119–57 (McGraw-Hill, N.Y., 1962).

Prochaska, George, *A Dissertation on the Functions of the Nervous System* (1784), trans. Th. Laycock (Sydenham Society, London, 1851).

Rand, Benjamin, *The Classical Psychologists* (Houghton Mifflin, Boston, 1912).

Reid, Thomas, *The Works of Thomas Reid. D.D.*, 6th edn., 2 vols. (Maclachlan and Stewart, Edinburgh, 1863).

Ribot, Th., *English Psychology*, trans. J. Fitzgerald (King, London, 1873).

Riese, Walther, 'The early history of aphasia', *Bull. Hist. Med.*, **21** (1947), 322–34.

— 'An outline of a history of ideas in neurology', *Bull. Hist. Med.*, **23** (1949), 111–36.

— 'The sources of Jacksonian neurology', *J.nerv. ment. Dis.*, **124** (1956), 125–34.

— 'Freudian concepts of brain function and brain disease', *J. nerv. and ment. Dis.*, **127** (1958), 287–307.

— *A History of Neurology* (MD, N.Y., 1959).

— and Hoff, Ebbel C., 'A history of the doctrine of cerebral localization. I. Sources, anticipations and basic reasoning', *J. Hist. Med.*, **5** (1950), 51–71; 'II. Methods and main results', Ibid., **6** (1951), 439–70.

ROBACK, A. A., *The Psychology of Character*, 3rd edn. (Routledge and Kegan Paul, London, 1952).

ROBERTSON, GEORGE C., 'Critical notice of "The Functions of the Brain", by David Ferrier' (1876), *Mind*, 2 (1877), 92–8.

— 'Association of ideas', in: *Encyclopedia Britannica*, 9th ed., II, 730–4 (Black, Edinburgh, 1875).

— 'Critical notice of Picavet, F. *Les Idéologues* (Paris, 1891), *Mind* (n.s.), 1 (1892), 118–26.

ROE, ANNE, and SIMPSON, GEORGE G. (eds.), *Behavior and Evolution* (Yale, New Haven, 1958).

ROGET, P. M., *Treatises on Physiology and Phrenology: from the Seventh Edition of the Encyclopedia Britannica*, 2 vols. (Black, Edinburgh, 1838).

ROLLESTON, GEORGE, et al., 'Referees' Reports on Ferrier', 1874, Archives of the Royal Society, RR.7. 299–305, RR.12.103.

ROLLESTON, J. D., 'Jean Baptiste Bouillaud (1796–1881), a pioneer in cardiology and neurology', *Proc. R. Soc. Med.*, 24 (1931), 1253–62.

ROMANES, GEORGE J., *Animal Intelligence* (Kegan Paul, London, 1882).

— *Mental Evolution in Animals* (Kegan Paul, London, 1883).

— *Darwin and After Darwin*, 3 vols. Vol. I *The Darwinian Theory* (Longmans, London, 1892), Vol. II *Post-Darwinian Questions. Heredity and Utility*, Vol. III *Post-Darwinian Questions. Isolation and Physiological Selection* Open Court, Chicago, 1916, 1914).

— *Essays* (Longmans, London, 1897).

ROSEN, GEORGE, 'The philosophy of ideology and the emergence of modern medicine in France', *Bull. Hist. Med.*, 20 (1946), 328–39.

ROSS, J., 'Review of treatise by Wernicke on brain', 3 vols., 1881–3, *Brain*, 6 (1883–4), 398–403.

ROYCE, JOSIAH, *The Spirit of Modern Philosophy* (Houghton, Mifflin, Boston, 1892).

RUCKMICH, CHRISTIAN A., 'The use of the term *function* in English textbooks of pyschology', *Am. J. Psychol.*, 24 (1913), 99–123.

RUSSELL, E. S., *Form and Function. A Contribution to the History of Animal Morphology* (Murray, London, 1916).

RUTHERFORD, WILLIAM, 'Address to the department of anatomy and physiology', *Report of the Forty-Third Meeting of the British Association for the Advancement of Science*, transactions, 119–23 (Murray, London, 1874).

SAWYER, CHARLES H., 'Reproductive behavior', in: Field, J. (ed.), *Handbook of Physiology. Neurophysiology*, II, 1225–40 (Am. Physiol. Soc., Wash., 1960).

SEWELL, CHARLES E., *Phrenology: Its Discovery and Re-Discovery*, The Presidential Address to The British Phrenological Society, 1932 (Gale, London, 1932).

— *Phrenology Stands the Test*, The Presidential Address to the British Phrenological Society, 1934 (S. Hearn, London, 1934).

SHEER, DANIEL E. (ed.), *Electrical Stimulation of the Brain* (Texas, Austin, 1961).

SHERRINGTON, CHARLES S., *The Integrative Action of the Nervous System* (Scribner's, N.Y., 1906).

— 'Sir David Ferrier, 1843–1928', *Proc. R. Soc.B*, **103** (1928), viii–xvi.

— 'Sir David Ferrier (1843–1928)', *Dictionary of National Biography*, 1922–1930, 302–4 (Oxford University Press, London, 1937).

— *Man on His Nature* (1940; 2nd edn., 1951, reprinted, Penguin, Harmondsworth, 1955).

SINGER, CHARLES, *Vesalius on the Human Brain* (1542), trans. Charles Singer (Oxford University Press, London, 1952).

— *A Short History of Anatomy from the Greeks to Harvey* (Dover, N.Y., 1957).

— *A History of Biology*, 3rd edn. (Abelard-Schuman, N.Y., 1959).

— and UNDERWOOD, E. A., *A Short History of Medicine*, 2nd edn. (Clarendon Press, Oxford, 1962).

SKINNER, B. F., *The Behavior of Organisms* (Appleton, N.Y., 1938).

SMITH, JOHN E., *The Spirit of American Philosophy* (Oxford University Press, N.Y., 1963).

SMITH, NORMAN, *Studies in the Cartesian Philosophy* (1902; Russell, N.Y., 1962).

SOURY, JULES, *Le système nerveux central: structure et fonctions: histoire critique des théories et des doctrines*, Vol. I (Carré et Naud, Paris, 1899).

SPEARMAN, CHARLES E., *The Abilities of Man. Their Nature and Measurement* (Macmillan, London, 1927).

— *Psychology Down the Ages*, 2 vols. (Macmillan, London, 1937).

SPENCER, HERBERT, *Social Statics* (Chapman, London, 1851).

— *The Principles of Psychology* (Longmans, London, 1855; 2nd edn., 2 vols. (Williams and Norgate, London, 1870–2); 3rd edn., 2 vols. (1890).

— *First Principles* (Williams and Norgate, London, 1862; 6th edn., revised, 1904).

— *Principles of Biology*, 2 vols. (Williams and Norgate, London, 1864, 1867; 2nd edn., 1898–99).

— *The Factors of Organic Evolution* (Williams and Norgate, London, 1887).

— *Social Statics, abridged and revised: together with Man Versus the State* (Williams and Norgate, London, 1892).

— *Various Fragments* (Williams and Norgate, London, 1900).

— *Essays: Scientific, Political and Speculative*, 3 vols. (Williams and Norgate, London, 1901).

— *Facts and Comments* (Williams and Norgate, London, 1902).

— *An Autobiography*, 2 vols. (Williams and Norgate, London, 1904).

— *The Life and Letters of Herbert Spencer*, Duncan, David (ed.) (Methuen, London, 1908).

SPOERL, HOWARD D., 'Faculties versus traits: Gall's solution', *Character and Personality*, **4** (1935–6), 216–31.

SPURZHEIM, JOHANN G., *The Physiognomical System of Drs. Gall and Spurzheim*, 2nd edn. (Baldwin, Cradock, and Joy, London, 1815).

— *The Anatomy of the Brain, with a General View of the Nervous System*, trans. R. Willis (Highley, London, 1826).

STENGEL, E. A., 'Introduction', in: Freud, Sigmund, *On Aphasia*, trans. E. Stengel, ix–xv. (International University Press, N.Y., 1953).

STENGEL, E. A., 'A re-evaluation of Freud's book "On Aphasia" ': Its significance for psycho-analysis. *Int. J. Psycho-Analysis*, **35** (1954), 85–9.
— 'Hughlings Jackson's influence in psychiatry', *Brit. J. Psychiat.*, **109** (1963), 348–55.
STEPHEN, LESLIE, *History of English Thought in the Eighteenth Century*, 2 vols., 3rd edn. (1902; Hart-Davis, London, 1962).
STEWART, DUGALD, *Elements of the Philosophy of the Human Mind* (1792; new edn., Tegg, London, 1842).
— 'Dissertation First: Exhibiting a General View of the Progress of Metaphysical and Ethical Philosophy, Since the Revival of Letters in Europe', in: *The Encyclopedia Britannica*, 8th edn., I, 1–289 (Black, Edinburgh, 1860).
STOUT, G. F., *A Manual of Psychology*, 2 vols. (Clive, London, 1898–1899).
— *Mind and Matter* (Cambridge University Press, 1931).
TAYLOR, JAMES, 'Biographical memoir', in: Jackson, J. H., *Neurological Fragments*, 1–26 (Oxford, Oxford, 1925).
TEMKIN, OWSEI, *The Falling Sickness* (Hopkins, Baltimore, 1945).
— 'The philosophical background of Magendie's physiology', *Bull. Hist. Med.*, **20** (1946), 10–35.
— 'Materialism in French and German physiology of the early nineteenth century', *Bull. Hist. Med.*, **20** (1946a), 322–27.
— 'Gall and the phrenological movement', *Bull. Hist. Med.*, **21** (1947), 275–321.
— 'Remarks on the neurology of Gall and Spurzheim', in: Underwood, E. A. (ed.), *Science Medicine and History*, II, 282–9 (Oxford University Press, London, 1953).
TENON, PORTAL, SABATIER, PINEL, and CUVIER, 'Report on a memoir of Drs Gall and Spurzheim, relative to the anatomy of the brain. By . . . presented to, and adopted by the Class of Mathematical and Physical Sciences of the National Institute', (Given at the Institute, 15 April, 1808), *Edinburgh Med. and Surg. J.*, **5** (1809), 36–66.
THOMSON, J. ARTHUR, *Herbert Spencer* (Dent, London, 1906).
THORNDIKE, EDWARD L., *The Elements of Psychology*, 2nd edn. (Seiler, N.Y., 1920).
THORNDIKE, LYNN, *A History of Magic and Experimental Sciences*, Vol. VIII, *The Seventeenth Century* (Columbia, N.Y., 1958).
THORPE, W. H., *Learning and Instinct in Animals*, 2nd edn. (Methuen, London, 1963).
THORWALD, JÜRGEN, *The Triumph of Surgery* (1957), trans. R. and C. Winston (Thames and Hudson, London, 1960).
TITCHENER, EDWARD B., 'The postulates of a structural psychology', *Philos. Rev.*, **7** (1898), 449–65; reprinted in Dennis, 1948, 366–76.
— 'Functional psychology and the psychology of act', *Am. J. Psychol.*, **32** (1921), 519–42; ibid., **33** (1922), 43–83.
TIZARD, BARBARA, 'Theories of brain localization from Flourens to Lashley', *Med. Hist.*, **3** (1959), 132–45.

TODD, ROBERT B., and BOWMAN, WILLIAM, *The Physiological Anatomy and Physiology of Man*, 2 vols. (Parker, London, 1845–56).

'TWO' (ANON.), *Home Life with Herbert Spencer* (Arrowsmith, Bristol, 1906).

VALLERY-RADOT, RENÉ, *The Life of Pasteur* (1901), trans. R. L. Devonshire Dover, N.Y., 1960).

VARTANIAN, ARAM, *La Mettrie's L' Homme Machine: A Study in the Origins of an Idea* (Princeton, Princeton, 1960).

VERWORN, MAX, *Irritability: A Physiological Analysis of the General Effect of Stimuli in Living Substance* (Yale, New Haven, 1913).

VIETS, HENRY R., 'West Riding, 1871–1876', *Bull. Inst. Hist. Med.*, **6** (1938), 477–87.

VON BONIN, GERHARDT (trans.), *Some Papers on the Cerebral Cortex* (Thomas, Springfield, 1960).

VON HOLST, ERICH, and SAINT PAUL, URSULA, 'The functional organization of drives', *Animal Behav.*, **11** (1963), 1–20.

WALKER, A. E., 'The development of the concept of cerebral localization in the nineteenth century', *Bull. Hist. Med.*, **31** (1957), 99–121.

WALLACE, ALFRED R., *The Wonderful Century* (Sonnenschein, London, 1901).
— *My Life. A Record of Events and Opinions*, 2 vols. (Chapman and Hall, London, 1905).

WALLACE, BRUCE, and SRB, ADRIAN M., *Adaptation* (Prentice-Hall, Englewood, N.J., 1961).

WALSHE, F. M. R., *Critical Studies in Neurology* (Livingstone, Edinburgh, 1948).
— 'Thoughts upon the equation of mind with brain', *Brain*, **76** (1953), 1–18.
— 'The contribution of clinical observation to cerebral physiology', *Proc. R. Soc.B*, **142** (1954), 208–24.
— 'The brain-stem conceived as the "highest level" of function in the nervous system; with particular reference to the "automatic apparatus" of Carpenter (1850) and to the "centrencephalic integrating system" of Penfield', *Brain*, **80** (1957), 510–39.
— 'Some reflections upon the opening phase of the physiology of the cerebral cortex, 1850–1900', in: Poynter, F.N.L. (ed.), *The Brain and its Functions*, 223–34 (Blackwell, Oxford, 1958).
— 'Contributions of John Hughlings Jackson to Neurology', *Archs Neurol.*, **5** (1961), 119–31.

WARD, JAMES, 'Psychology', in: *The Encyclopedia Britannica*, 9th edn., XX, 37–85 (Black, Edinburgh, 1886).
— *Psychological Principles* (Cambridge University Press, 1918).
— et al., 'Ward Commemoration Number', *Monist*, **36** (1926), 1–175.

WARDEN, C. J., 'The historical development of comparative psychology', *Psychol. Rev.*, **34** (1927), 57–85, 135–68.

WARREN, HOWARD C., *A History of the Association Psychology* (Constable, London, 1921).

WATSON, JOHN B., 'Psychology as the behaviorist views it', *Psychol. Rev.*, **20** (1913) 158–77; reprinted in Dennis, 1948, 457–71.
— *Psychology from the Standpoint of a Behaviorist* (Lippincott, Philadelphia, 1919; 2nd edn., 1924).

WEISENBERG, THEODORE, and McBRIDE, K. E., *Aphasia. A Clinical and Psychological Study* (Oxford University Press, London, 1935).

WEISKRANTZ, LARRY, 'Review of "Brain Mechanisms and Learning".' *Q. Jl exp. Psychol.*, **14** (1962), 125–6.

WEISS, ALBERT P., 'Relation between structural and behavior psychology', *Psychol. Rev.*, **24** (1917), 301–17.

WELSH, DAVID, *Account of the Life and Writings of Thomas Brown, M.D.* (Tait, Edinburgh, 1825).

WHITE, MORTON G., *The Origin of Dewey's Instrumentalism* (Columbia, N.Y., 1943).

WHITEHEAD, ALFRED N., *Science and the Modern World* (Cambridge, 1925).

WHYTE, LANCELOT L., *The Unconscious Before Freud* (Basic, N.Y., 1960).

WIENER, PHILIP P., *Evolution and the Founders of Pragmatism* (Harvard University Press, Cambridge, 1949).

WIGHTMAN, W. P. D., 'Wars of ideas in neurological science—from Willis to Bichat and from Locke to Condillac', in: Poynter, F.N.L. (ed.), *The Brain and its Functions*, 135–45 (Blackwell, Oxford, 1958).

WILKS, SAMUEL, 'Notes on the history of the physiology of the nervous system. Taken more especially from writers on phrenology', *Guy's Hosp. Rep.*, 3rd Series, **24** (1879), 57–94.

WILLEY, BASIL, *The Eighteenth-Century Background. Studies on the Idea of Nature in the Thought of the Period* (1940; Penguin, Harmondsworth, 1962).

WILLIAMS, H. MATTIEU, *A Vindication of Phrenology* (Chatto and Windus, London, 1894).

WILSON, J. WALTER, 'Biology attains maturity in the nineteenth century', in: Clagett, Marshall (ed.), *Critical Problems in the History of Science*, 401–18 (Madison, Wisconsin, 1959).

WOLF, A., *A History of Science, Technology and Philosophy in the Eighteenth Century*, 2nd edn., revised by D. McKie (Allen and Unwin, London, 1952).

WOODWORTH, ROBERTS S., *Contemporary Schools of Psychology* (1931); 8th edn., (Methuen, London, 1951).

WOOLLAM, D. H. M., 'Concepts of the brain and its function in classical antiquity', in: Poynter, F.N.L. (ed.), *The Brain and Its Functions*, 5–18 (Blackwell, Oxford, 1958).

YAKOVLEV, PAUL I., 'The "crowbar skull" and mementoes of "phrenological hours",' *Harvard Med. Alumni Bull.*, Oct., 1958, 6 pp.

YOUNG, ROBERT M., 'Scholarship and the history of the behavioural sciences', *History of Science*, **5** (1966), 1–51.

— 'The development of Herbert Spencer's concept of evolution', *Actes du XIe Congrès International d'Histoire des Sciences*, 1965, II, 273–78 (Ossolineum, Warsaw, 1967).

— 'Animal Soul', in: Edwards, Paul (ed.), *The Encyclopedia of Philosophy*, I, 122–7 (Macmillan, N.Y., 1967a).

— 'Philosophy of mind and related issues', *Br. J. Phil. Sci.*, **18** (1967b), 325–30.

— 'The functions of the brain: Gall to Ferrier (1808–1886)', *Isis*, *59* (1968), 251–68.

YOUNG, ROBERT M., 'The impact of Darwin on conventional thought', in: Symondson, Anthony (ed)., *The Victorian Crisis of Faith* (S.P.C.K., London, 1970).

— 'Malthus and the evolutionists: the common context of biological and social theory', *Past and Present*, No. 43 (1969), 109–45.

ZANGWILL, OLIVER L., *Cerebral Dominance and its Relation to Psychological Function* (Oliver and Boyd, London, 1960).

— 'Speech', in: Field J. (ed.), *Handbook of Physiology. Neurophysiology III*, 1709–22 (Am. Physiol. Soc., Washington, 1960b).

— 'Lashley's concept of cerebral mass action', in: Thorpe, W. H., and Zangwill, O. L. (eds)., *Current Problems in Animal Behaviour*, 59–86 (Cambridge University Press, 1961).

— 'The cerebral localization of psychological functions', *Advancement of Science*, **20** (1963–4), 335–44.

ZILBOORG, GREGORY, and HENRY, G. W., *A History of Medical Psychology* (Norton, N.Y., 1941).

# INDEX

There is an exceedingly subtle and insidious danger in positivism. If you cannot avoid metaphysics, what kind of metaphysics are you likely to cherish when you sturdily suppose yourself to be free from the abomination? Of course it goes without saying that in this case your metaphysics will be held uncritically because it is unconscious; moreover, it will be passed on to others far more readily than your other notions inasmuch as it will be propagated by insinuation rather than by direct argument.

E. A. Burtt, 1932, p. 225.

Now it may well be that science, despite its rejection of final causes, reveals the presence and functioning of values in the fundamental categories it selects and the way it applies them. If so, then an adequate scientific metaphysic will not be able to manage without teleology in some form, and it becomes a question of first-rate importance what that form is to be.

*Ibid.*, p. 308.